Non-Euclidean Adventures on the LÉNÁRT SPHERE

Investigations in Planar and Spherical Geometry

István Lénárt

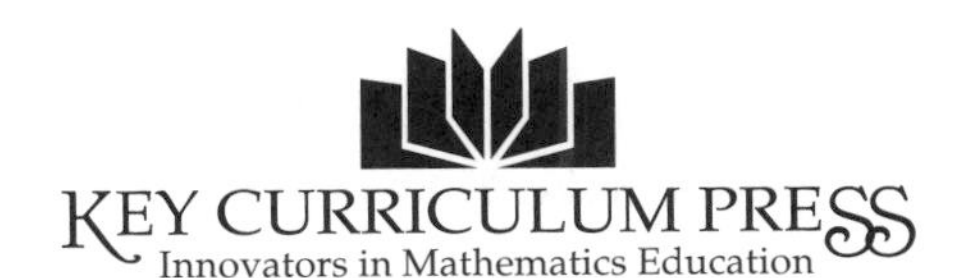

The LÉNÁRT SPHERE™ Construction Materials

The Lénárt Sphere Construction Materials and *Non-Euclidean Adventures on the Lénárt Sphere* are the result of research begun in 1969 by Hungarian mathematics educator István Lénárt. Over the years, hundreds of Hungarian teachers and their students have used Mr. Lénárt's spheres and ideas in their classrooms. In 1992, Key Curriculum Press met Mr. Lénárt at the seventh meeting of the International Congress on Mathematical Education and joined with him to make the Lénárt Sphere known and available outside of Hungary.

Editors
Masha Albrecht and Peter Rasmussen

Editorial Assistance
Bill Marthinsen, Leslie Nielsen, and Steven Rasmussen

Copyeditor
Greer Lleuad

Cartography
Joseph Roubal
Roubal Mapping Company

Cover and Design
Terry Lockman
Lumina Designworks

Production
Ann Rothenbuhler, Luis Shein, and Susan Parini

Illustrations
István Lénárt

Technical Art
A. W. Kingston Publishing

Photo Credits
Images provided by The Image Bank®.
Key Curriculum Press would like to thank all of the students
involved in creating the Lénárt Sphere materials.
Photo on page 77 by Lesley Lovell.

10 9 8 7 6 5 4 3 2 99 98 97

ISBN 1-55953-103-7
Printed in the United States of America.

Key Curriculum Press
P.O. Box 2304
Berkeley, CA 94702
510-548-2304
editorial@keypress.com

TABLE OF CONTENTS

A Letter from the Author

Why explore spherical geometry?

The high school geometry curriculum is primarily based on Euclidean concepts and constructions. Often, non-Euclidean ideas appear in high school geometry books as topological curiosities or historical asides, relegated to footnotes or visual activity boxes. Students are asked to consider these ideas only briefly if at all. Rarely is non-Euclidean geometry handled with the same depth or rigor that is used to study plane geometry. Even rarer are instances of non-Euclidean exploration with manipulatives.

This book is a collection of comparative geometry activities—or *adventures*—for students. Most of the adventures deal with the basic concepts of spherical geometry, such as points, lines, circles, distance, angle, and area. These concepts are compared and contrasted with the corresponding ideas of elementary plane geometry.

The adventures are presented in two forms to accommodate two different learning styles. First each adventure is succinctly described on an *Adventure Card* as an unguided investigation in which students determine their own paths of exploration. Then the same adventure is repeated in the more structured *Student's Guide* with step-by-step constructions, guided investigations, and questions for further exploration. Following the Student's Guide is the *Teacher's Guide* with solutions and hints.

Spherical geometry, studied in tandem with plane geometry, offers students and teachers opportunities for learning that require creative thought, that allow for discovery, and that have applications in the real world. Given a sphere and construction tools to use on that sphere, students can experience non-Euclidean constructions as an integral part of their geometry class. After all, the sphere is not a foreign object; rather, it is a geometric shape familiar to young and old. Remember, ball games are universal, and we live on a sphere. There are many applications of spherical geometry—just ask any engineer, physicist, astronomer, navigator, or pilot. You can share this rich topic with your students and make it a meaningful part of their geometry curriculum.

Student Audience

The adventures on the Lénárt Sphere are designed primarily for upper middle school and high school students. The Teacher's Guide indicates the appropriate student audience for each adventure.

However, the successful use of this material with any age group depends largely on the teacher's intentions and the students' interest and ability. Younger students have successfully explored several of the adventures, mostly in classes without an advanced program in mathematics. At the same time, this material has been favorably received in college mathematics and teacher education classes. In Hungary, my own country, the adventures are widely used with students of all ages.

Techniques Applied

Most of the adventures introduce a new topic in the traditional, planar method, then translate the steps from the plane to the sphere as closely as possible. We turn to new methods only if planar methods prove inadequate for solving a problem on the sphere. Thus the challenge for students is to shift their thinking from the plane to the sphere and to compare two different worlds of geometry.

In the adventures, students only use mathematical skills and techniques commonly used in high school geometry classes. The arithmetic procedures applied in this book do not go beyond the four basic operations. In Adventure 6.3, "How can you approximate the area of a circle?" trigonometric functions are mentioned, but the adventure does not involve trigonometric computations. The geometric constructions are also well within the reach of first- and second-year high school students.

Background Knowledge on the Teacher's Part

When designing the adventures, one of our main ambitions was to make them accessible to teachers who have experience with Euclidean plane geometry and who understand the geometric concepts and definitions that are usually taught in middle and high schools. Teachers do not have to have previous experience with spherical geometry or any form of non-Euclidean geometry to successfully embark on the adventures.

A taste for thinking wildly and an affinity to new ideas are welcomed!

Some Elementary Concepts

Most of the adventures are based on a few elementary concepts of spherical geometry. Each of these concepts is dealt with separately in the introductory adventures. However, to give you an idea about the nature of the spherical geometry discussed in this book, here is a brief summary of these fundamental concepts.

- The simplest shape in spherical geometry is the **spherical point**, just as the planar point is the simplest shape in plane geometry. Each spherical point determines another point on the sphere called the **opposite point**. The North and South poles on the globe are an example of a spherical point and its opposite point.

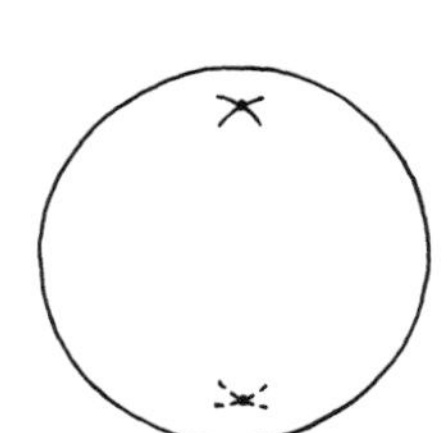

- The simplest line is the **great circle**, the largest of all the circles that can be drawn on the sphere. A globe's longitudes and equator are examples of great circles. (A globe's other latitudes are circles but not great circles!) The great circle on the sphere is the spherical equivalent of the straight line on the plane.

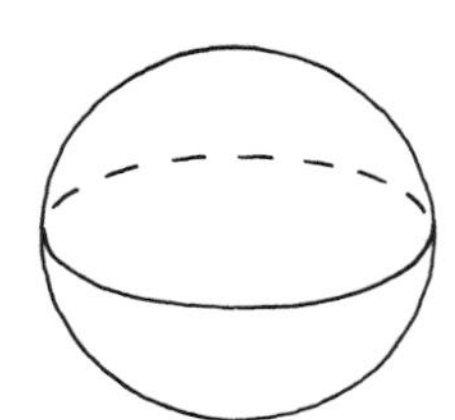

- **Two different great circles always intersect** in two opposite points of intersection. Parallel great circles on the sphere do not exist. You can draw one and only one great circle through two spherical points that are not opposite. If the points are opposite, then there are infinitely many great circles passing through them.

- Two points on a great circle divide it into two separate and measurable arcs. If the two points are not opposite, then we define their **spherical distance** as the measure of the shorter of the two arcs. We use degrees to measure distance along a great circle. If the two points are opposite, then their spherical distance measures 180°.

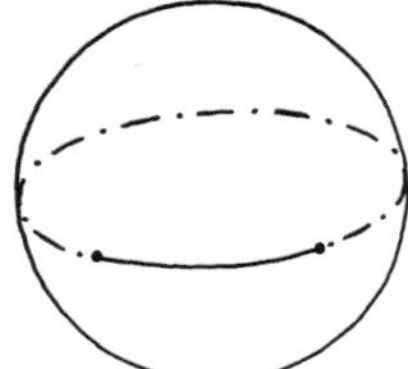

- Each great circle has two centers on the sphere, called the **pole points** or **poles** of the great circle. As a pole, each spherical point determines one and only one great circle, called the **equator**.

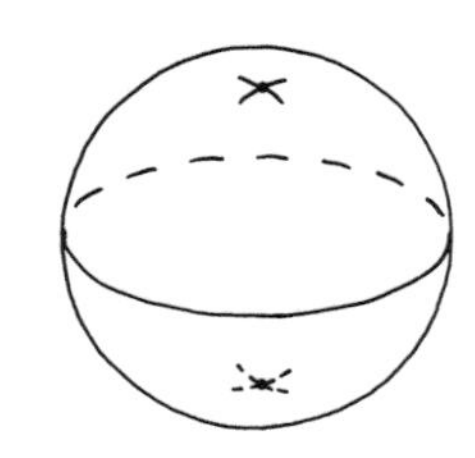

Manipulative Devices

To successfully explore geometry on a sphere, it is not enough to imagine the spherical figures or to draw figures on a sheet of paper. Students absolutely must experiment on real spheres! Could you teach plane geometry by drawing only on a globe? It is just as hopeless to teach spherical geometry without drawing on a sphere and, more importantly, without your students drawing on it!

Luckily, spherical forms are so prevalent that you can perform many simple experiments on objects from your everyday environment. You can draw with marking pens on Ping-Pong balls, balloons, basketballs, or melons. You can construct arcs of great circles with the help of a string stretched taut on a sphere. You can even tape a marker to one leg of a regular planar compass, put a piece of transparent tape on the surface of the sphere, stick the point of the compass into it, and draw any circle on a sphere.

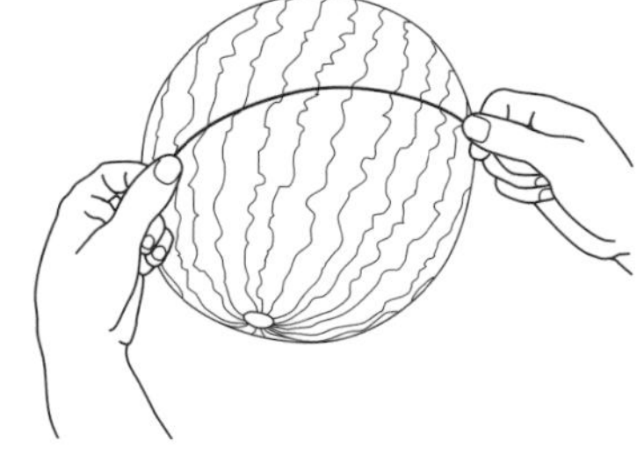

However, one critical problem presents itself when you work on most spherical objects. On a plane you can carefully measure and draw shapes with a ruler, a protractor, and a compass. It is impossible to make accurate constructions and observations on the surface of an orange.

The Lénárt Sphere Construction Materials not only provide you with a smooth spherical surface to work on but also with a set of tools that you can use to make constructions that are as accurate as you and your students are accustomed to making on the plane. You can find a detailed list of these tools, and instructions for their use, in the Using the Lénárt Sphere Construction Tools section of the introduction.

The Main Goals of the Lénárt Sphere Curriculum

Almost all branches of mathematics abound in topics that can be adapted to classroom use in one form or another. Spherical geometry studied in tandem with plane geometry is just one possibility among many others, yet we believe this topic has some features that make its study particularly interesting and useful.

Here are the main goals of this curriculum.

- To teach the basics of spherical geometry
- To explain the concepts and the definitions of plane geometry by comparing them with their corresponding ideas in spherical geometry
- To develop an understanding of what an axiomatic system is and of how more than one axiomatic system can exist at the same time in the same field of study
- To develop understanding of other viewpoints

Spherical Geometry

The Lénárt Sphere curriculum clearly focuses on teaching a detailed spherical geometry in middle and high schools through the use of manipulatives. This raises the question of whether the topic should play a greater role in school mathematics than it currently does. We believe that spherical geometry is not at all inferior to plane geometry from a mathematical, educational, or even aesthetical point of view. What is more, it has an unquestionable advantage over plane geometry: It is built on a finite rather than an infinite surface. All the wonders of spherical geometry are entirely realized in a student's hands on a finite, tangible, and understandable solid, with minimal reference to the notion of infinity.

Another advantage to spherical geometry is that many of its concepts have always been present in the curriculum of another school subject: geography. The geographic coordinate system makes it easy to introduce most of the elementary concepts of spherical geometry at a relatively early stage in a student's education. These concepts, however, are too often introduced without adequate experience on a real sphere. Working on the Lénárt Sphere may prove helpful in this respect, leading to a fruitful connection between geography and geometry. This experience can help students realize the significance of spherical geometry in real life, on the surface of the round earth on which we live.

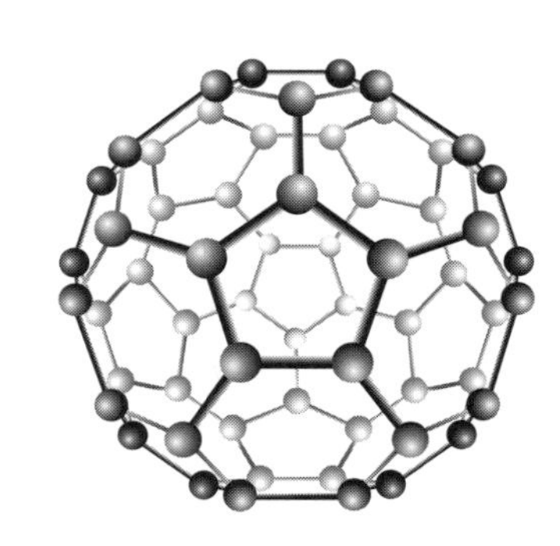

Spherical geometry plays an important and vital role in a number of fundamental subjects. Within mathematics, spherical geometry is widely used in solid geometry, trigonometry, topology, infinitesimal calculus, projective and differential geometry, finite geometries, complex number theory, and the theory of functions. One sometimes has the feeling that the mystery of higher mathematics rests on the mystery of spherical geometry! Beyond the boundaries of mathematics, spherical geometry has many applications in classical and modern physics, inorganic and organic chemistry, crystallography, earth sciences, astronomy, navigation, artistic and technical drawing, industrial design, engineering, and many other sciences.

Plane Geometry Versus Spherical Geometry

Teaching spherical geometry along with the more familiar concepts of plane geometry not only helps students understand ideas on the sphere but also heightens students' insights into plane geometry. The adventures in this book are designed to allow a two-way comparison between the two geometries. When working with spherical geometry, students are often fascinated by how much new information they gather about well-known ideas in plane geometry. The counterexamples in spherical geometry show the limits of validity of a given theory or definition, or the significance of a nuance in a theorem or a proof in plane geometry that may appear trivial or superfluous at first sight.

Students understand that each time they pose and solve a problem in one of the two geometries, a similar problem arises in the other geometry. They learn to translate a problem in plane geometry into another problem in spherical geometry and vice versa. In most cases, this action is far from being trivial, but, on the contrary, it needs a good deal of inventiveness and creativity. That is why students feel that they not only solve a given problem but also pose and formulate problems on their own. They learn that the same problem may have a different solution in a different context in which there is a different set of rules.

Principle of Balance: The Game

When students understand the idea of contrasting plane geometry with spherical geometry, they may begin to play—intuitively or intentionally—a game between the two geometries: "Which of the two is simpler? Which is better? Which do I prefer?"

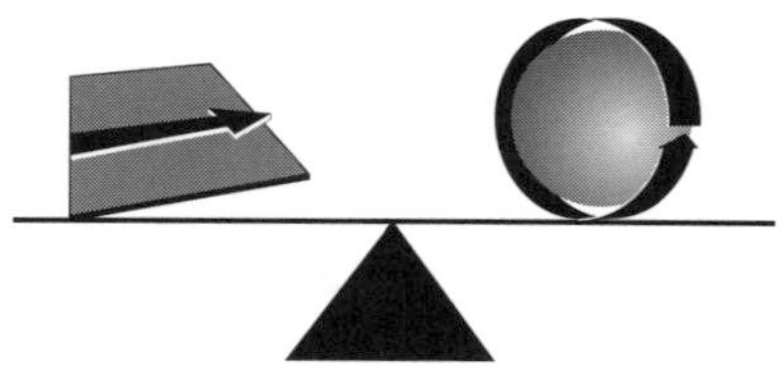

Students' curiosity regarding the outcome of this game is one of the forces behind completing the adventures. For that very reason, the game should not be decided conclusively in favor of either of the two geometries. The match must always be nearly a draw.

This principle of balance was considered throughout the adventures, although, we were a bit biased in favor of the sphere because most students are educated to be biased in favor of the plane. If there is a lack of balance within a single adventure, the scale should tip back into balance in the following adventure. If you run into an adventure concluding with a definite "victory" for the plane, turn to the next adventure—you will probably find a victory for the sphere.

Approaching spherical geometry as a game emphasizes the human face of the subject. Mathematics changes from a monologue into a living drama about the rivalry between plane and sphere, with teacher and students arguing and reasoning in search of the truth.

Proofs

We strongly believe that the Lénárt Sphere curriculum can contribute to success in the teaching of proof in mathematics classes. Proof is an integral part of mathematics. For that reason, proof must be part of mathematics education as well. However, there is strong evidence that many high school students are indifferent to, or even dislike, proof. Many view proof as superfluous verification of statements of which they are already convinced.

Given this skeptical attitude, the best way to raise students' interest in proof is to shift the rationale for proof from verification, its traditional role in school geometry, to understanding and explanation. Investigations and experience using geometry tools will convince students that statements are true: "I measured the angles of four different triangles on the plane and they always added up to 180°." But if you then ask students to explain why the measures add up to 180°, they must move beyond their experience and search for logical argument. Proof in the context of comparison, explanation, and communication can yield insights and understanding.

The contrasts between planar and spherical geometry offer wonderful opportunities to ask students "why" questions. Why do theorems that students accept on the plane behave differently on the sphere? Why were students convinced of the validity of these theorems on the plane? What were the assumptions behind their conviction? Proof in this context becomes interesting. To quote the words of a high school student who took part in a four-day Lénárt Sphere minicourse: "Each day I looked forward to disproving another theory I took for granted." Her interest in proof was raised by the fact that an understandable theory on two understandable surfaces behaved in two totally different manners, working perfectly on one surface but failing to work on the other.

The Axiomatic Method

Mathematics has gone through a fundamental change in the last two centuries. It has grown from a science built on a few fixed axiomatic systems into one with a multitude of axiomatic systems, no strict boundaries between its different branches, and widened areas of application both within and outside the field. Despite many efforts, this change has only partly been reflected in mathematics education. Teaching different axiomatic systems has proved to be a complicated and often thankless task. Students seem to adhere to their chosen axioms in arithmetic or geometry just as stiffly as mathematicians did in the past.

We hope working with the Lénárt Sphere has a positive effect in this regard. Spherical geometry is just as real and understandable as plane geometry. Therefore, students can develop an understanding of what an axiomatic system is and how more than one axiomatic system can exist in geometry at the same time. What is more, they can accept that other areas of mathematics can also be described with various axiomatic systems. They can understand that mathematics is more than universal because it encompasses a multiplicity of universes.

Working in Small Groups

The Lénárt Sphere makes it possible for students to experiment on real spheres. Teachers who have used the spheres suggest that students work in small groups of two to four persons each, each group working on its own sphere. Make sure that each student in a group has the chance to actually work on the sphere. Students learn best when they communicate about what they are learning, and students working together can better stimulate ideas and lend help to one another.

Encourage this process by letting students select for their four-member group, a spokesperson, a recorder to keep a written record of the process, and someone to make sure everyone participates. Have the students rotate the roles within their group.

Changing One's Way of Thinking

As you have been reading, the geometric properties of the sphere are by no means more difficult to grasp than those of plane geometry. Thus it is not the complexity of spherical geometry that may cause problems in the classroom. One of the main problems students encounter when they study the sphere is that they sometimes want to transfer geometric properties from the plane to the sphere without giving sufficient consideration to the differences between the two surfaces.

Consider asking your students questions such as these: Why are you sure that the point is simpler than the straight line or the great circle? Why do you think that the straight line is less complex than the other lines on the plane? Do your reasons hold for the great circle and the other lines on the sphere? Is it possible that parallelism among straight lines has no direct equivalent among great circles? If so, what other concepts and definitions must fail, or at least change, on the sphere? What is the difference between measuring distances and measuring angles? Can area be measured in the same way on the sphere as it is on the plane? Shall we consider it an advantage or a disadvantage that the sum of the measures of the angles of a spherical triangle is not a constant? How many centers of a circle can be found on the plane? On the sphere?

These questions, if properly presented, lead students to even deeper problems. What concepts and statements can be taken for the simplest? If you consider something to be the simplest, can you take it for granted that another person thinks as you do? If we agreed on the simplest elements, how can we deduce other concepts and definitions from our "simplest" ones? What does "simple" mean in mathematics? What does "obvious" mean? (You may have heard this famous definition: We call a statement obvious if we cannot prove it!) By working through this curriculum, students will have the opportunity to inquire into the notions—conscious or unconscious—on which their own concept of geometry is built. Comparing plane geometry with spherical geometry helps students get rid of some of their own mathematical preconceptions and biases. This is exactly what Girolamo Saccheri, Johann Lambert, Carl Friedrich Gauss, János Bolyai, Nikolai Lobachevsky, Bernhard Riemann, and other mathematicians did when they laid the foundations of non-Euclidean geometry in the eighteenth and nineteenth centuries.

Let us digress for a moment from the middle and high school level to the elementary grades. Teaching spherical geometry in tandem with plane geometry to students who have not begun to study geometry gives rise to quite different problems and results. Younger children who initially learn both planar and spherical geometry can avoid developing biases that are so hard to get rid of later. It becomes natural for these children to compare and contrast different aspects of geometry. However, this curriculum also involves the risk of making children prefer the sphere to the plane!

Developing Multicultural Understanding

The type of thinking used in mathematics is an integral part of human thinking. Students who learn to use cautious judgment in mathematical problems and to accept different approaches in geometry are more likely to apply these ways of thinking in other areas of life.

This curriculum offers many opportunities for teachers to develop and strengthen these tendencies. It encourages students both to ask questions of teachers and other students, and to experiment and investigate on their own. It urges students to compare their ideas with those of others, to reason and argue in a constructive manner, and to look at people with different points of view as partners in finding the truth, not as enemies.

Teaching spherical geometry side-by-side with plane geometry may help individuals develop tolerance toward and understanding of those who are different in their cultural, traditional, or social background. It can help students gain the skills needed to excel in a diverse and multicultural world and can lead them to more clearly understand how relative and human all axioms and theorems of science are. Our greatest hope is that these studies on the sphere may increase the number of those with whom students will be able to communicate, live, and work on this globe.

Sincerely,

István Lénárt

István Lénárt

Using the Lénárt Sphere Curriculum

Fitting Spherical Geometry into Your Curriculum

Now that you have read the arguments for learning and teaching spherical geometry on the Lénárt Sphere, perhaps you are wondering "How am I going to fit spherical geometry into my mathematics curriculum?" The intention of this section is to give you different ideas for using these spherical geometry adventures in your classroom.

First of all, do not be deceived by the sequential appearance of the book. Only a few concepts are essential as prerequisites for many of the adventures. In fact, if students know that great circles are the spherical equivalent of straight lines, they are ready to tackle almost any adventure in this book. Check the Prerequisites section in the Teacher's Guide to a given adventure to find a more detailed description of any previous mathematical experience your students may need. Because different adventures contain overlapping mathematics, students have a chance to discover the same concept in different contexts.

Here are a few ways to use the material in this book.

Introducing the Lénárt Sphere to Your Class and Your Colleagues

The introductory adventure, "What color is the bear?" is short and informal and stimulates students to think about a spherical surface. The adventure contains a riddle that you can solve only when you realize that the riddle's scenario occurs on the curved surface of the earth.

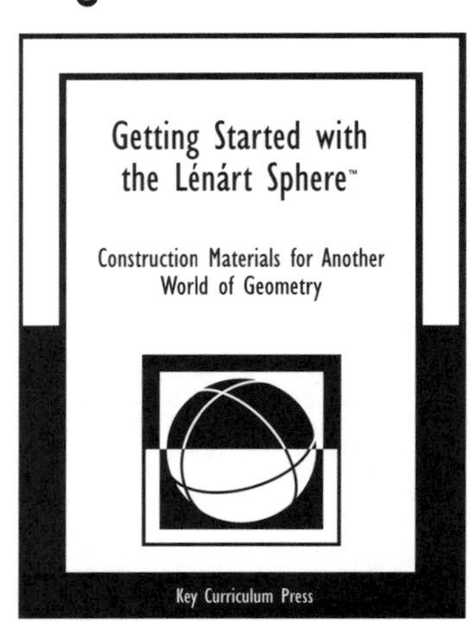

The booklet that comes with your Lénárt Sphere Construction Materials, *Getting Started with the Lénárt Sphere,* also contains an introduction to some of the basic ideas of spherical geometry. After a short introduction, the booklet features two lessons that introduce the construction tools and that provide a context for comparing some essential aspects of spherical and planar geometry. You can use this booklet to introduce Lénárt Sphere materials to your students and colleagues.

Teaching a Spherical Geometry Unit

You may want to devote more than one day to spherical geometry and teach an entire unit. Units can last a few days, or they may span an entire semester. The adventures in this book are organized into chapters by topic, so you can teach each chapter as a separate unit. Alternately, you can reorder and mix adventures from different chapters to make units of your own.

Appendix A suggests thirteen units, each of which may take your students about five days to complete. Because some of the book's later adventures make more sense if you've explored earlier adventures, several of the units begin with an adventure from Chapter 1, "Basic Concepts." These suggested units are only meant to help you in your planning; they are not meant to be a recommended curriculum. We encourage you to pursue spherical geometry in any direction that you and your students find most interesting.

Enriching Your Plane Geometry Class

If you are teaching a traditional plane geometry class, reinforce and enhance your curriculum with adventures in spherical geometry. Appendix B contains a chart to help you correlate a traditional geometry curriculum with the adventures in this book. If in your class students work together to perform investigations in plane geometry, give each group a Lénárt Sphere and ask them to perform the corresponding spherical investigations on it. Let students investigate the results for extra credit if there is insufficient class time for their explorations. In classes with widely varied performance levels among students, the Lénárt Sphere allows you to add significant and useful extra challenge for students who need it.

Spherical Geometry Projects

Use adventures as projects for students to complete inside or outside of class. Students can work independently on the projects or together in groups. Almost every adventure is a possible project. The tessellation adventures in Chapter 9 and the maps adventures in Chapter 7 require a lot of careful work and produce results that are appealing and decorative, so these adventures make very rewarding projects. Have each group pick a different adventure from these chapters and present it to the rest of the class as a completed project.

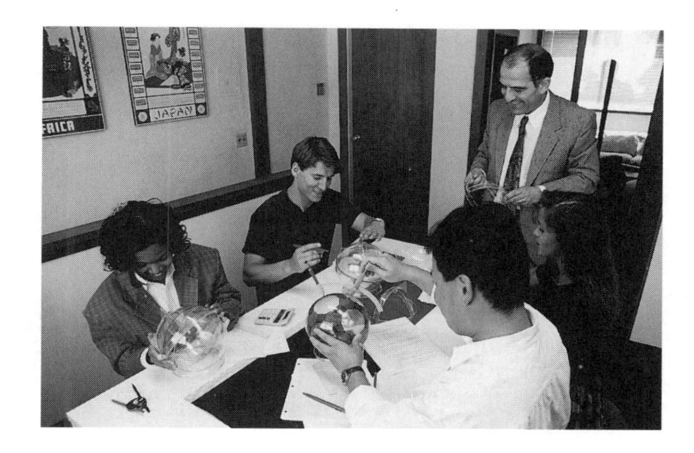

The Adventures and the Adventure Cards

We have designed this book to accommodate different styles of mathematical exploration. Some adventurers prefer to discover and explore without a guide. Maybe this is because they are more experienced travelers, because they are already familiar with the area they are exploring, or because they simply prefer the thrill of going places on their own.

Each adventure is presented in the form of an Adventure Card to accommodate the most adventurous type of explorer. If you and your students want a truly open-ended approach to spherical geometry, simply use these cards, which are in blackline master form. There is room on most Adventure Cards to write additional instructions of your own or instructions that you've taken from the Investigate and Explore More sections of the Student's Guides to the adventures. You can photocopy these cards onto paper or card stock and distribute them to individuals or groups. Keep copies of the Student's Guides handy so that students who get stuck or lost have somewhere to turn for help.

How can you tile the sphere with three different types of regular polygons?

The soccer ball is a spherical tessellation that uses two different regular polygons as its tiles. Can you make a spherical tessellation that uses more?

- Using three different types of regular polygons as tiles, construct a spherical tessellation.

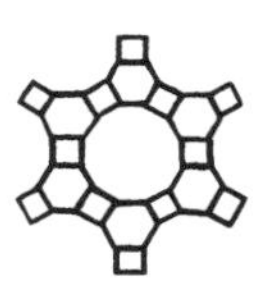

We suggest that you hang a large two-column comparison chart on a wall in your classroom so that students can summarize their results on the plane and on the sphere. Keep adding to the chart as your class adventures further. After completing some of the Basic Concepts adventures together as a class, students can divide into groups, then work and report on different adventures. Then the class comparison chart can serve as a useful reference for all groups.

Lines on the Plane	Lines on the Sphere
A segment of a straight line is the shortest path between two points.	An arc of a great circle is the shortest path between two points.
A straight line is infinite.	A great circle is finite.
A straight line has no center.	A great circle has two centers.
Two straight lines can be parallel.	Two great circles can never be parallel.
Two nonparallel straight lines intersect in exactly one point.	Two great circles intersect in exactly two points.

Student's Guides to the Adventures

One risk of exploring without guidance is getting completely lost. Sometimes it's impossible to know the best places to visit without the help of a knowledgeable guide.

For some adventures, you and your students may choose to explore the relatively uncharted territory of spherical geometry with some guidance. Use the Student's Guide version of the adventures for this purpose. Copy the entire adventure and provide your students with a more structured lesson. This structure helps adventurers travel more securely and ensures they don't miss any of the important attractions along the way.

Even if your students are using the Adventure Cards, keep copies of the Student's Guides handy so that students who get stuck or lost have a place to turn for help. Use the Student's Guides to better understand how to informally guide students who have trouble.

Contents of the Student's Guides

Construction on the Plane

Many of the adventures compare a concept in geometry on the plane with the corresponding concept on the sphere. Each of these adventures contains a Construction on the Plane and a Construction on the Sphere. These constructions are usually very similar. Students perform the first on a planar surface such as a piece of paper or a computer screen, then perform the second on their Lénárt Sphere. Each construction is followed by an Investigate section in which students make discoveries about their constructions.

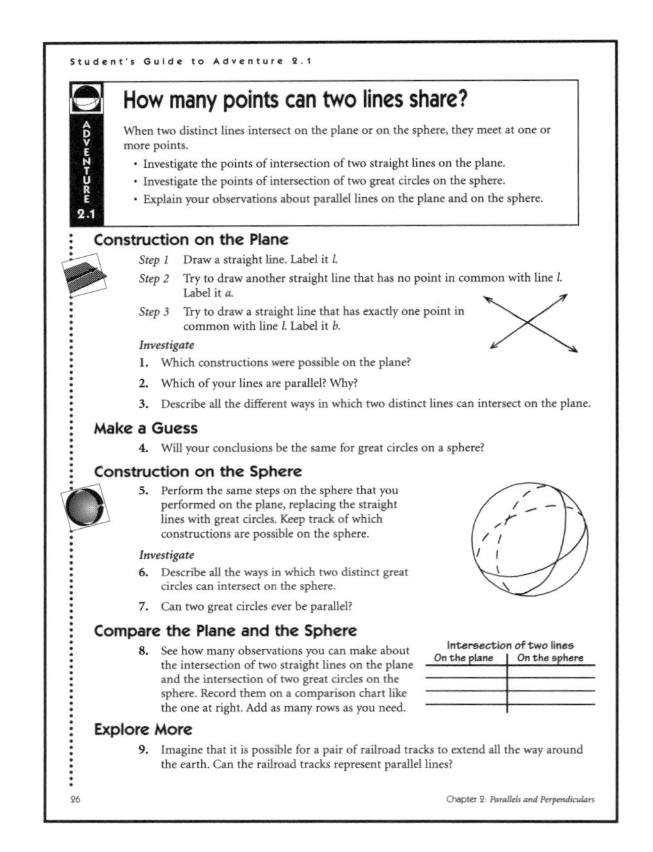

Student's Guide to Adventure 2.1

ADVENTURE 2.1

How many points can two lines share?

When two distinct lines intersect on the plane or on the sphere, they meet at one or more points.

- Investigate the points of intersection of two straight lines on the plane.
- Investigate the points of intersection of two great circles on the sphere.
- Explain your observations about parallel lines on the plane and on the sphere.

Construction on the Plane

Step 1 Draw a straight line. Label it *l*.

Step 2 Try to draw another straight line that has no point in common with line *l*. Label it *a*.

Step 3 Try to draw a straight line that has exactly one point in common with line *l*. Label it *b*.

Investigate

1. Which constructions were possible on the plane?
2. Which of your lines are parallel? Why?
3. Describe all the different ways in which two distinct lines can intersect on the plane.

Make a Guess

4. Will your conclusions be the same for great circles on a sphere?

Construction on the Sphere

5. Perform the same steps on the sphere that you performed on the plane, replacing the straight lines with great circles. Keep track of which constructions are possible on the sphere.

Investigate

6. Describe all the ways in which two distinct great circles can intersect on the sphere.
7. Can two great circles ever be parallel?

Compare the Plane and the Sphere

8. See how many observations you can make about the intersection of two straight lines on the plane and the intersection of two great circles on the sphere. Record them on a comparison chart like the one at right. Add as many rows as you need.

Intersection of two lines	
On the plane	On the sphere

Explore More

9. Imagine that it is possible for a pair of railroad tracks to extend all the way around the earth. Can the railroad tracks represent parallel lines?

26 Chapter 2: Parallels and Perpendiculars

Make a Guess

After students have finished the Construction on the Plane and have learned (or reviewed) a particular concept in plane geometry, they are asked to Make a Guess. This gives them an opportunity to predict the corresponding outcome in spherical geometry. There are no wrong answers in the Make a Guess section. Encourage students to make wild guesses, and reward them for free and brave thought. You will find that very often the most unusual idea is nearest to the truth.

Construction on the Sphere

This section contains steps for using the spherical construction tools to perform a construction on the Lénárt Sphere. The Construction on the Sphere section usually contains directions for a spherical construction which is equivalent to the planar construction.

Compare the Plane and the Sphere

After exploring one aspect of geometry on both the plane and the sphere, students compare the two geometries. This section almost always asks students to fill out a comparison chart. The first column charts their exploration into plane geometry, the second contains the corresponding information they discovered in spherical geometry. You may want to hang a large version of this chart on a wall in your classroom and continue adding to it as your class adventures further. If different groups of students are working on different adventures, this class chart will be a useful reference for all groups.

After building the chart, we ask students to identify which geometric surface they thought was simpler to work with in that particular adventure. Once they pick the simpler surface, the next question asks them to try to reverse their argument and give some reasons why the other surface might be simpler. For some topics—such as the sum of the angles of a triangle—one surface clearly seems simpler and more elegant than the other and it is hard to argue both ways. For other topics, neither surface is an obvious victor.

Explore More

Every adventure has an Explore More section with extended construction and application problems. The Explore More problems enrich the adventure, and you may want to use them even with adventures for which you are not using the rest of the Student's Guide.

Teacher's Guides to the Adventures

Because you will probably lead these adventures, you'll want to know what equipment to bring along, how long the adventure might take, and what to do in an emergency. The Teacher's Guide helps you prepare for the adventure. This guide contains information about any prerequisite knowledge your students will need to bring along, any additional materials to have in the classroom, and a predicted length for each adventure. The Teacher's Guide also contains detailed answers to questions in the Student's Guide.

Using the Lénárt Sphere Construction Tools

The tools for working on the Lénárt Sphere correspond to the traditional drawing and measuring tools used to study geometry on the plane.

Tools for geometry on the plane	Tools for geometry on the sphere
You draw and write on a **flat surface** or on a **flat computer screen.**	You draw and write on the **Lénárt Sphere** or on **hemispherical transparencies** fitted onto the sphere.
You use a **straightedge** to draw straight lines, line segments, and rays.	You use a **spherical straightedge** to draw great circles and arcs of great circles.
You use a **ruler** to measure line segments.	You use a **spherical ruler** to measure great circles and arcs of great circles.
You use a **protractor** to measure angles.	You can use the spherical ruler as a **spherical protractor** to measure angles. Alternately, you can create a smaller spherical protractor out of a circular piece of transparency (see Adventure 1.5).
You use a **compass** to draw circles.	You use a **spherical compass** and a **center locator** to draw circles.
If you use a **pencil**, you can erase your work with an eraser.	If you use a **non-permanent marking pen**, you can erase your work with a damp cloth or paper towel.

Sphere

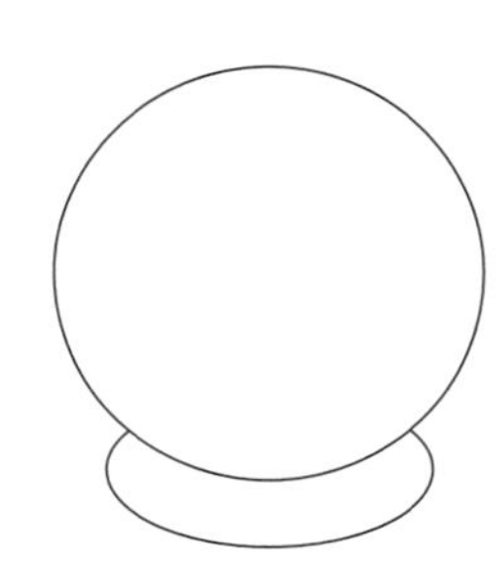

Your Lénárt Sphere set contains one transparent plastic sphere. This is the surface you will use to investigate spherical geometry. You can draw with non-permanent markers directly on the sphere or on hemispherical transparencies that fit over the sphere. When the sphere is not being held, always rest it on the torus or the spherical ruler. *To guard against breakage, never throw or drop your sphere.*

Torus

Your set also contains a torus, or donut-shaped surface. The torus serves as a base for the sphere and as another interesting surface on which to experiment.

Transparencies

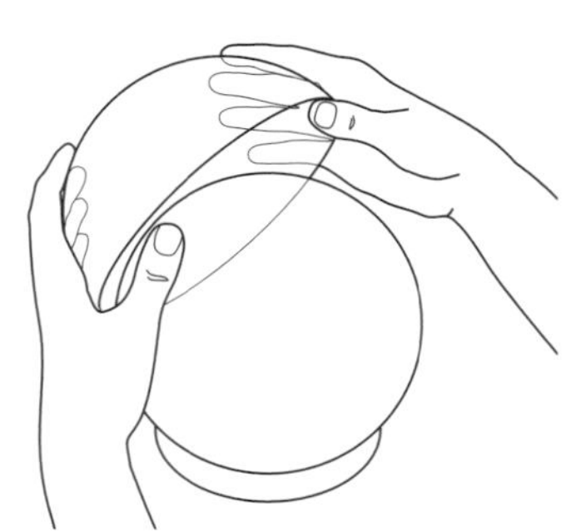

Each Lénárt Sphere set contains four hemispherical transparencies that fit over the sphere. These transparencies are the "paper" for your spherical "tabletop." You can draw on these transparencies with non-permanent markers and erase your drawings with a damp cloth or paper towel. You can cut transparencies into various shapes with scissors, and you can connect two hemispherical transparencies with a special hanger to make a hanging sphere.

If more than one class needs to use the spheres on a given day and you expect that students will need more than one class period to complete their constructions, have them work on transparencies rather than directly on the sphere. They can save their work, and they won't have to clean off the sphere for the next group of students.

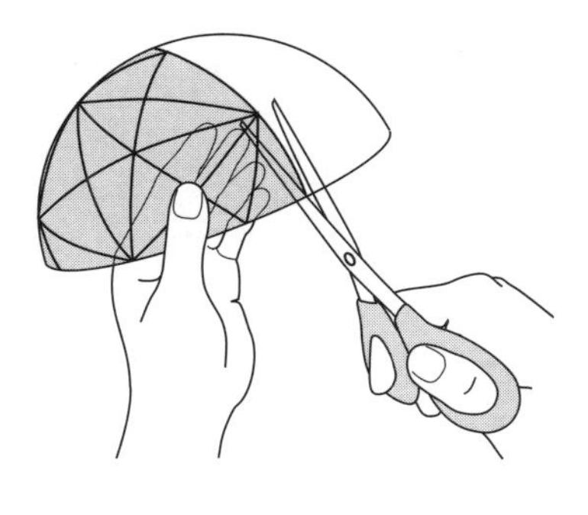

Some adventures require students to cut up transparencies. Often you can save the pieces from one class for use in another class. (For example, in Adventure 4.2, students explore AAA correspondence in a pair of triangles. They need to cut transparencies into three large pieces so that each piece can be the angle of a spherical triangle.)

Use transparencies so that you can collect students' work or save important constructions. Your own spherical library of transparencies can come in handy when you want to demonstrate a new concept or reinforce a previous one.

Sometimes you may want to sketch over a background drawing you want to preserve for future use. (For example, when students construct the time zones on their globe in Adventure 7.3, they may need to reuse the map.) In these cases you can make the background drawing on the sphere itself and do additional work on transparencies. Optionally, you can use permanent markers to trace the background drawing on a transparency, then use non-permanent markers to do additional work. Transparencies and marking pens are the only "consumable" components in the Lénárt Sphere set. Replacement supplies of both items are available from Key Curriculum Press.

Hangers

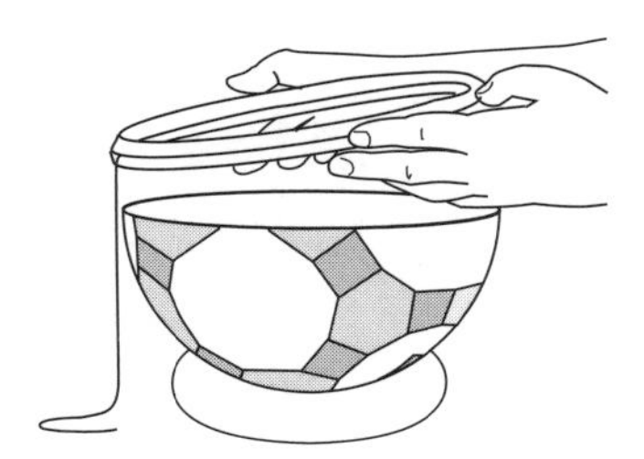

Each Lénárt Sphere set contains one plastic hoop or hanger. You can join two transparencies with a hanger to form a hanging sphere. The tessellation adventures in Chapter 9 and the maps adventures in Chapter 7 make especially decorative constructions to hang in your classroom.

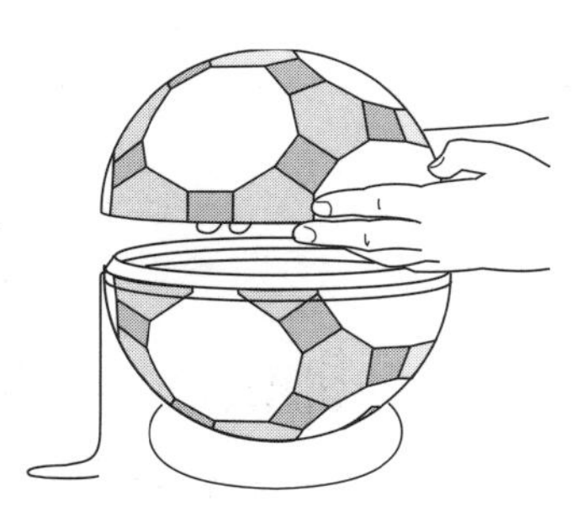

To suspend a pair of transparencies with the hanger perpendicular to the ground, tie a knot near the end of a piece of string, and thread the string, with the knot inside, through the hole of the hanger. Then set one transparency on the torus and fit the hanger into the transparency. Finally, fit the second transparency onto the hanger.

If you choose to hang the transparencies with the hanger parallel to the ground, tie a knot on a string, and thread the string, with the knot inside, through the hole of one transparency. Then complete the assembly. (If necessary, you can use two small pieces of transparent tape to ensure that the hanging sphere does not come apart.)

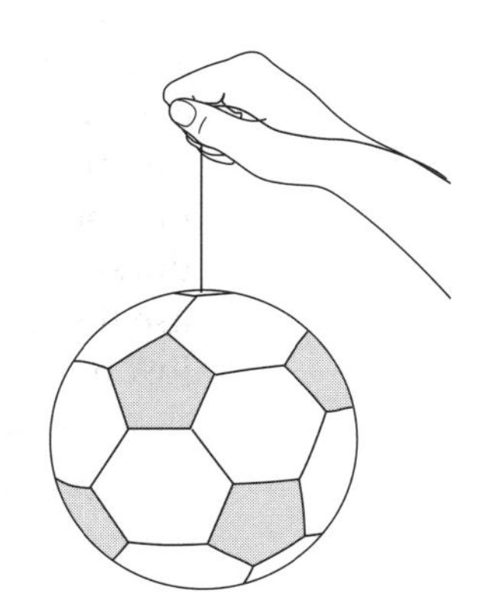

Spherical Straightedge/Ruler/Protractor

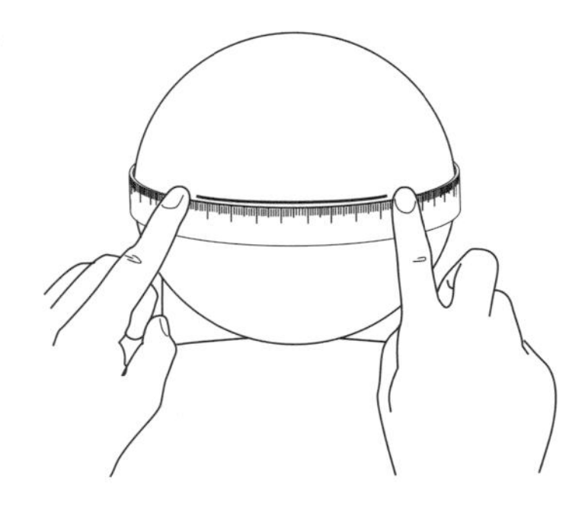

Use your spherical straightedge or ruler to draw and measure the sphere's great circles and arcs of great circles. This construction tool also works as a protractor for measuring spherical angles.

The spherical ruler has three "feet" that allow it to stand on a table and hold the sphere. With the sphere cradled in the ruler it is easy to draw a great circle. The two *scaled* edges trace arcs of great circles; the other edges do not. To measure distance with the spherical ruler, align the arc you are measuring with one of these scaled edges. The markings on the ruler indicate degrees, which are used to measure distance on the sphere. (When the spherical ruler is sitting on its feet and holding the sphere, the great circle along its scaled edge has the same inclination as the earth's equator relative to the sun.)

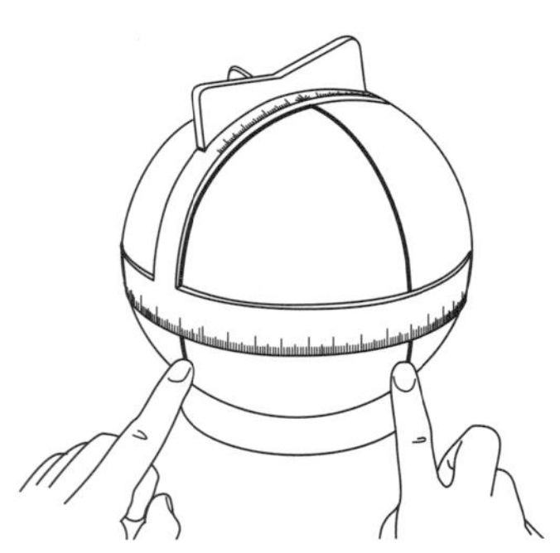

There are several ways to use the spherical ruler as a protractor to measure (or draw) spherical angles. The simplest, but also the least accurate, way is to make use of the mini-protractor, with 30° divisions on it, at the top of the shorter ruled edge. You can choose another method that is more tedious but more precise. Place the midpoint of the shorter ruled edge at the vertex of the angle. Then line up one side of the angle with this ruled edge. Count the degrees that are along the great circle (longer ruled edge) and that are between the two sides of the angle. You may need to extend the sides of the angles so that they intersect this great circle.

Use both ruled edges to construct right angles with the spherical ruler. Finish the corner of the right angle by extending one of the sides.

You can make a smaller protractor from a circular piece of a transparency. The instructions for making this protractor are in Adventure 1.5. This protractor can be very handy, especially for measuring angles in smaller constructions.

Spherical Compass and Center Locator

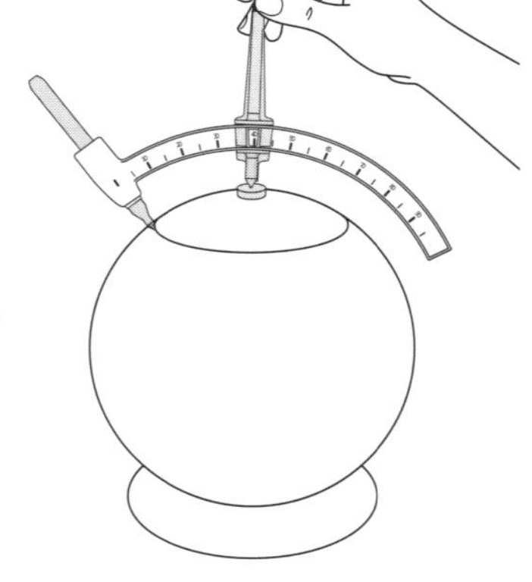

Your construction set contains a spherical compass and a center locator for drawing circles on the sphere and the transparencies. The center locator has a hole in its center to fix the position of the compass point. To draw a spherical circle, first mark its center on the sphere. Position the sphere on the torus so that the center mark for your circle is on top of the sphere. Place the center locator on the sphere so that the center mark shows through the hole. Then use the spherical compass as you would use its planar counterpart. Just hold the grooved tip between your thumb and forefinger and slowly twist it around.

The spherical compass does not measure degrees as accurately as the ruler. So for constructions where accuracy is important, use the ruler to verify the compass setting. *(Warning: Be sure that ink from permanent markers is dry before coming into contact with the center locator.)*

Non-Permanent Marking Pens and Collars for Holding the Pens

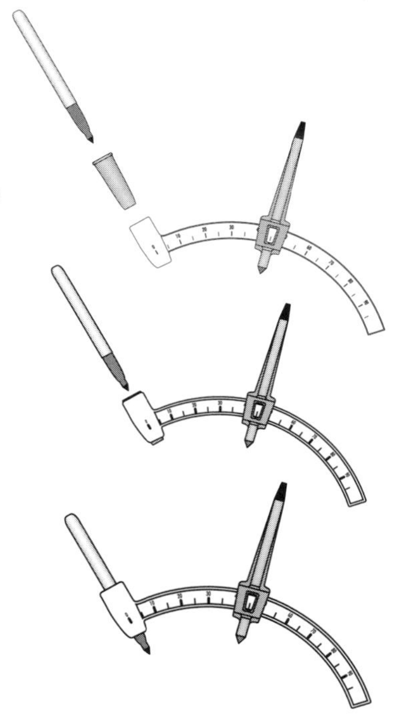

Your set contains four non-permanent marking pens (red, blue, green, and black) for drawing on the sphere, the torus, and the transparencies. Use water to erase these surfaces, just as you would on an overhead transparency. You can use a spray bottle and paper towels, or you can keep a damp cloth handy.

Occasionally you may want to use permanent overhead markers to preserve an especially nice or important construction on a transparency. Use rubbing alcohol on a tissue or a paper towel to erase permanent markers. *(Only write on the sphere with permanent markers made specifically for use with overhead transparencies. Ink from "dry erase" markers, for example, cannot be removed from the sphere.)*

The four collars included in your set are designed to hold Vis-à-Vis® and Stabilo®-OH markers snugly in the barrel of the compass. Simply push the appropriate collar into the barrel of the compass arc until it snaps into place. Then push the marking pen into the collar as far as it will go. *To prevent your marking pens from drying out, always remove the pen from the collar and replace its cap when not in use.*

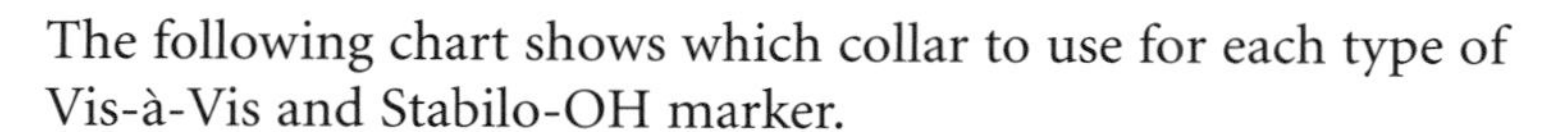

The following chart shows which collar to use for each type of Vis-à-Vis and Stabilo-OH marker.

Type of marking pen	Collar identification	Collar color
Vis-à-Vis Wet-Erase Fine Point (non-permanent)	V-WF	Light blue
Vis-à-Vis Wet-Erase Extra Fine Point (non-permanent) Vis-à-Vis Permanent Extra Fine Point	V-XF	Clear
Vis-à-Vis Permanent Fine Point	V-PF	White
Stabilo-OH Water Soluble Medium Point (non-permanent) Stabilo-OH Water Soluble Fine Point (non-permanent) Stabilo-OH Permanent Medium Point Stabilo-OH Permanent Fine Point	S-OH	Red

To work with a different brand of marker, use a length of string in place of a collar. Simply wind the string around the marker until it fits snugly into the empty barrel of the compass arc. The string should keep the marker from wobbling or falling out of the barrel.

The Living Earth Poster and Globe

The Living Earth on the Lénárt Sphere poster includes polyconic projections of the earth's northern and southern hemispheres. You can mount the poster and display it as a flat map, or you can cut out the polyconic projections and make a spherical map to display as a globe on your Lénárt Sphere. The directions for making the globe are printed on the poster.

In Adventure 7.1, you use polyconic projections to trace a spherical map onto two transparencies.

Storage Container

The cubical box in which each Lénárt Sphere set was packed is its permanent storage container. Simply remove the loose piece of protective cardboard that surrounded the sphere during shipping, and the box will easily hold a complete set of materials. To avoid loss, you should store extra transparencies (with foam spacers between them), hangers, and collars separately from the rest of the set.

CHAPTER 0
Getting Started

Chapter 0: Getting Started

Adventure 0.1: What color is the bear?

Getting Started is a short chapter with only one adventure. This adventure provides an opportunity for students to explore their new spherical surface and to use the spherical tools but does not require them to formalize their mathematics. The adventure presents a riddle. As students solve the riddle, they explore some of the basic differences between a plane and a sphere. A more formal approach to the geometric differences between the sphere and the plane begins in Chapter 1.

Another purpose of this chapter is to show how geometry on a sphere models the geography of our planet earth. The solution to the riddle of the bear highlights the inaccuracy of mapping a nearly spherical surface onto a flat plane. In Chapter 7, students will explore the geographical applications of spherical geometry in more depth. Students begin Chapter 7 by creating a more accurate global map of the earth on their Lénárt Sphere.

This adventure about the bear is valuable for students of any age and mathematical ability. Younger students will be entertained by the story of the bear and her trip. We have also seen this adventure inspire adult mathematicians to argue for weeks about which direction on the earth is truly due west.

Use the Adventure Card below if you prefer a completely open-ended discussion of the riddle. If you prefer a more structured approach, use the Student's Guide to Adventure 0.1 instead.

ADVENTURE 0.1

What color is the bear?

You may be familiar with the following riddle:

A wandering bear leaves home and walks 100 kilometers south. After a rest, she turns west and walks straight ahead for 100 kilometers. Then she turns again and walks north. To her surprise she finds that she arrives back home again. What color is the bear?

Adventure Cards and Student's Guides: Two Formats for Two Styles of Learning

Each activity—or *adventure*—in this book is presented in two forms to accommodate two different learning styles. First each adventure is succinctly described on an *Adventure Card* as an unguided investigation in which students determine their own paths of exploration. Then the same adventure is repeated in a more structured *Student's Guide* with step-by-step constructions, guided investigations, and questions for further exploration. Following the Student's Guide is the *Teacher's Guide* with solutions and hints.

The Adventure Cards are designed to accommodate the most adventurous type of explorer. If you and your students want a truly open-ended approach to spherical geometry, simply use these cards, which are in blackline master form. There is room on most Adventure Cards to write additional instructions of your own or instructions that you've taken from the Investigate and Explore More sections of the Student's Guides to the adventures.

The Adventure Cards are found at the beginning of each chapter. You can photocopy these cards onto paper or card stock and distribute them to individuals or groups. Keep copies of the Student's Guides handy so that students who get stuck or lost have somewhere to turn for help.

This introductory chapter has only one adventure, and the Adventure Card is above. The corresponding Student's Guide and Teacher's Guide are on the following two pages.

ADVENTURE 0.1

What color is the bear?

You may be familiar with the following riddle:

A wandering bear leaves home and walks 100 kilometers south. After a rest, she turns west and walks straight ahead for 100 kilometers. Then she turns again and walks north. To her surprise she finds that she arrives back home again. What color is the bear?

Construction on the Plane

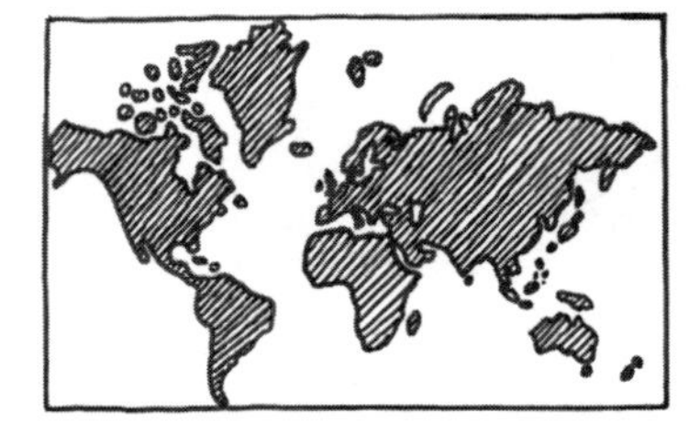

Sketch on a sheet of paper a drawing of the bear's trip.

Investigate

1. Is it possible for the bear to end up at the same place she started?

Construction on the Sphere

Sketch on your sphere a drawing of the bear's trip.

Investigate

2. Is it possible for the bear to end up at the same place she started?
3. Where does the bear live?
4. What color is the bear?

Welcome to the World of Spherical Geometry

In this adventure you noticed that the story of the bear has a different ending depending on what kind of surface the bear uses for her travels. Geometry can change quite a bit when you draw and study it on two different surfaces!

In this book you will investigate geometry on the surface of a sphere. You will draw and experiment on your Lénárt Sphere, just as you use a flat piece of paper or a flat computer screen to experiment with geometry on a plane.

You are already familiar with many aspects of plane geometry. In these adventures you will often compare what you know is true on the plane with what you discover on the sphere.

5. Which surface do you prefer?
6. Which makes a simpler geometry?
7. Which geometric system is more intriguing?

As you discover geometry on a surface shaped like our planet earth, enjoy your explorations!

What color is the bear?

Student Audience: Any

Prerequisites: Students should be able to locate the North Pole, the South Pole, and the equator on maps and globes. They should know the relationships among the directions north, south, east, and west.

Class Time: 20 minutes

Tips for the Adventure

The only home possible for the bear is the North Pole. Therefore she is a polar bear and must be white. (In Hungary, polar bears are called ice bears.)

This adventure is an invitation to the topic, an appetizer for the material. We can't and shouldn't expect precise solutions because our students are not yet familiar with the concepts indispensable for the correct solution. Let them conduct their experiments and offer statements like: "Two parallel straight lines never go through a common point" or "It must be the North Pole."

Construction on the Plane

The bear's trip on the plane looks like three sides of a square.

Construction on the Sphere

Students are likely to come up with two types of drawings to represent the bear's path on the sphere. One type of drawing will contain two "straight" paths of equal length meeting at the North Pole, both connected to a "curved" path (the western trip) that follows a latitude of the globe.

The other type of drawing contains all straight paths. Only the southern trip and the western trip are perpendicular. The third northern trip connects back to the North Pole and is of a different length than the other two.

At this point both drawings are acceptable, although the second one is probably more correct geographically. (The two drawings at right are exaggerations of the actual route of the bear, since the distance of 100 km is too short to be adequately shown.)

If students do come up with the second drawing, you might ask them: "How far should the bear travel south if we want her to go straight, equal distances in the south, west, and north directions?" The answer is one fourth of the whole equator, or about 10,000 km in each direction. So in this case, her first trip would take her all the way to the equator.

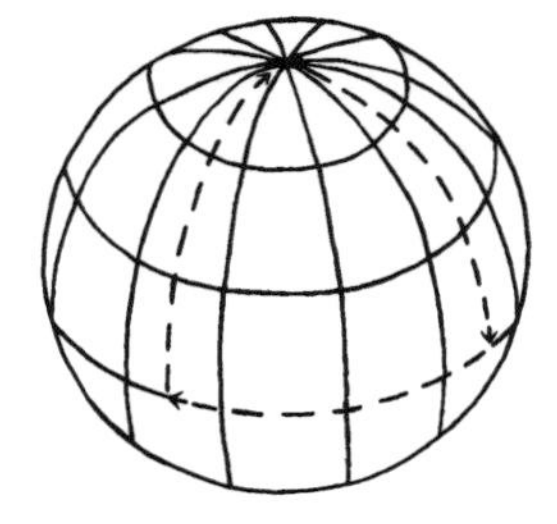

If you do get into a detailed discussion about what the geographic directions really are on the sphere, you can define them as follows (as long as you are not at the North or South Pole):

Connect your point of location with the North and South poles. This path tells you which way north and south are. Now, if you turn so that you are facing north, west will be to your left and east will be to your right.

CHAPTER 1
Basic Concepts

Chapter 1: Basic Concepts

Adventure 1.1: What is the simplest shape?

Adventure 1.2: Can you draw a straight line on a sphere?

Adventure 1.3: How do you measure distance?

Adventure 1.4: How can you construct equators and pole points?

Adventure 1.5: How can you use a protractor to measure angles on a sphere?

This chapter contains five adventures that provide students with the basic ideas and skills they will need for working on the Lénárt Sphere. In Adventures 1.1 and 1.2, students determine the spherical equivalents of a point and a straight line. Just as they do in plane geometry, they must agree on these simplest elements before they can build more complex shapes. Because there are no straight lines on a sphere, Adventure 1.2 is crucial to the student's understanding of a basic difference between the two geometries and is a prerequisite for almost all the other adventures.
In Adventure 1.3, students learn how to use a spherical ruler to measure distance on the sphere. In Adventure 1.4, students find methods for constructing pole points and equators—shapes that do not exist on the plane but are important in many spherical constructions. In Adventure 1.5, students build a small spherical protractor out of a piece of spherical transparency.

Use these first adventures as an introduction to spherical geometry, but don't let your students get stuck dealing with these basic concepts too long. The ideas in this chapter will adequately prepare them for the more sophisticated adventures that appear later in the book. See Appendix A for some suggested five-day units that will help you plan an appropriate sequence of adventures.

Use the Adventure Cards at the beginning of the chapter if you prefer a more open-ended approach to the lessons. If you prefer structured lessons, use the Student's Guides instead. The Teacher's Guide that follows each Student's Guide contains solutions and suggestions.

ADVENTURE 1.1

What is the simplest shape?

In these adventures you will learn about geometry on the surface of the sphere. The first step in building a geometric system on any surface is to decide what the simplest shape is on that surface. The simplest geometric shape will help you in your further investigations, and you will use it to develop other shapes and ideas.

- Determine which shape is the simplest on the plane.
- Determine which shape is the simplest on the sphere.

ADVENTURE 1.2

Can you draw a straight line on a sphere?

Let's consider the point to be the simplest shape on the plane and on the sphere.

- Describe the simplest, shortest path between two points on the plane.
- Describe the simplest, shortest path between two points on the sphere.
- Describe the shape you get when you extend each of these two paths.

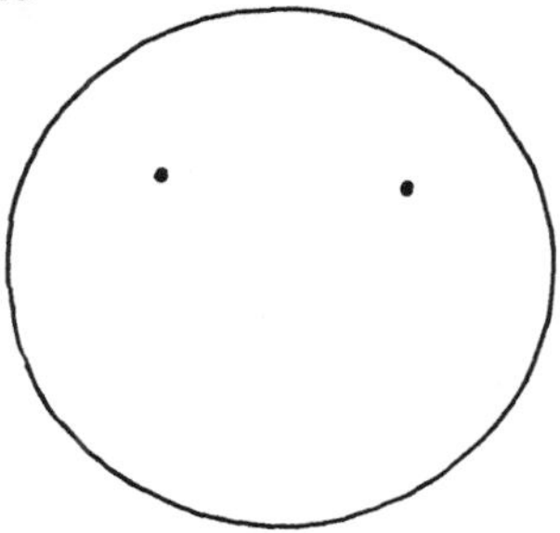

ADVENTURE 1.3

How do you measure distance?

You often need to measure the distance between two figures.

- Describe how to measure distance on the plane.
- Describe how to measure distance on the sphere.
- In each case, explain what units of measure you can use.

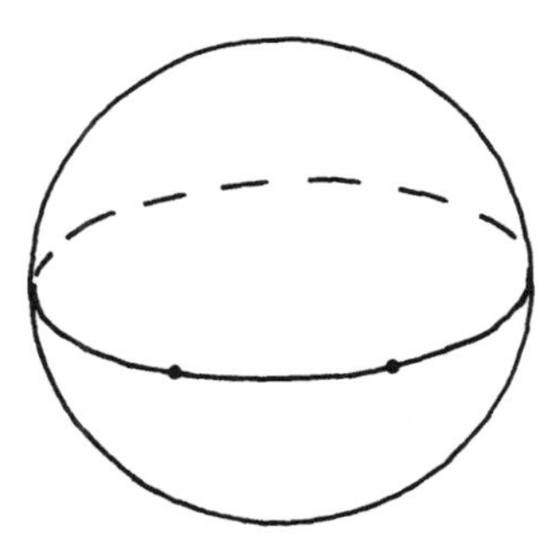

ADVENTURE 1.4

How can you construct equators and pole points?

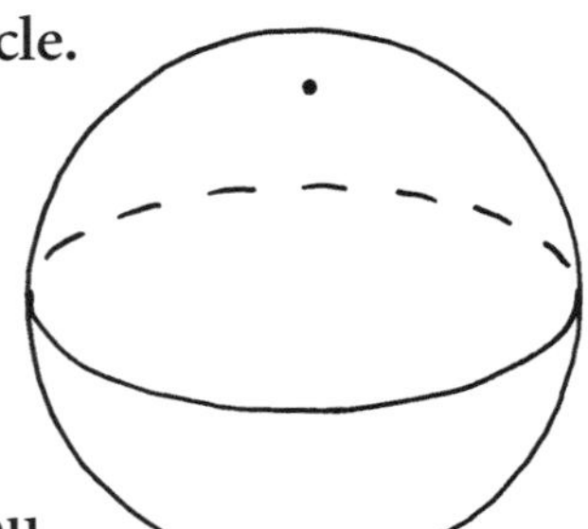

The equator of the planet earth is approximately a great circle. This great circle has two centers or *pole points:* the North and South poles. On a sphere we call any great circle an *equator* and we call a great circle's pole points its *poles.*

- Determine how to construct an equator if you know one of its pole points.
- Determine how to construct a pair of pole points if you know their equator.

ADVENTURE 1.5

How can you use a protractor to measure angles on a sphere?

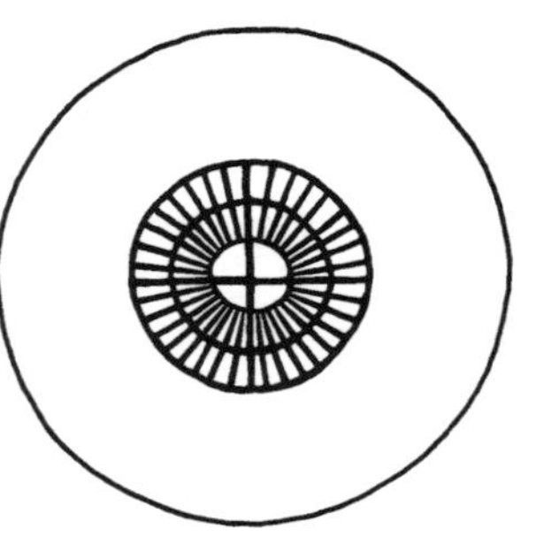

You know how to use a flat protractor to measure angles on a plane. Can you use a flat protractor to measure angles on a sphere?

- Use a piece of a spherical transparency to make a protractor that can measure angles on a sphere.

ADVENTURE 1.1

What is the simplest shape?

In these adventures you will learn about geometry on the surface of the sphere. The first step in building a geometric system on any surface is to decide what the simplest shape is on that surface. The simplest geometric shape will help you in your further investigations, and you will use it to develop other shapes and ideas.

- Determine which shape is the simplest on the plane.
- Determine which shape is the simplest on the sphere.

The Simplest Shape on the Plane

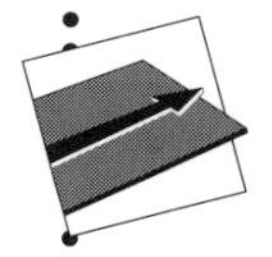

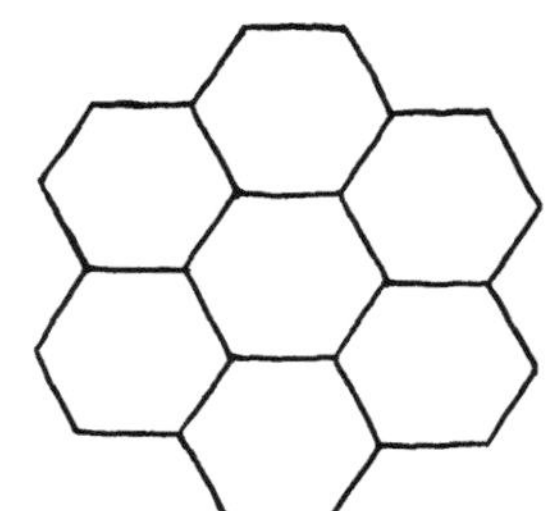

1. There are many different kinds of geometric shapes on the plane: points, lines, circles, tiles on a floor, and streets on a map of your neighborhood. Decide which shape you think is the simplest shape on the plane. Give your reasons for your choice.

The Simplest Shape on the Sphere

2. There are also many different kinds of geometric shapes on the sphere: points, lines, circles, polygons on a soccer ball, and land masses on a globe. Use your marker, spherical ruler, and spherical compass to draw many different geometric shapes on your sphere.

3. Review your reasons for the choice you made for the simplest shape on the plane. Decide if these reasons also hold true on the sphere.

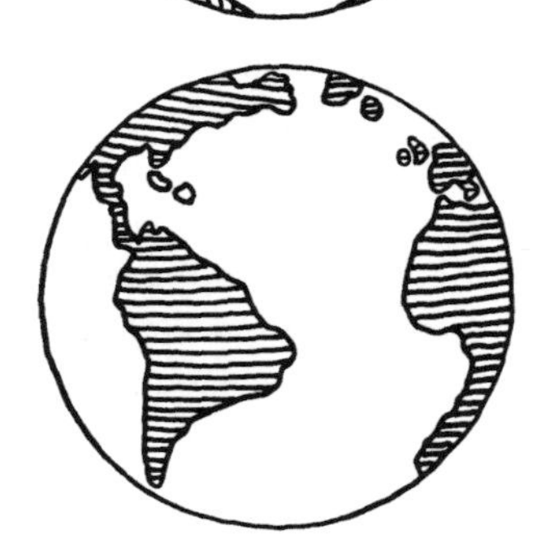

Compare the Plane and the Sphere

4. **a.** Draw at least two shapes on your sphere that you cannot draw on a plane.

   b. Describe the shapes and explain why you cannot draw these shapes on the plane.

5. **a.** Draw at least two shapes on your sphere that you can draw on a plane.

   b. Describe the shapes and explain why you can draw these shapes on the plane.

6. Discuss your findings with your partner or group. See how many differences you can find between the plane and the sphere.

What is the simplest shape?

Student Audience: Any

Prerequisites: None

Class Time: 20–40 minutes

Tips for the Adventure

Your class can complete this adventure without student handouts. In this case, the Student's Guide simply offers you some guidelines for discussion.

The Simplest Shape on the Sphere

Suggest that students choose the point both on the plane and on the sphere. We do not expect absolutely valid reasons for this choice because there are many other possibilities besides the point, such as straight lines, great circles, and pairs of points. Typical answers are "The point is the easiest to draw" or "It is the smallest, so it must be the simplest, too." We have no better reasons ourselves.

Compare the Plane and the Sphere

4. An example of a shape that can be drawn on the sphere but not on the plane is a spherical triangle with two right angles.

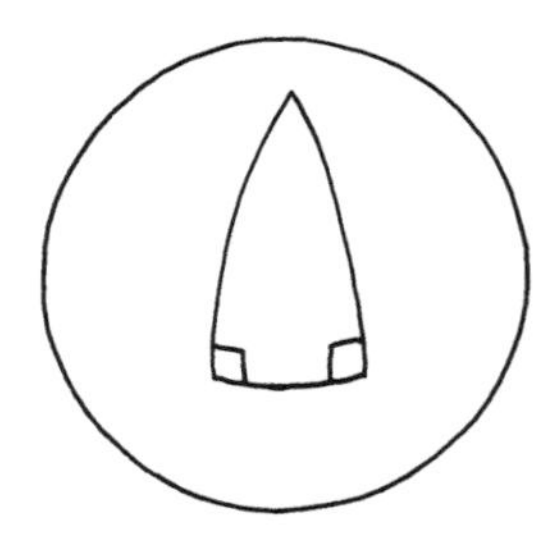

5. The intersection of a plane and a sphere is a circle or a point. Thus a shape that can be drawn both on the plane and on the sphere must be a point, an entire circle that is not bigger than an equator of the sphere, or any part of the perimeter of such a circle.

ADVENTURE 1.2

Can you draw a straight line on a sphere?

Let's consider the point to be the simplest shape on the plane and on the sphere.

- Describe the simplest, shortest path between two points on the plane.
- Describe the simplest, shortest path between two points on the sphere.
- Describe the shape you get when you extend each of these two paths.

Construction on the Plane

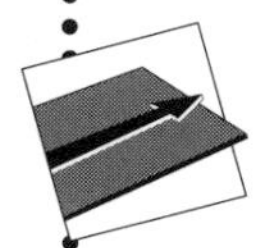

Step 1 Draw two different points on the plane. Label them *A* and *B*.

A B

Step 2 Connect points *A* and *B* with three different lines or curves.

Step 3 Draw the shortest path between points *A* and *B* if you have not yet done so. Use a taut string to show that you have really drawn the shortest path.

Step 4 Use a straightedge to extend your shortest path until it reaches the edges of your paper.

Investigate

1. If you could extend the ends of your line forever, would they ever meet?

2. How is the shortest path between points *A* and *B* different from the other paths you drew?

3. **a.** Into how many sections do points *A* and *B* divide your line?

b. How many of these sections are finite?

c. How many are infinitely long?

4. How many different straight lines can you draw through one point on a plane?

5. How many different straight lines can you draw through two points on a plane?

Make a Guess

6. What shape will you get when you connect two points on a sphere with the shortest possible path?

7. What will happen when you extend this path in both directions around the sphere?

Construction on the Sphere

Step 1 Draw two different points on your sphere. Label them *A* and *B*.

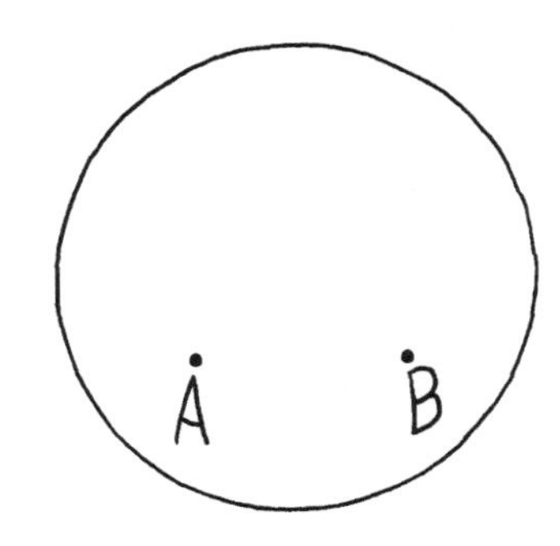

Step 2 Stretch a piece of string on the sphere between the two points to find the shortest path between them. Have your partner draw a line along the taut string with a marker.

Step 3 Pick either of the two ruled edges of your spherical ruler and try to align it with your line on the sphere. What do you observe?

Step 4 Continue drawing the line along the spherical ruler and extend it as far as possible in both directions.

Investigate

8. You have just created a **great circle** on a sphere. Describe it.

9. a. Into how many **arcs** do points *A* and *B* divide your great circle?

b. How many of these arcs are finite?

c. How many are infinitely long?

10. Determine which edges of your spherical ruler trace arcs of great circles and which don't.

11. How many great circles can you draw through one point on a sphere?

12. a. How many great circles can you draw through two points on a sphere?

b. Is your answer true for any two points on a sphere?

Compare the Plane and the Sphere

13. See how many observations you can make about straight lines on the plane and great circles on the sphere. Record them on a comparison chart like the one at right. Add as many rows as you need.

Lines

On the plane	On the sphere

14. Decide which you think is simpler: straight lines on the plane or great circles on the sphere. Why?

15. Now try to reverse your argument. Give reasons why lines are simpler on the surface you *didn't* choose above.

Explore More

16. a. Put a drop of water onto a tilted flat surface and allow the drop to run down the surface. Describe the path of the drop of water.

b. Put a drop of water near the top of your sphere and allow the drop to run down the surface. Describe the path of the drop of water. Does it follow a great circle?

17. Use a globe that depicts the earth.

a. Find two places on the globe between which there is more than one shortest route.

b. Find another such pair of places.

18. An airplane flies from San Francisco, California, to Moscow, Russia.

a. Use a globe and describe the shortest route for the flight.

b. Explain why there is only one shortest route.

c. Follow the same route on the planar map at right. Does the route appear to be straight?

19. The *great* in *great circle* means large. What's so great about a great circle?

Can you draw a straight line on a sphere?

Student Audience: Middle School/High School

Prerequisites: Students must understand the concept of a point on the plane and on the sphere.

Class Time: 30–45 minutes

Construction/Investigation on the Plane

Draw pieces of the straight line on the plane with either a taut string or a straightedge. You get the same line whether you hold the straightedge in the upright or in the upside-down position. We shift from the string to the straightedge as quickly as possible because the straightedge is much more precise than the string.

3. Points *A* and *B* divide the line into three separate sections. Only the middle section is finite and can be measured. The other two are infinite and thus cannot be measured. Discuss how a segment is measured with a ruler.

Some propose that points *A* and *B* constitute two sections themselves, so the two points actually determine five parts of the line. This is no doubt true. Thus we should state that we exclude the division points from this type of division. We shall follow this convention throughout the book. When we ask the students to divide the spherical surface into parts with two great circles, we will deliberately exclude the great circles from the resulting parts.

Make a Guess

6. Before performing the experiment, students may express doubts about whether the line along the taut string on the sphere is unique, that is, whether two given points on the sphere determine a line.

Construction/Investigation on the Sphere

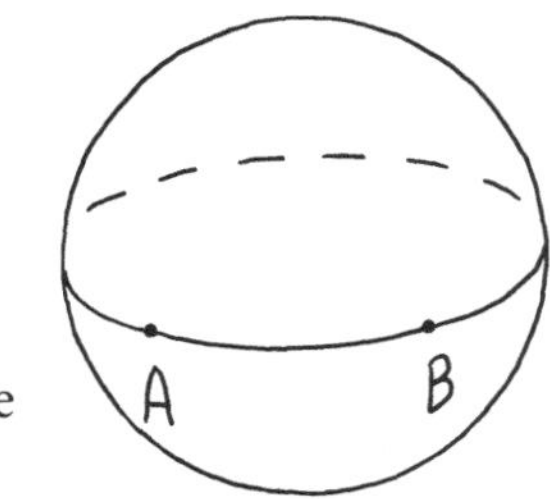

Use either a taut string or the scaled edges of the spherical ruler to draw pieces of the great circle on the sphere, the greatest of all the spherical circles. You get the same great circle whether the ruler is in the upright or the upside-down position. We shift from the string to the ruler as quickly as possible because the ruler is much more precise than the string. Students must draw all the way around the sphere and get back to the starting point, and this is easier with the ruler than with the string.

8. The term *great circle* is used because it is the greatest circle possible on the sphere. Students sometimes propose the term *spherical straight line* for the great circle. This is okay, but make it clear that straight lines of the plane do not exist on the sphere.

9. Points *A* and *B* divide the great circle into two separate arcs. Each arc is finite.

10. Students are often surprised to learn that only the two scaled edges of the ruler draw arcs of great circles. All the other edges draw smaller circles. If students have doubts, let them check their lines with the ruler in the upside-down position. They get a drawing like the one shown.

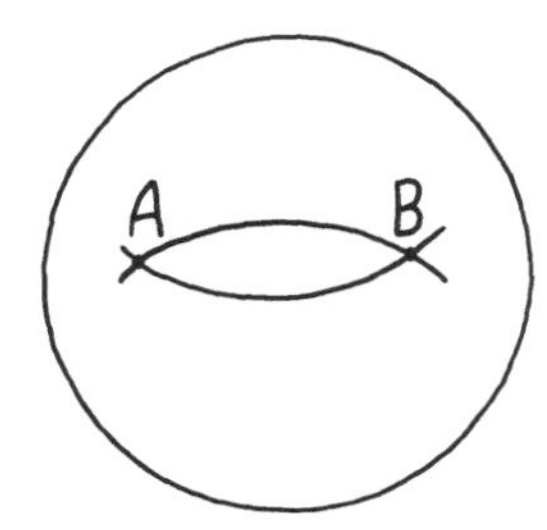

Compare the Plane and the Sphere

Lines

On the plane	On the sphere
The straight line is infinite.	The great circle is finite.
The straight line has no center.	The great circle has two centers. (For example, the equator on the globe has the North Pole and the South Pole as centers.)
If you follow a straight line on a plane, you will never return to your starting point.	If you follow a great circle on a sphere, you will always return to your starting point.
There is a unique straight line passing through any pair of points. The points divide the line into three sections, two infinite and one finite.	There is a unique great circle passing through any pair of points unless the points are pole points. The two points divide the great circle into two finite sections. If the points are pole points, there are infinitely many great circles that pass through them.
A straight line segment is the shortest path between two points.	An arc of a great circle is the shortest path between two points.

Explore More

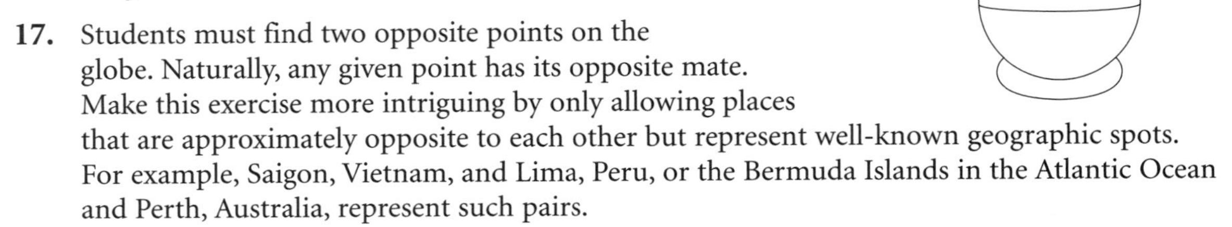

16. **a.** If all goes well, the water will trace the path of a straight line.

b. The water should trace the arc of a great circle.

17. Students must find two opposite points on the globe. Naturally, any given point has its opposite mate. Make this exercise more intriguing by only allowing places that are approximately opposite to each other but represent well-known geographic spots. For example, Saigon, Vietnam, and Lima, Peru, or the Bermuda Islands in the Atlantic Ocean and Perth, Australia, represent such pairs.

18. **a.** The shortest route goes over the northwest United States, western Canada, the Canadian Arctic, the northern tip of Greenland, and the northern tip of Finland.

b. There is only one shortest route because San Francisco and Moscow do not represent opposite poles of the earth.

c. If you look at a fixed sphere from a fixed point, you see a circle. The center of this circle will be the point of the sphere which is nearest to you. The great circles on the sphere which pass through this center will appear to you as straight lines. All the other great circles will be seen as curved lines. Take a planar map of the earth. It can be constructed in such a way that a given great circle is projected into a straight line, or it can be projected into a curved line. In most cases, the horizontal and vertical axes of symmetry of the planar map represent great circles. If the route between San Francisco and Moscow coincides with such an axis, then it will appear on the map as a straight line. If, as it often happens, the axes of symmetry coincide with the Greenwich meridian and the Equator, then the San Francisco–Moscow route will appear as a curved line.

19. The great circle deserves its name both because it is the largest of all the circles that can be drawn on the sphere and because it is the spherical equivalent of the straight line on the plane.

ADVENTURE 1.3

How do you measure distance?

You often need to measure the distance between two figures.

- Describe how to measure distance on the plane.
- Describe how to measure distance on the sphere.
- In each case, explain what units of measure you can use.

Construction on the Plane

Step 1 Draw two distinct points on a plane. Label them *A* and *B*.

Step 2 Measure the distance between points *A* and *B*.

Step 3 Draw the path along which you measured the distance.

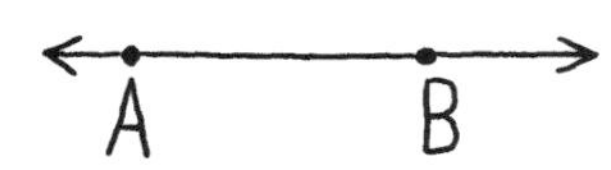

Investigate

1. Why is this the only path along which you can measure the distance between points *A* and *B*?

Make a Guess

2. How can you measure the distance between two points on a sphere?

Construction on the Sphere

Step 1 Draw two distinct points on your sphere. Label them *A* and *B*.

Step 2 Draw the entire great circle that passes through these two points.

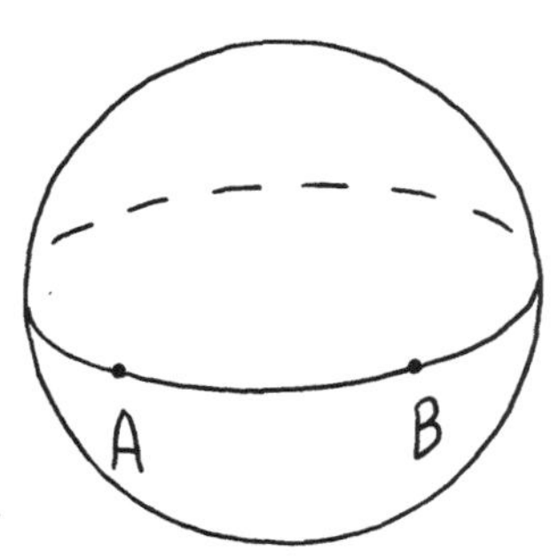

Investigate

3. **a.** How many arcs connect points *A* and *B*?

b. Use the degree markings on your spherical ruler to measure the length of each arc in degrees.

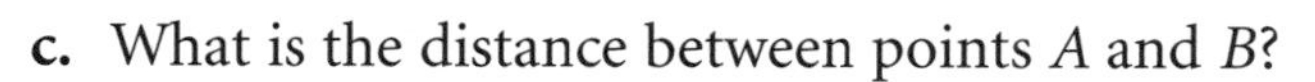

c. What is the distance between points *A* and *B*?

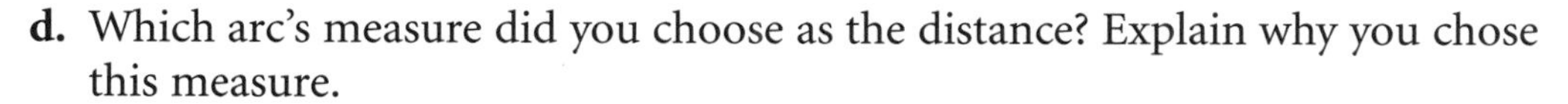

d. Which arc's measure did you choose as the distance? Explain why you chose this measure.

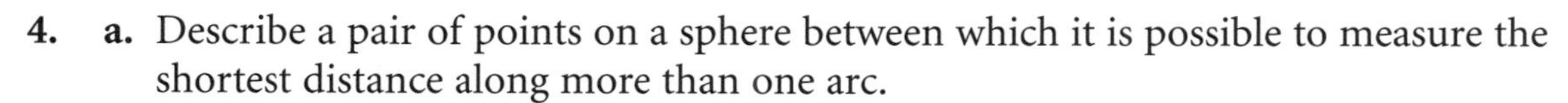

4. **a.** Describe a pair of points on a sphere between which it is possible to measure the shortest distance along more than one arc.

b. Is there a pair of points on a plane between which it is possible to measure the distance along more than one segment?

5. **a.** What is the longest possible distance between two points on a plane?

b. What is the longest possible distance between two points on a sphere?

c. What is the shortest possible distance between two points on a plane?

d. What is the shortest possible distance between two points on a sphere?

Compare the Plane and the Sphere

6. See how many observations you can make about measuring distance on the plane and on the sphere. Record them on a comparison chart like the one at right. Add as many rows as you need.

Measuring the distance between two points

On the plane	On the sphere

7. Do you think measuring distance is simpler on the plane or on the sphere? Why?

8. Now try to reverse your argument. Give reasons why measuring distance is simpler on the surface you *didn't* choose above.

Explore More

9. **a.** Find the length of an entire great circle on your sphere. Express your answer in degrees.

   b. Find the length of the earth's equator. Express your answer in degrees.

   c. Find the length of the equator of a tennis ball. Express your answer in degrees.

   d. What is the advantage of measuring spherical distance in degrees?

10. The radius of the earth measures approximately 6,400 km.

    a. Pick two cities on the globe and find the distance between them. Express your answer in degrees.

    b. What is the distance in kilometers?

11. **a.** Find a place on the globe that is 90° from your home town.

    b. How many places can you find that are this distance away?

    c. Calculate this distance in kilometers.

12. **a.** Find a place on the globe that is 180° from your home town.

    b. How many places can you find that are this distance away?

    c. Calculate this distance in kilometers.

13. The distance from a point to a line is always measured along the perpendicular line that passes through the point.

    a. What is the shortest possible distance between a point and a straight line on the plane?

    b. What is the longest possible distance between a point and a straight line on the plane?

    c. What is the shortest possible distance between a point and a great circle on the sphere?

    d. What is the longest possible distance between a point and a great circle on the sphere?

    e. In each case above, where is the point located?

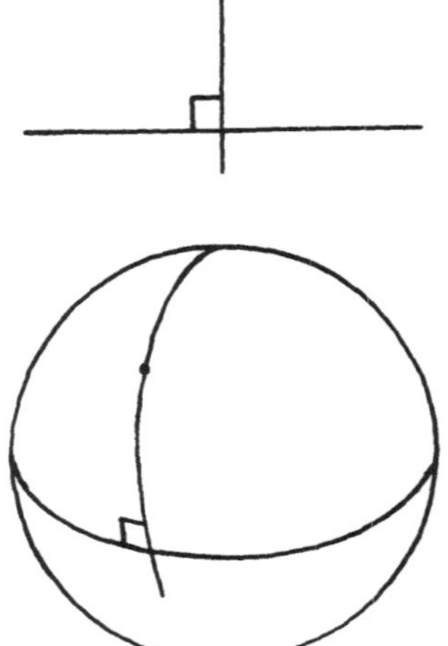

How do you measure distance?

Student Audience: Middle School/High School

Prerequisites: Students should know the terms **line**, **great circle**, and **opposite points**. They should know how to measure a segment on the plane.

Class Time: 25–40 minutes

Construction/Investigation on the Sphere

3. Points *A* and *B* divide the great circle into two separate arcs. Each arc is finite and can thus be measured. Theoretically, either arc is suitable for defining distance on the sphere. We usually choose the shorter, or minor, arc for the purpose.

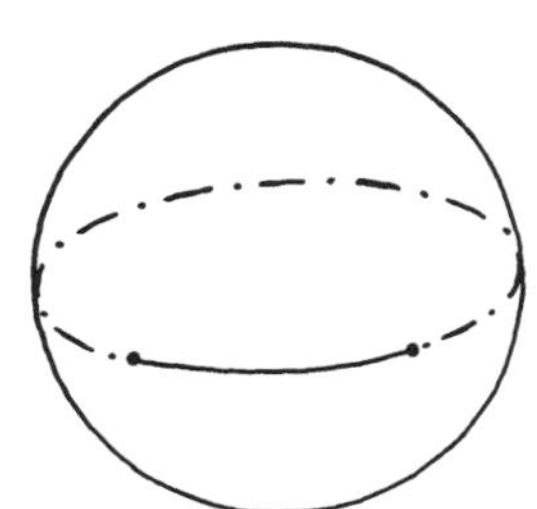

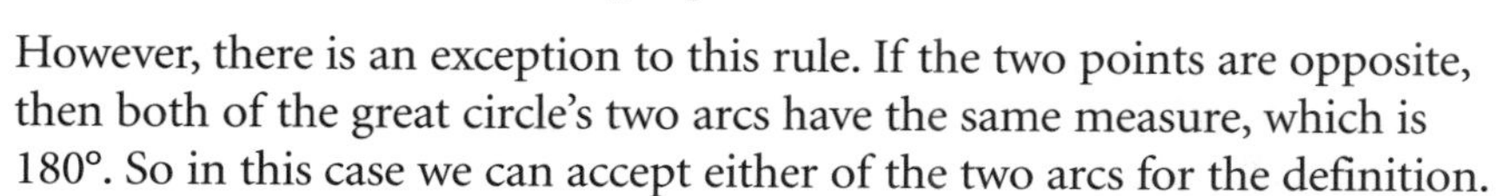

However, there is an exception to this rule. If the two points are opposite, then both of the great circle's two arcs have the same measure, which is 180°. So in this case we can accept either of the two arcs for the definition.

4. a. If the two points are opposite, their spherical distance is the measure of one of any great circle's two parts passing through these two points. Therefore the measure of any two opposite points' spherical distance is always 180°.

Compare the Plane and the Sphere

Measuring the distance between two points

On the plane	On the sphere
You measure the distance between two points along the straight line connecting them. There is only one distance that you can measure.	You measure the distance between two points along the great circle connecting them. There are two distances you can measure, so you must decide which one to use. Usually we pick the shorter one.
Two points can be any distance apart. There is no greatest distance between two points.	The greatest distance between two points measures 180°.
Between any two points there is only one shortest path along which you can measure the distance.	Between any two points that are not pole points there is only one shortest path along which you can measure the distance. If the two points are pole points, there are infinitely many shortest paths between them, but they all have the same length of 180°. Therefore the distance between two pole points measures 180°.

7. Because we have to deal separately with two opposite points on the sphere, the definition of distance on the plane is simpler than that on the sphere.

8. An advantage of the spherical distance is that it is always finite; in contrast, the planar distance is not.

Explore More

13. The shortest distance is zero centimeters on the plane and zero degrees on the sphere. In both cases the point is on the line. The longest distance cannot be determined on the plane; the longest distance measures 90° on the sphere. In the latter case, the point is the pole of the great circle.

How can you construct equators and pole points?

The equator of the planet earth is approximately a great circle. This great circle has two centers or **pole points**: the North and South poles. On a sphere we call any great circle an **equator** and we call a great circle's pole points its **poles**.

- Determine how to construct an equator if you know one of its pole points.
- Determine how to construct a pair of pole points if you know their equator.

Constructions on the Sphere

Following are three separate constructions on the sphere. Begin each construction with a clean sphere.

Construction 1 Draw a point on your sphere. This will be a pole point. Use your spherical ruler and compass to construct the equator that corresponds to this pole point. Describe your method of construction.

Construction 2 Draw a point on your sphere. This will be your first pole point. Find a way to construct the opposite pole point. Describe your method.

Construction 3 Draw a great circle. Find a way to construct the pole points that correspond to this great circle. Describe your method.

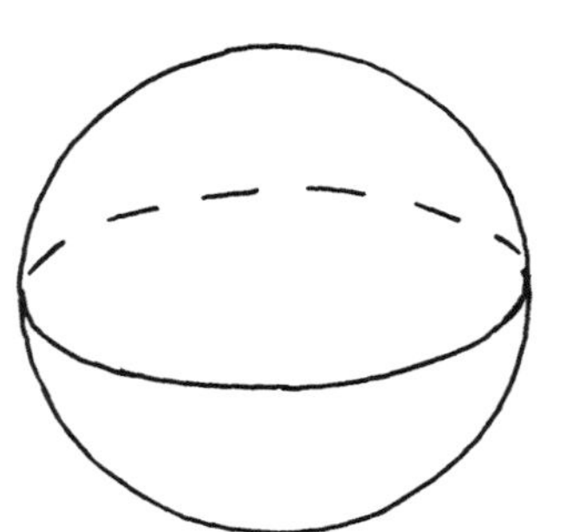

Investigate

1. Compare your construction methods with others in your class.

2. What is the distance between any pair of pole points?

3. What is the distance between a pole point and its equator?

Compare the Plane and the Sphere

4. Would it make sense in this case to make a comparison chart between the plane and the sphere as we did in previous adventures? Why or why not?

Explore More

5. Suppose the town you live in is a pole of the earth.

a. Describe the location of your opposite pole.

b. Describe your home town's equator.

6. Find the Greenwich meridian (0° longitude) on the globe. Where are the pole points of the great circle that includes this meridian?

How can you construct equators and pole points?

Student Audience: Middle School/High School
Prerequisites: None
Class Time: 15–35 minutes

Construction/Investigation on the Sphere

2. The distance between a pair of pole points measures 180°.

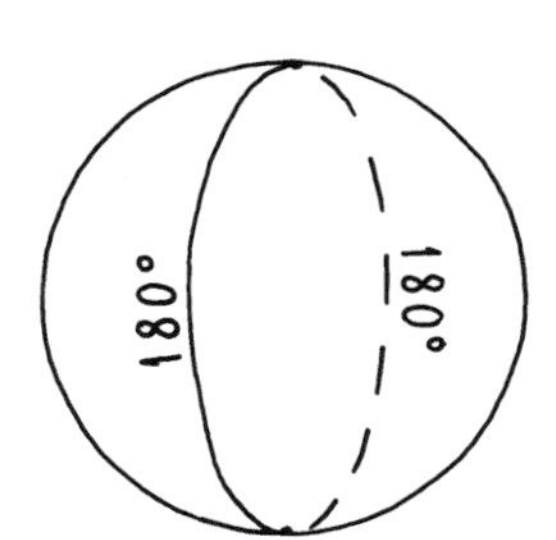

3. The distance between a pole point and its equator measures 90°.

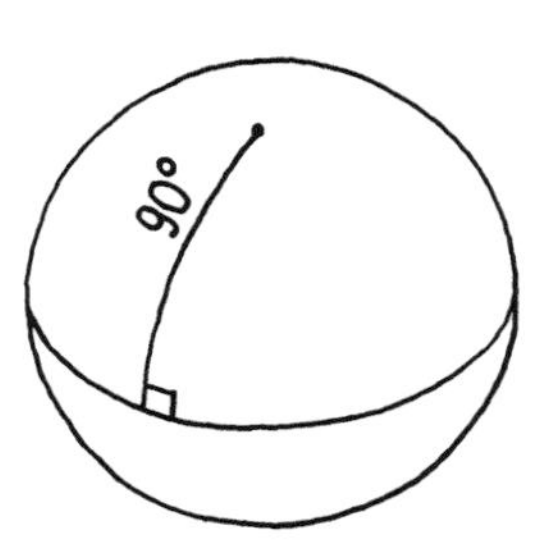

Compare the Plane and the Sphere

4. It doesn't make sense to compare equators and pole points on the plane and the sphere because there are no equators and pole points on the plane. There are no pole points on the plane because a straight line has no center, so the fundamental correspondence between poles and equators on the sphere has no parallel on the plane. (However it is interesting to mention that there are various ways of making a line on the plane correspond to a point in the same plane with the help of a figure such as a circle or an ellipse. In this connection the point is called a pole and the line the polar.)

Explore More

5. Answers will vary.

6. The pole points of the great circle that includes the Greenwich meridian are 90° W (approximately at the Galápagos Islands, Ecuador) and 90° E (in the Indian Ocean 10° west of Sumatra).

How can you use a protractor to measure angles on a sphere?

You know how to use a flat protractor to measure angles on a plane. Can you use a flat protractor to measure angles on a sphere?

- Use a piece of a spherical transparency to make a protractor that can measure angles on a sphere.

Making a Spherical Protractor

Only one group in your class should do Step 1.

Step 1 You need to cut a transparency into pieces so that every group in your class can make its own protractor. Put a transparency onto your sphere. Use your spherical compass to draw a circle that has the transparency's hole as its center and that has a radius of 25°. Mark a point about midway between the circle and the edge of the transparency. Use this point as a center and draw another circle that has a radius of 25°. Mark additional points as centers, and use each center to draw a circle that has a radius of 25°. Choose your center points so that your circles are close together but do not touch. Remove the transparency from the sphere and use scissors to carefully cut it into pieces, with one circle on each piece. Distribute one of these transparency pieces to each group in your class. If needed, use another transparency to make additional pieces.

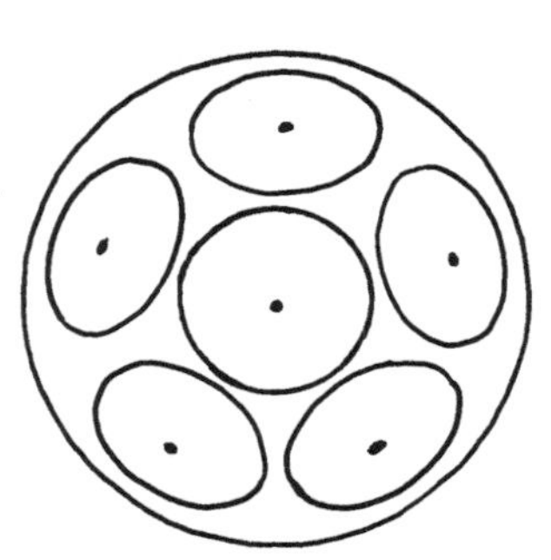

Each group in your class should perform the remaining steps.

Step 2 Mark a pole point on your sphere. Use your spherical ruler to draw the corresponding equator. Then mark every tenth degree along the equator.

Step 3 Make your transparency piece into a disk by carefully trimming around the outside edge of the circle. Then use a loop of transparent tape to stick this disk onto the sphere so that its center point coincides with the pole you marked on the sphere.

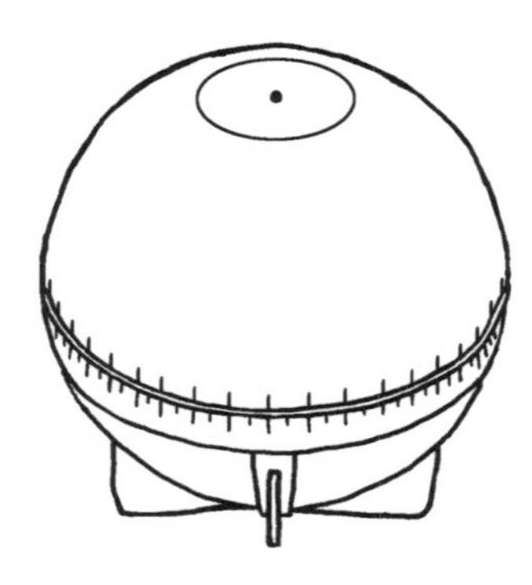

Step 4 Use your ruler to align each pair of opposite markings on the sphere's equator with the center point of the disk. Then draw a thin arc every ten degrees across the disk.

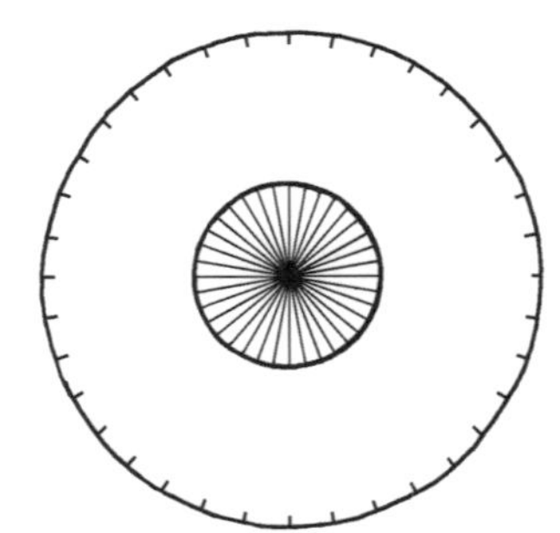

Step 5 Select a pair of perpendicular arcs and thicken these lines. Finish your handy disk protractor by punching a small hole exactly in its center.

Step 6 (Optional) To make your disk protractor last longer, use your ruler and a permanent marker to trace over your arcs. (Try not to get any permanent ink on your sphere. If you do, you can wipe it off with rubbing alcohol.)

Investigate

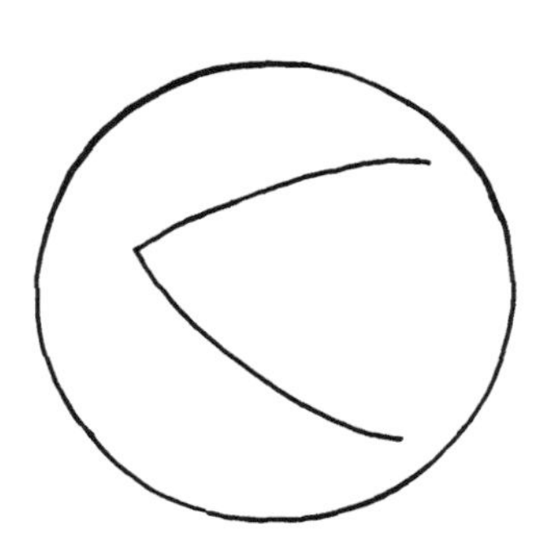

1. On your sphere draw two arcs of great circles that have a common endpoint. Use your disk protractor to measure both spherical angles formed. What do you observe about these angles?

2. Use your disk protractor and your spherical ruler to construct a 50° angle. Construct a 100° angle, a 200° angle, and a 300° angle.

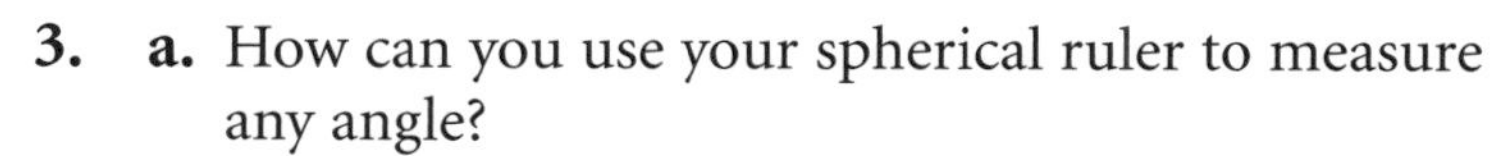

3. **a.** How can you use your spherical ruler to measure any angle?

   b. What are the practical advantages of the smaller disk protractor you have just made?

Compare the Plane and the Sphere

4. Compare methods of measuring angles on the plane and on the sphere. Which is the simpler? Which is more interesting?

Explore More

5. **a.** Draw a triangle on the plane, and use an ordinary planar protractor to measure its three interior angles. Add up the angle measures. What do you find?

   b. Now do the same with a spherical triangle and your disk protractor. What do you find?

   c. Draw a different spherical triangle and add up the measures of its three interior angles. What do you find?

6. **a.** Extend one side of a planar triangle beyond one of its vertices. The extended part of the line and the other side of the triangle sharing the same vertex form an **exterior angle** of the triangle. Construct all three exterior angles. Then use your planar protractor to find their measures and add them up. What is the sum of the exterior angles of a triangle on the plane?

   b. Now do the same with a spherical triangle, using your disk protractor. What do you find? What is the sum of the exterior angles of a triangle on the sphere?

ADVENTURE 1.5

How can you use a protractor to measure angles on a sphere?

Student Audience: Middle School/High School

Prerequisites: Students should know how to measure angles on the plane. They should also know that a great circle can be divided into 360 degrees.

Class Time: 35–50 minutes

Making a Spherical Protractor

1. The sum of the measures of the two angles is always 360°.

3. **a.** The spherical ruler is also a perfect spherical protractor. First extend both sides of the angle to a measure of at least 90°. Then place the top point of the ruler's saddle at the vertex of the angle. Measure the length of the equatorial arc between the two sides along the base edge of the ruler. This experiment clearly demonstrates that the spherical angle can be measured by the arc of a great circle, as can the spherical distance. Thus both the spherical angle and the spherical distance can be measured with the same unit.

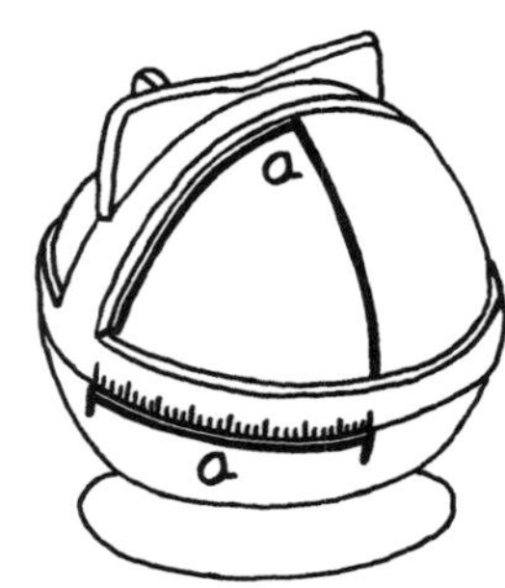

b. The main practical advantage of a smaller spherical protractor is that you don't need to extend the sides of the angle to 90°. For example, if you draw a spherical triangle, you can measure its angles without extending the sides of the triangle.

Compare the Plane and the Sphere

4. On the plane the measurement of distances differs from the measurement of angles. Thus you cannot add centimeters to degrees. On the sphere, however, both distances and angles are measured with the help of the same geometric shape, an arc of a great circle. Thus spherical distances and angles can be measured in the same units and can safely be added or subtracted. Here is a striking example: On the plane, it is nonsense to ask "What is the sum of the measure of an angle of a triangle and the measure of a side of another triangle?" On the sphere, this is an absolutely logical, and very interesting, question. (See Adventure 10.2.)

Explore More

5. The sum of the angle measures of a triangle is always 180° on the plane. The sum of the angle measures of a triangle on the sphere is always greater than 180° and less than 540°, provided that the three vertices are not on the same great circle. The sum of the angle measures of a spherical triangle is not a constant.

6. If the three angles of the triangle have measures a, b, and c, then the exterior angles measure $180° - a$, $180° - b$, and $180° - c$ on both the plane and the sphere. Now, if the sum of the angle measures of a planar triangle is always 180°, then the sum of the measures of the exterior angles is $(180° - a) + (180° - b) + (180° - c) = 540° - (a + b + c) = 540° - 180° = 360°$. On the sphere, the sum of the angle measures varies from 180° to 540°, so the sum of the measures of the exterior angles varies from $540° - 180° = 360°$ to $540° - 540° = 0°$; that is, from 0° to 360°.

180°–c
c
a
b
180°–a
180°–b

Parallels and Perpendiculars

Chapter 2: Parallels and Perpendiculars

Parallel lines and perpendicular lines have some surprising differences on the plane and the sphere. The adventures in this chapter highlight these differences.

In Adventure 2.1, students explore parallel and intersecting pairs of lines. Because parallel lines cannot exist on a sphere, this adventure provides an important example of how spherical geometry is inconsistent with one of the most basic axioms of Euclidean plane geometry: the parallel postulate. Adventure 2.1 is essential if you are using this book for a formal study of spherical geometry, since it demonstrates a fundamental reason that spherical geometry is a non-Euclidean geometry.

Adventure 3.2 makes a nice follow-up lesson to 2.1 because it investigates the possible intersections of *three* distinct lines.

Adventures 2.2 and 2.3 explore some of the differences between perpendicular lines on the two different surfaces. Adventure 2.2 defines and explores the properties of a line perpendicular to one other line. In Adventure 2.3, students investigate properties of a line that is perpendicular to at least two other lines. Both adventures compare these notions in planar and spherical geometry. Adventure 2.2 is helpful as an introduction to 2.3 but is not essential.

Use the Adventure Cards at the beginning of the chapter for more open-ended lessons. Use the Student's Guides for more structured lessons. The Teacher's Guide that follows each Student's Guide contains solutions and suggestions.

ADVENTURE 2.1

How many points can two lines share?

When two distinct lines intersect on the plane or on the sphere, they meet at one or more points.

- Investigate the points of intersection of two straight lines on the plane.
- Investigate the points of intersection of two great circles on the sphere.
- Explain your observations about parallel lines on the plane and on the sphere.

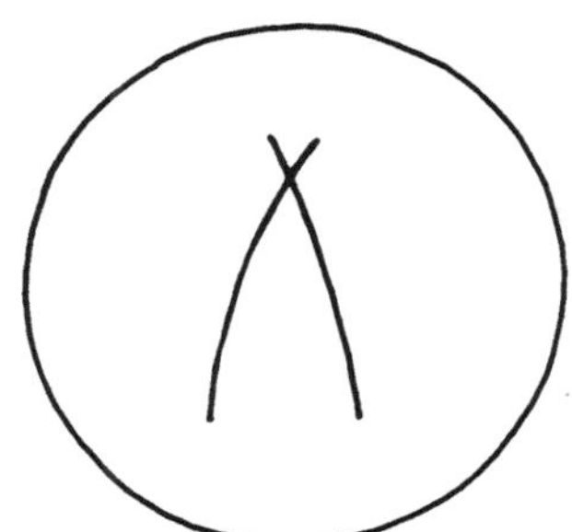

ADVENTURE 2.2

What do perpendicular lines look like on a sphere?

Perpendicular lines intersect in a special way on the plane and on the sphere.

- Describe two perpendicular straight lines on the plane.
- Describe two perpendicular great circles on the sphere.

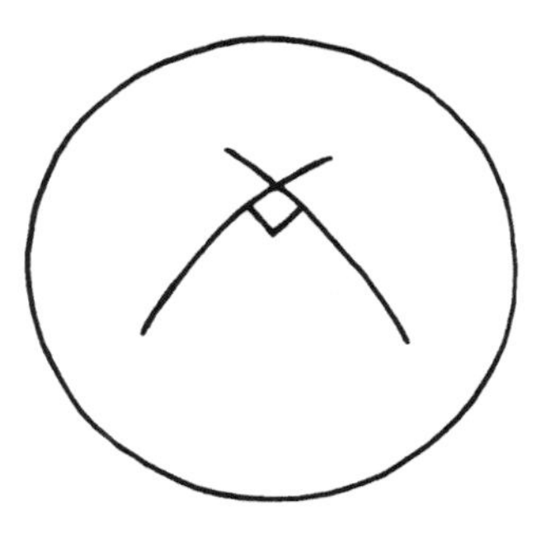

ADVENTURE 2.3

How many perpendiculars can two lines have in common?

If a line is perpendicular to two other lines at once, it is a *common perpendicular* to those lines.

- Investigate the common perpendiculars of two straight lines on the plane.
- Investigate the common perpendiculars of two great circles on the sphere.

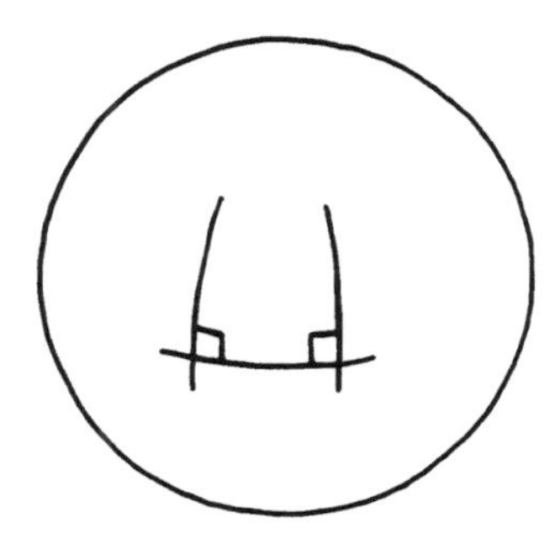

ADVENTURE 2.1

How many points can two lines share?

When two distinct lines intersect on the plane or on the sphere, they meet at one or more points.

- Investigate the points of intersection of two straight lines on the plane.
- Investigate the points of intersection of two great circles on the sphere.
- Explain your observations about parallel lines on the plane and on the sphere.

Construction on the Plane

Step 1 Draw a straight line. Label it *l*.

Step 2 Try to draw another straight line that has no point in common with line *l*. Label it *a*.

Step 3 Try to draw a straight line that has exactly one point in common with line *l*. Label it *b*.

Step 4 Try to draw a straight line that has exactly two points in common with line *l*. Label it *c*.

Step 5 Try to draw a straight line that has more than two points in common with line *l*. Label it *d*.

Investigate

1. Which constructions were possible on the plane?

2. Which of your lines are parallel? Why?

3. Describe all the different ways in which two distinct lines can intersect on the plane.

Make a Guess

4. Will your conclusions be the same for great circles on a sphere?

Construction on the Sphere

5. Perform the same steps on the sphere that you performed on the plane, replacing the straight lines with great circles. Keep track of which constructions are possible on the sphere.

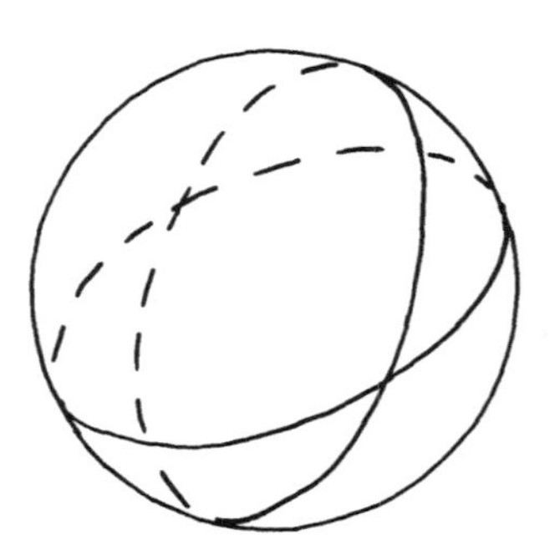

Investigate

6. Describe all the ways in which two distinct great circles can intersect on the sphere.

7. Can two great circles ever be parallel?

Compare the Plane and the Sphere

8. See how many observations you can make about the intersection of two straight lines on the plane and the intersection of two great circles on the sphere. Record them on a comparison chart like the one at right. Add as many rows as you need.

Intersection of two lines

On the plane	On the sphere

9. Do you think the intersection of two lines is simpler on the plane or on the sphere? Which case is more intriguing? Why?

10. Now try to reverse your argument. Give reasons why the intersection of two lines is simpler or more intriguing on the surface you *didn't* choose above.

Explore More

11. Imagine that it is possible for a pair of railroad tracks to extend all the way around the earth. Can the railroad tracks represent parallel lines?

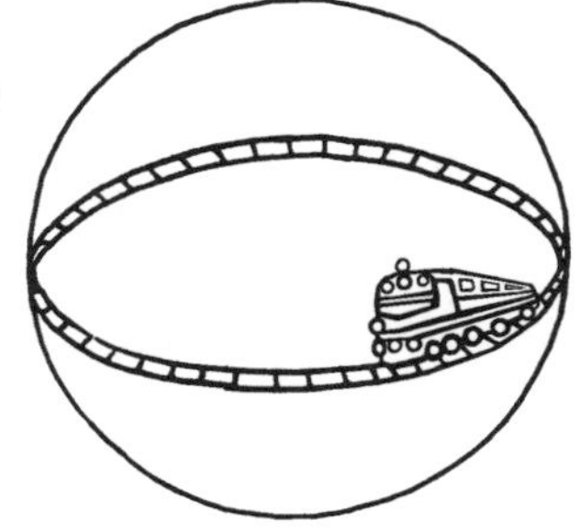

12. Parallel lines on the plane are always the same distance apart. Draw a great circle on your sphere. Then draw a different figure that is always the same distance from your great circle.

a. Describe this figure.

b. Decide if the figure could be a great circle.

13. A boat travels in a such a way that it is always 50 km from the equator. Explain why the boat is not traveling in the most direct path between two points.

14. Euclid was a mathematician from ancient Greece who is famous for being one of the first to organize the ideas of geometry. In his treatise titled *Elements,* Euclid lists a set of **axioms** for geometry. Euclid's axioms were statements that he believed were so obviously true that he was willing to accept them without proof. Almost two and a half thousand years later, we still base plane geometry on Euclid's axioms. However his last axiom, commonly called the parallel postulate, has always been open to debate. Here is one form of Euclid's parallel postulate: Given a straight line and a point not on this straight line, you can draw only one straight line through the given point that is parallel to the given straight line.

a. On a piece of paper draw a straight line and a point not on the line. Draw as many lines as you can through the point that are parallel to the first line. Use your drawing to explain why Euclid's parallel postulate makes sense on the plane.

b. Rewrite the parallel postulate for the sphere by replacing the words *straight line* with *great circle.* Then make a construction on your sphere similar to the construction you just made on the plane. Now explain why Euclid's parallel postulate does not make sense on the sphere.

c. Write your own parallel postulate that is true for geometry on a sphere.

15. Describe all the ways that three distinct great circles can intersect.

How many points can two lines share?

Student Audience: Middle School/High School

Prerequisites: Students should know the terms line and great circle.

Class Time: 25–40 minutes.

Construction/Investigation on the Plane

In Step 2, students can use the parallel edges of the straightedge. Step 4, of course, cannot be constructed. The only construction in Step 5 is found in two coincidental lines with infinitely many points in common.

Two distinct lines are either parallel to each other, with no common point, or intersecting, with exactly one point of intersection.

Construction/Investigation on the Sphere

Students may be surprised to learn that parallel great circles (with no common point) do not exist. Sometimes they construct a parallel circle that is not a great circle, using the upper unscaled rim of the base hoop of the spherical ruler. To help students see this, ask them to stretch a taut string between two points of a "false" circle. On the sphere, Step 4 is the only possible construction. The only solution in Step 5 is found in coincidental great circles, just as it is with lines.

Two distinct great circles always intersect in exactly two points.

Compare the Plane and the Sphere

Intersection of two lines

On the plane	On the sphere
Two distinct straight lines with no point of intersection are called parallel lines.	Two distinct great circles can never be parallel to each other.
Two distinct straight lines with exactly one point in common are called intersecting lines.	Two distinct great circles can never have exactly one point of intersection.
Two distinct straight lines can never have more than one point of intersection.	Two distinct great circles always have exactly two points of intersection.

9. We must consider three cases on the plane: parallel, intersecting, and coincident lines. On the sphere, however, we must only consider two because parallel great circles do not exist. Therefore in this investigation, the sphere is simpler than the plane.

Explore More

11. Presumably the two tracks never intersect. Because every pair of great circles intersects, it follows that both tracks cannot lie on great circles. Therefore both of the tracks cannot represent great circles on the sphere.

12. The figure is a circle with a radius between 0° and 90°. If the distance in question measures 0°, then the circle is the original great circle with radius 90°. If the distance measures 90°, then the circle is the pole point of the original great circle.

13. The boat isn't traveling in the most direct path between two points because a line that is always at a 50-km distance from the equator must be a circle smaller than a great circle.

14. c. Answers should sound something like this: Given a great circle and a point not on the great circle, there is no great circle through the point that is parallel to the given great circle.

As you see, there is one straight line through a given point that is parallel to a given straight line on the plane. There is no great circle through a given point that is parallel to a given great circle on the sphere. Logically, the third possibility is a surface with some kind of simplest line on it, which adheres to the following property: There is more than one simplest line through a given point that is parallel to a given simplest line. Can we find such a surface? This question was first answered in the nineteenth century by Carl Friedrich Gauss, János Bolyai, Nikolai Lobachevsky, and others. Indeed, we can find such surfaces, but these are a bit more complicated and less demonstrative than the plane with the straight line or the sphere with the great circle. For example, if we replace the straight lines of the plane or the great circles of the sphere with certain arcs of certain circles as the simplest lines, then we can build up geometries of the third kind.

15. If the three great circles are concurrent, then they have two points of intersection. If they are not concurrent, then there are six points of intersection on the whole sphere.

ADVENTURE 2.2

What do perpendicular lines look like on a sphere?

Perpendicular lines intersect in a special way on the plane and on the sphere.

- Describe two perpendicular straight lines on the plane.
- Describe two perpendicular great circles on the sphere.

Construction on the Plane

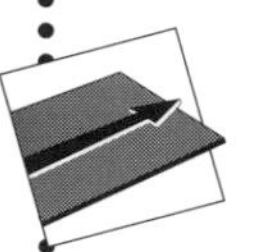

Step 1 Draw two intersecting straight lines that divide the plane into regions that are all congruent.

Step 2 Measure and label all the angles at each point of intersection of these two lines.

Investigate

1. The two straight lines you constructed are perpendicular to each other. Record any observations you can make about perpendicular lines on a plane.

Make A Guess

2. What do perpendicular lines look like on a sphere?

Construction on the Sphere

Step 1 Draw two distinct great circles that divide your sphere into regions that are all congruent.

Step 2 Measure and label all the angles at each point of intersection of these two perpendicular great circles.

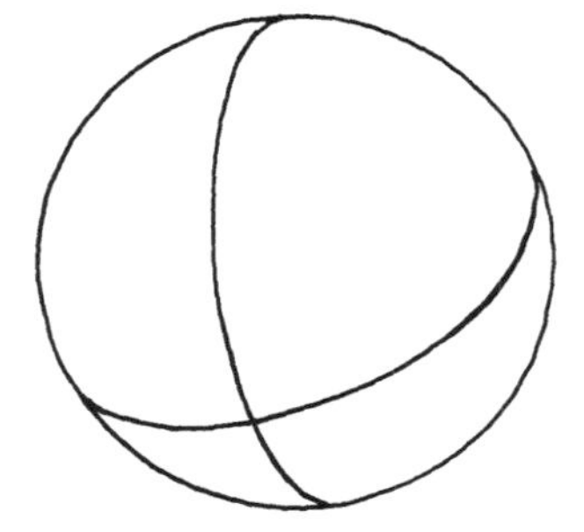

Investigate

3. The two great circles you constructed are perpendicular to each other. Record any observations you can make about perpendicular great circles on a sphere.

Compare the Plane and the Sphere

4. See how many observations you can make about perpendicular straight lines on the plane and perpendicular great circles on the sphere. Record them on a comparison chart like the one at right. Add as many rows as you need.

Perpendicular lines

On the plane	On the sphere

5. Do you think perpendicular lines are more interesting on the plane or on the sphere? Why?

6. Now try to reverse your argument. Give reasons why perpendicular lines are more interesting on the surface you *didn't* choose above.

Explore More

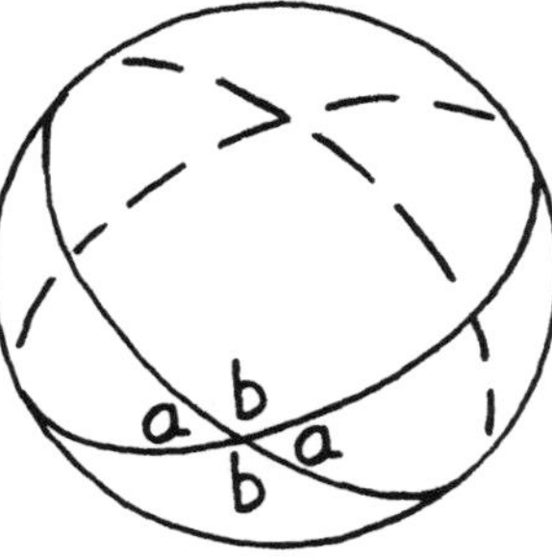

7. Pairs of vertical angles are always congruent on the plane. Construct some pairs of vertical angles on your sphere and determine if the same is true on the sphere.

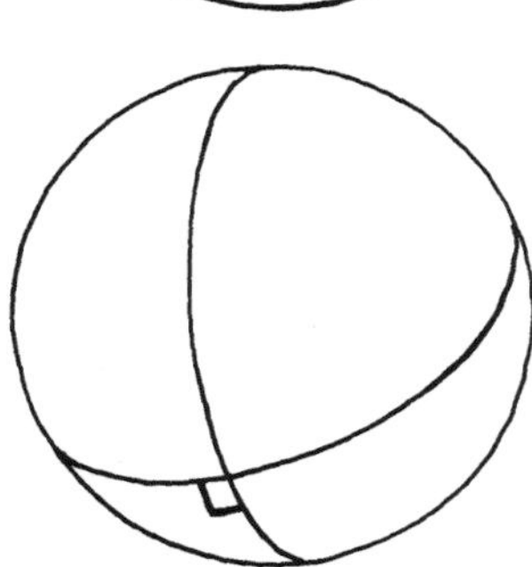

8. **a.** Draw two perpendicular great circles and draw their pole points. What do you notice about these pole points? Describe your findings.

   b. Can you find an equivalent situation on the plane? Why or why not?

9. Draw two distinct great circles on the sphere that are not perpendicular. Describe the regions they create.

What do perpendicular lines look like on a sphere?

Student Audience: Middle School/High School

Prerequisites: Students should know how to measure an angle on the sphere. They need to know that each great circle has two centers on the sphere, called the **pole points** or **poles** of the great circle. The great circle is called the **equator** of the points.

Class Time: 25–40 minutes

Construction/Investigation on the Sphere

Two distinct great circles divide the spherical surface into four regions. Each of these regions has two congruent angles in it. These regions are called biangles. The two great circles have two points of intersection; there are four angles at each of these points. The opposite angles at the same point are always congruent; thus the Vertical Angle Theorem is valid for great circles on the sphere.

3. If any one of the angle measures at the two points of intersection equals 90° then all the angles equal 90°, and the two great circles divide the spherical surface into four congruent regions (four congruent biangles).

Two great circles are perpendicular to each other if they divide the spherical surface into four congruent regions.

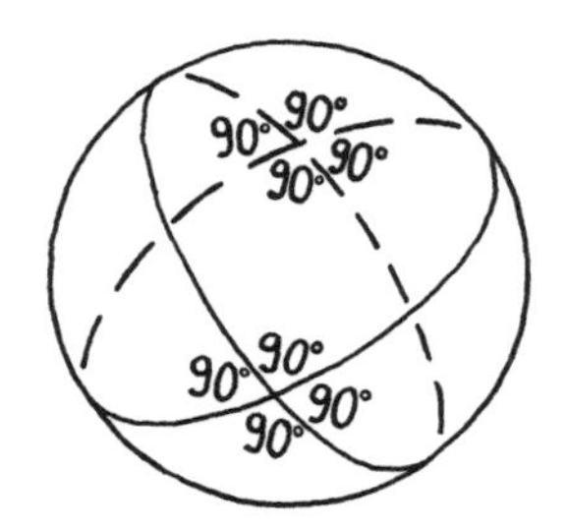

Compare the Plane and the Sphere

Perpendicular lines

On the plane	On the sphere
A pair of perpendicular straight lines intersects once and creates four right angles.	A pair of perpendicular great circles intersects twice and creates eight right angles.
A pair of perpendicular straight lines divides the plane into four infinite (but congruent) regions.	A pair of perpendicular great circles divides the sphere into four finite congruent regions.

5. It's easier to understand dividing the finite spherical surface into four congruent parts than to understand infinite regions of the infinite plane. Here are some of the similarities between perpendiculars on the plane and the sphere: All four regions are congruent, and each angle measures 90°. Here are some of the differences: The regions are finite on the sphere, and there are eight angles at the two points of intersection of the two great circles.

Explore More

8. If the two great circles are perpendicular to each other, then the pole points of each great circle lie on the other great circle. Conversely, if one of the pole points of the first great circle lies on the other great circle, then the two great circles are perpendicular to each other. This property of perpendicular great circles is of fundamental importance in spherical geometry and has no corresponding property pertaining to perpendicular straight lines in plane geometry.

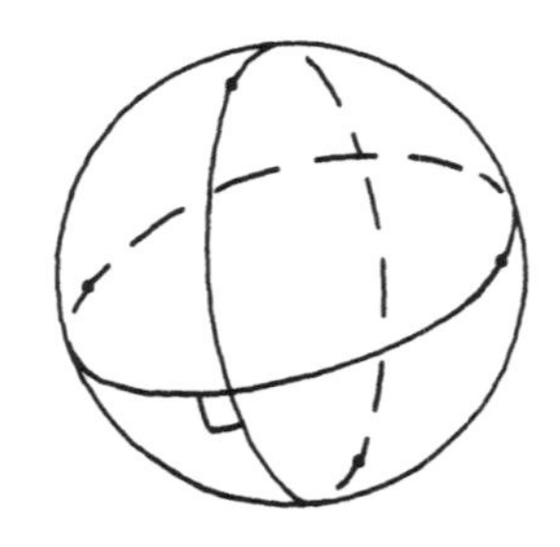

9. Two distinct great circles divide the sphere into four finite regions. Any two of these regions that are opposite each other are congruent. Each of these regions has two opposite vertices, two congruent angles, and two sides that each measure 180°. Such a region is called a **biangle**.

ADVENTURE 2.3

How many perpendiculars can two lines have in common?

If a line is perpendicular to two other lines at once, it is a **common perpendicular** to those lines.

- Investigate the common perpendiculars of two straight lines on the plane.
- Investigate the common perpendiculars of two great circles on the sphere.

Construction on the Plane

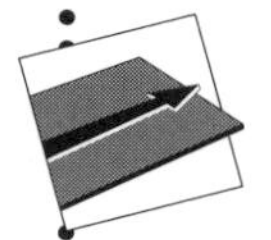

Step 1 Draw two intersecting straight lines. Then try to draw some straight lines that are perpendicular to both of them.

Step 2 Draw two parallel straight lines. Then try to draw some straight lines that are perpendicular to both of them.

Investigate

1. How many common perpendiculars could you draw in Step 1?

2. How many common perpendiculars could you draw in Step 2?

Make a Guess

3. Will your conclusions about common perpendiculars be the same on the sphere?

Construction on the Sphere

Step 1 Draw two different great circles.

Step 2 Try to draw some great circles that are perpendicular to both of them.

Investigate

4. For any two great circles, how many common perpendiculars can you draw?

Compare the Plane and the Sphere

5. See how many observations you can make about common perpendiculars on the plane and common perpendiculars on the sphere. Record them on a comparison chart like the one at right. Add as many rows as you need.

Common perpendiculars

On the plane	On the sphere

6. Do you think common perpendiculars are simpler on the plane or on the sphere? Why?

7. Now try to reverse your argument. Give reasons why common perpendiculars are simpler on the surface you *didn't* choose above.

Explore More

8. Each great circle has two pole points, just as the earth's equator has the North and South poles. Draw two great circles and a common perpendicular to these two great circles. Describe the location of the pole points of the common perpendicular.

9. **a.** Determine if it is possible to draw three straight lines on the plane so that each line is perpendicular to the other two.

   b. Show that it is possible to draw three great circles on a sphere so that each great circle is perpendicular to the other two. Explain the location of each great circle's pole points.

10. Use your spherical ruler to draw a triangle on your sphere. Then extend each side of the triangle until you have drawn an entire great circle. Label the great circles *a*, *b*, and *c*. Draw the common perpendicular to great circles *a* and *b*. Label it *p*. Draw the common perpendicular to *a* and *c*. Label it *q*. What do you notice about the common perpendicular to great circles *p* and *q*?

11. Describe at least two different ways of constructing the common perpendicular to two great circles.

ADVENTURE 2.3

How many perpendiculars can two lines have in common?

Student Audience: Middle School/High School

Prerequisites: Students should know how to construct a perpendicular to a straight line on the plane or to a great circle on the sphere.

Class Time: 25–40 minutes

Construction/Investigation on the Plane

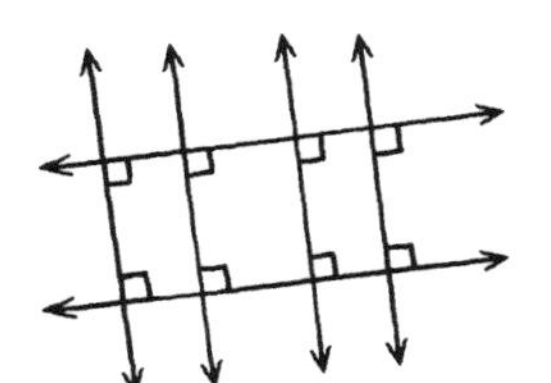

1. Two intersecting straight lines have no common perpendicular.
2. Two parallel straight lines have infinitely many common perpendiculars.

Construction/Investigation on the Sphere

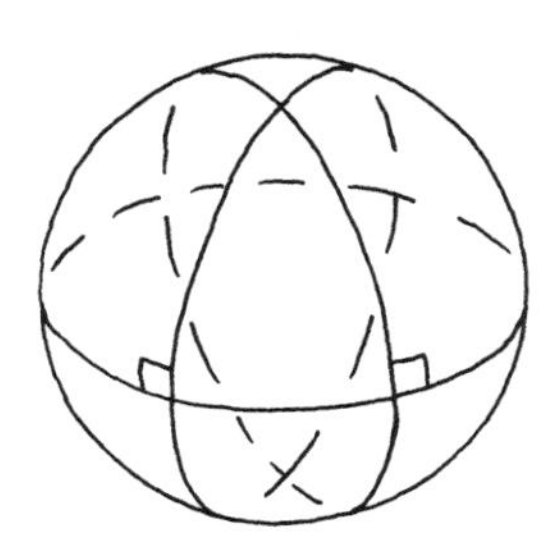

If the two great circles are different, then only one great circle perpendicular to both of the other two exists, as shown. If the two great circles are perpendicular to each other, again, they have one and only one common perpendicular.

Compare the Plane and the Sphere

Common perpendiculars

On the plane	On the sphere
Two intersecting straight lines do not have a common perpendicular.	Two intersecting great circles have exactly one common perpendicular. (Even two great circles that are perpendicular to each other have exactly one common perpendicular.)
Parallel straight lines have infinitely many common perpendiculars.	Parallel great circles do not exist on the sphere.

Explore More

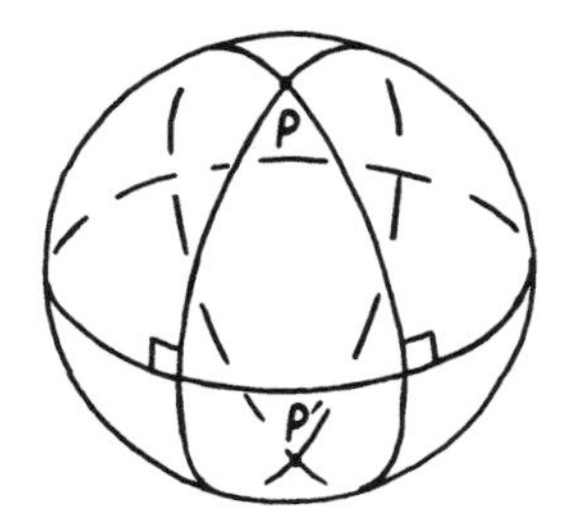

8. The pole points of the common perpendicular are the two great circles' two points of intersection.

9. **a.** No. If you draw two perpendicular straight lines, you cannot find a third one that is perpendicular to both of the other two.

   b. Draw two perpendicular great circles and construct their common perpendicular. Any of these three great circles is perpendicular to the other two.

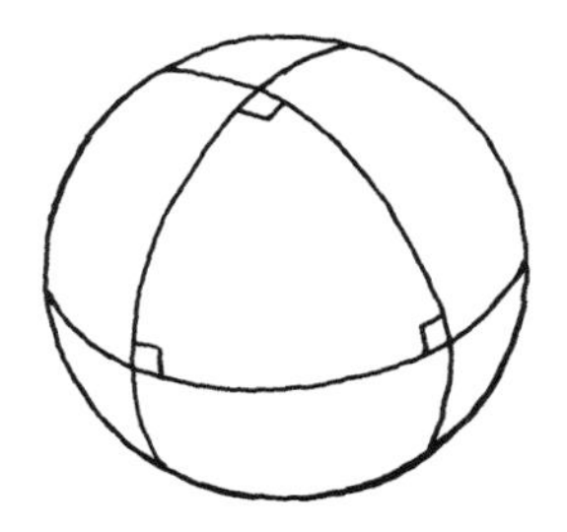

10. According to the construction, a and p are perpendicular to each other. Likewise, a and q are also perpendicular to each other. This means that a is perpendicular to both p and q. However, p and q have exactly one common perpendicular, so this common perpendicular must be great circle a.

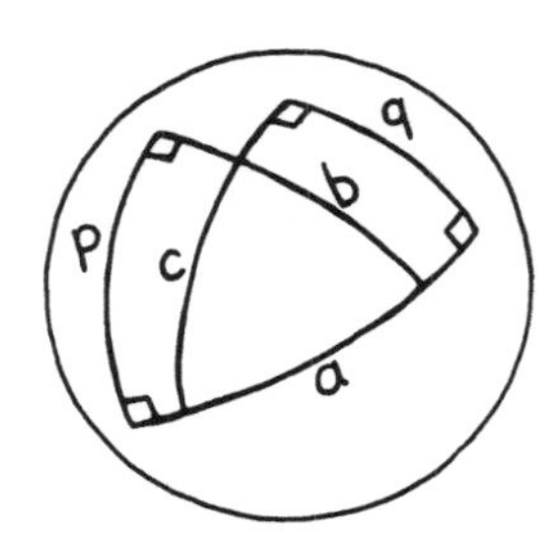

11. The simplest way to construct the common perpendicular is to place the top of the ruler's saddle at either point of intersection of the two great circles. In this position, the base edge of the ruler will trace the common perpendicular. Alternately, you can construct the midpoints of the four 180°-long arcs and connect them with a great circle.

CHAPTER 3
Polygons

Chapter 3: Polygons

Adventure 3.1: Is it possible to make a polygon with only two sides?

Adventure 3.2: What regions can you create using three lines?

Adventure 3.3: How many triangles can have the same three vertices?

Adventure 3.4: What is the sum of the angle measures of a triangle?

Adventure 3.5: Can a triangle have more than one right angle?

Many of the rules about polygons that seem obvious on the plane are no longer true on the sphere. To examine these differences in the simplest possible way, this chapter focuses on triangles (although in Adventure 3.1, students discover that a triangle is not the simplest polygon on a sphere!). Students can extend all their observations about triangles to conjectures about polygons with more than three sides.

In Adventure 3.4, when students add up the measures of the angles of a triangle on a sphere, they come upon what is probably the biggest surprise of the chapter. Before they measure the angles of a triangle, it helps to be sure which spherical shapes they define to be triangles. This is trickier than it seems. In Adventures 3.2 and 3.3, students clarify what it means for a shape to be a triangle. If your class is feeling adventurous, skip Adventures 3.2 and 3.3 and go directly to Adventure 3.4. By doing so, students will develop their own definition of a spherical triangle when they need to.

Adventure 3.5 compares right triangles on the two different surfaces. This adventure contains some surprises of its own, and, as in Adventure 3.4, students can explore this topic without first doing the previous adventures in the chapter. In Adventure 3.5, students also begin their investigation of the triangle congruence properties, which they will continue in Chapter 4.

Use the Adventure Cards at the beginning of the chapter for more open-ended lessons. Use the Student's Guides for more structured lessons. The Teacher's Guide that follows each Student's Guide contains solutions and suggestions. For a really open-ended approach to the whole chapter, use Adventure Card 3.4 and give students quite a few days to think and explore on their own. It is likely that they will independently discover many of the ideas covered in the other adventures.

ADVENTURE 3.1

Is it possible to make a polygon with only two sides?

You've created many different kinds of polygons, such as triangles, quadrilaterals, pentagons, and hexagons.

- Determine if it is possible to create a two-sided polygon.

ADVENTURE 3.2

What regions can you create using three lines?

When three lines intersect, they divide a surface into several regions.

- Investigate the regions you can create using three straight lines on a plane.
- Investigate the regions you can create using three great circles on a sphere.

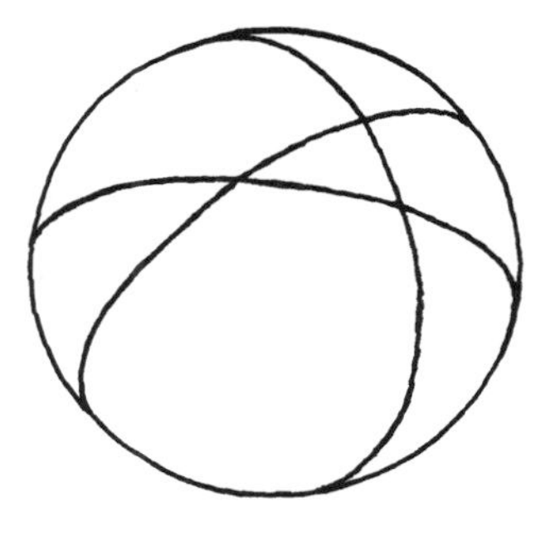

ADVENTURE 3.3

How many triangles can have the same three vertices?

Suppose you pick three points.

- Investigate how many different triangles you can get by connecting the points with line segments on the plane.
- Investigate how many different triangles you can get by connecting the points with arcs on the sphere.

ADVENTURE 3.4

What is the sum of the angle measures of a triangle?

If you add the measures of the angles of a triangle, do you always get the same sum?

- Investigate the sum of the angle measures of planar triangles.
- Investigate the sum of the angle measures of spherical triangles.

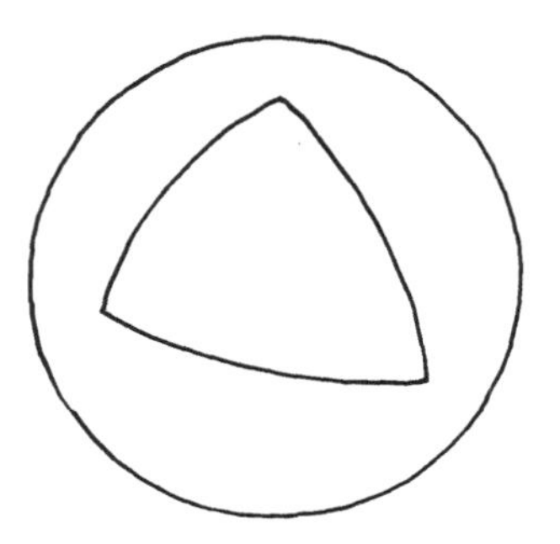

ADVENTURE 3.5

Can a triangle have more than one right angle?

You may have already learned some special properties of right triangles.

- See if you can construct a triangle with more than one right angle.

Is it possible to make a polygon with only two sides?

You've created many different kinds of polygons, such as triangles, quadrilaterals, pentagons, and hexagons.

- Determine if it is possible to create a two-sided polygon.

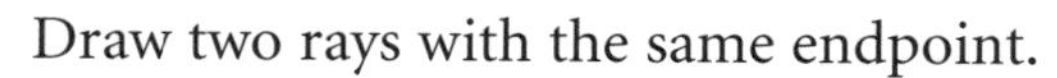

Construction on the Plane

Draw two rays with the same endpoint.

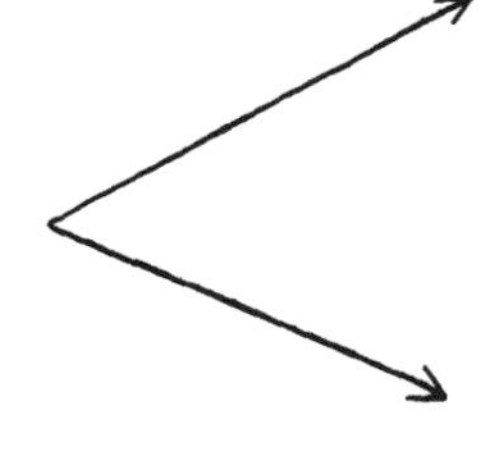

Investigate

1. Will the two rays meet in another point if extended indefinitely?
2. The two rays divide the plane into different regions. Describe the size and the shape of the regions.
3. A **polygon** is a closed figure with straight sides. Explain whether it is possible to create a two-sided polygon on the plane.

Make A Guess

4. Can you make a two-sided polygon on a sphere?

Construction on the Sphere

Draw arcs of two different great circles, starting from the same point on your sphere.

Investigate

5. Extend the two arcs. Do the two arcs meet in another point?
6. The two arcs divide the sphere into different regions. Describe the size and shape of the regions.
7. **a.** Write a definition for a polygon on a sphere.

   b. Are any of the regions you created on your sphere polygons?
8. A polygon on the sphere that has exactly two angles is called a **biangle**. The measure of each angle in a biangle cannot be greater than 180°. Shade in one of the biangles on your sphere.
9. Measure both angles of the biangle and describe a property that holds for the angles of any biangle.
10. Measure both sides of the biangle and describe two properties that hold for the sides of any biangle.

Compare the Plane and the Sphere

11. See how many observations you can make about two rays with a common endpoint on the plane and two arcs of great circles with a common endpoint on the sphere. Record them on a comparison chart like the one at right. Add as many rows as you need.

Two rays (arcs) with a common endpoint	
On the plane	On the sphere

12. Which surface do you think is simpler in this case: the plane or the sphere? Why?

13. Now try to reverse you argument. Give reasons why the surface you *didn't* choose above might be simpler.

Explore More

14. Draw two great circles.

a. How many biangles do your two great circles create?

b. Determine if any of these biangles are congruent.

15. Name some examples of biangles that occur in your environment.

16. See if you can draw two great circles so that all the biangles they create are congruent.

17. A **regular polygon** has all of its sides the same length and all of its angles the same measure. Explain why biangles are always regular.

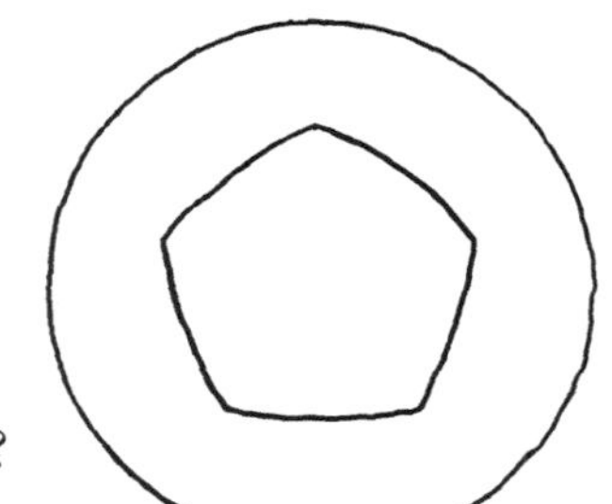

18. Biangles are also called **lunes** or **digons**.

a. The word *lune* has the same Latin root as the word *lunar*. Why do you suppose these two words are related?

b. What do you think is the origin and meaning of the word *digon*?

c. Which name among these three do you prefer? Why?

19. a. A shape **tiles** a surface if the shape and its duplicates cover the entire surface without gaps or overlaps. A tiling like this is also called a **tessellation**. If the shape you use as a tile is a regular polygon, then the tessellation is called a **regular tessellation**. Use your knowledge of biangles to find some regular tessellations of the sphere.

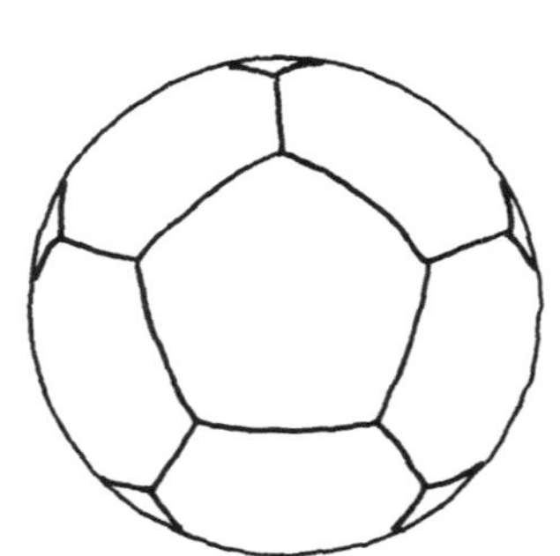

b. Find all possible biangles that can tile the sphere.

20. Is it possible to create a one-sided polygon?

Is it possible to make a polygon with only two sides?

Student Audience: Middle School/High School

Prerequisites: None

Class Time: 25–45 minutes

Construction/Investigation on the Plane

1. The rays will not intersect again.
2. The rays determine two infinite regions.

Construction/Investigation on the Sphere

5. The two arcs meet in two opposite points of intersection.
6. The arcs determine two finite regions on the sphere, both bounded by two arcs of great circles. Each arc, called a *meridian,* measures 180°. Each of the two regions is two-angled. Let us agree to choose the smaller of the two regions and call it a *biangle.*

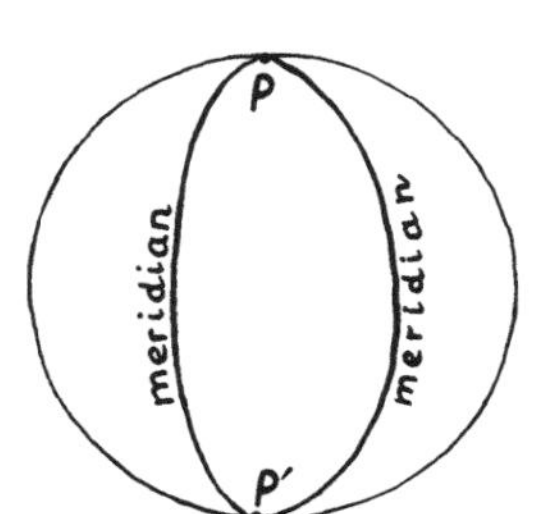

7. Here is one possible definition: A spherical polygon is a closed geometric figure on the sphere, formed by connecting one or more arcs of great circles endpoint to endpoint.
8. Here is a practical tip: Shading that is too dense consumes too much of the marker's ink!
9. The two angles of a biangle are always congruent with each other.
10. Each side of a biangle measures 180° and connects two opposite points. We call such a side a **meridian.**

Compare the Plane and the Sphere

Two rays (arcs) with a common endpoint

On the plane	On the sphere
Two rays with a common endpoint will never meet.	Two arcs of great circles will meet at a pair of pole points to form a biangle.
It is impossible to create a two-sided polygon.	It is possible to create a two-sided polygon called a biangle. Every biangle has exactly two congruent angles and two congruent sides. Each side has a length of 180°. We call such a side a meridian.
Two rays with a common endpoint divide the plane into two infinite regions.	Two meridians with two common endpoints divide the sphere into two (finite) biangles.

12. Students may have mixed impressions about whether the plane or the sphere is superior in this adventure. The plane yields a simpler result, but the result on the sphere is elegant and appealing.

Explore More

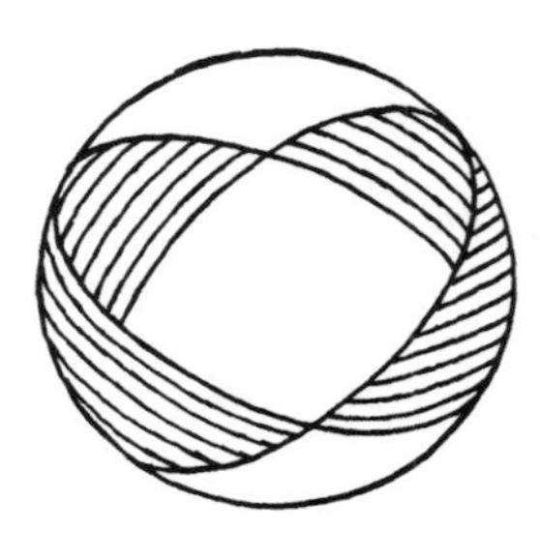

14. Two complete great circles determine four biangles on the spherical surface. The opposite biangles are always congruent.

15. Some occurrences of biangles in the environment are the network on basketballs, the outer appearance of a peeled orange, and the peel of a slice of a watermelon.

16. If the two great circles are perpendicular, then all the four biangles are congruent with one another.

18. **b.** *Digon* comes from the Greek language and means "double angle."

19. **a.** For example, the four biangles determined by two perpendicular great circles form a regular tessellation.

    b. In general, if k is any natural number, then you can make a regular tessellation of k biangles with angles of measure $360/k$ in each. For example, 10 biangles with angles of measure 36° in each will cover the sphere with a regular tessellation.

20. Surprisingly, a great circle with one point on it satisfies the definition of a polygon, so it is a one-sided polygon.

ADVENTURE 3.2

What regions can you create using three lines?

When three lines intersect, they divide a surface into several regions.

- Investigate the regions you can create using three straight lines on a plane.
- Investigate the regions you can create using three great circles on a sphere.

Construction on the Plane

Every pair of distinct straight lines on the plane is either parallel or intersecting. Make drawings to demonstrate every possible case for three distinct straight lines on the plane.

Investigate

1. For each drawing determine how many regions the three lines create.
2. For each drawing determine how many regions have a finite area, and how many regions have an infinite area.

Make a Guess

3. What kinds of regions can you create with three great circles on a sphere?

Construction on the Sphere

Draw three distinct great circles on your sphere.

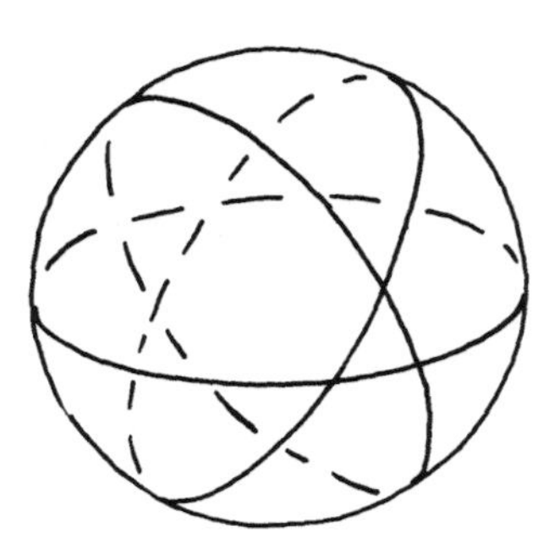

Investigate

4. How many regions can you create with three distinct great circles on a sphere? List every possible answer to this question.
5. For each example you gave in your answer above, determine how many regions have a finite area and how many have an infinite area.
6. In one of the cases above, you created regions that are triangular. Triangles are **congruent** if we can make their sides and angles correspond to each other in such a way that the corresponding sides are congruent and the corresponding angles are congruent. Use the drawing you made for this case and find a pair of congruent triangles on opposite sides of your sphere.

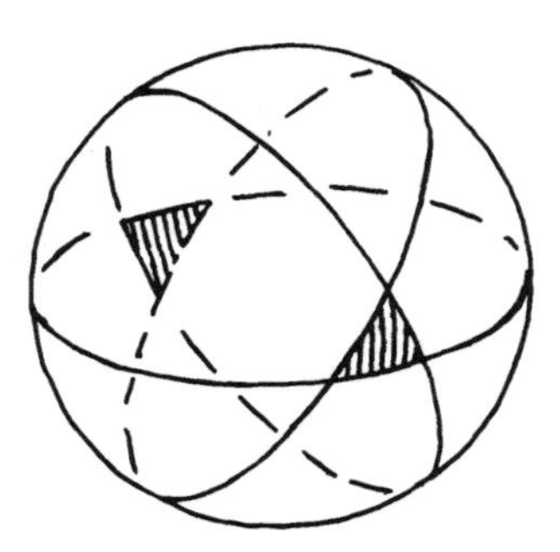

   a. Mark each such pair of triangles in your drawing with a different color.

   b. How many such pairs of triangles do your three great circles create?

7. Trace one of these triangles onto a transparency.

   a. Does the triangle fit exactly onto its congruent partner?

   b. Explain how you could make it fit exactly.

   c. Such a pair of triangles is called a **reflexive** pair of triangles. Explain why this is a good name for these pairs of triangles.

Compare the Plane and the Sphere

8. See how many observations you can make about three distinct straight lines on the plane and three distinct great circles on the sphere. Record them on a comparison chart like the one at right. Add as many rows as you need.

Three distinct lines	
On the plane	On the sphere

9. Which do you think is simpler, three straight lines on the plane or three great circles on the sphere? Why?

10. Now try to reverse your argument. Give reasons why three lines are simpler on the surface you *didn't* choose above.

Explore More

11. The adjacent triangle formed by extending two sides of a spherical triangle enlarges the original triangle into a biangle. Take a triangle on the sphere and its three adjacent triangles, as shown. What is the total area of these four triangles? Hint: If two triangles are reflexive, they have the same area.

12. The more lines you draw on the plane or on the sphere, the more regions you create. As you add more lines, you will notice a pattern.

   a. Find the maximum number of regions you can create on the plane by using a given number of straight lines. Record your data in a chart like the one below. Then generalize the pattern for n lines.

Number of straight lines	1	2	3	4	5	6	n
Maximum number of regions you can create with the straight lines							

   b. Find the maximum number of regions you can create on the sphere by using a given number of great circles. Record your data in a chart like the one below. Then generalize the pattern for n great circles.

Number of great circles	1	2	3	4	5	6	n
Maximum number of regions you can create with the great circles							

What regions can you create using three lines?

Student Audience: Middle School/High School

Prerequisites: Students should know how to measure distance and angles on the sphere.

Class Time: 30–50 minutes

Construction/Investigation on the Plane

1 & 2. There are four possible cases on the plane. (a) Three parallel lines determine four infinite regions. (b) Two parallel lines and a third one that intersects both of them determine six infinite regions. (c) Three concurrent lines determine six infinite regions. (d) Three nonconcurrent lines with no parallels among them determine seven regions, six of which are infinite and one of which is finite.

Construction/Investigation on the Sphere

4 & 5. There are two possible cases on the sphere.

a. Three concurrent great circles determine six finite regions: six biangles that cover the whole sphere. Each of these biangles has one reflexive mate with the same angles and sides. Thus the six biangles consist of three reflexive pairs.

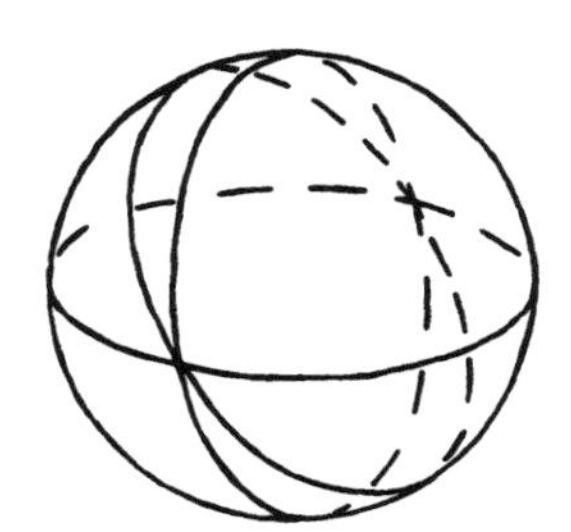

b. Three nonconcurrent great circles determine eight finite regions: eight triangles that cover the whole sphere. Each of these triangles has one reflexive mate with the same angles and sides. Thus the eight triangles consist of four reflexive pairs.

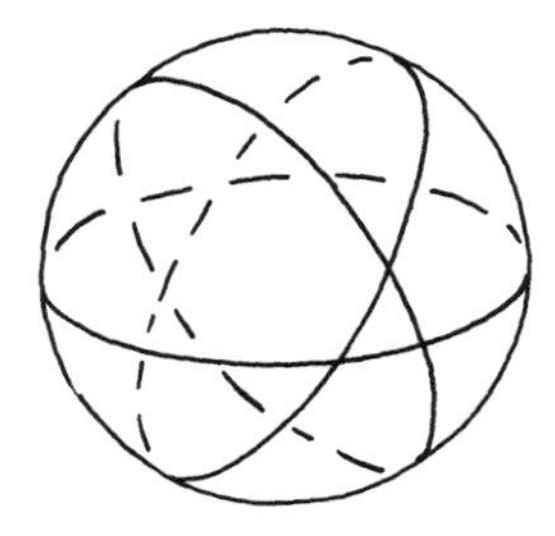

7. Planar and spherical reflexive triangles differ in that two planar reflexive triangles can be made to exactly coincide with each other by moving them in three-dimensional space; this is not possible for spherical reflexive triangles. In contrast with the plane, reflexive spherical triangles cannot be placed over each other so that they coincide. However, if you trace one of the reflexive spherical triangles onto a transparency and turn the transparency inside out, the triangles will coincide. On the other hand, if you place the triangle on the transparency adjacent to its reflexive mate without first turning the triangle inside out, you can easily see that it is a reflection of its mate; hence the name *reflexive triangles.* A pair of reflexive spherical triangles can be made to coincide with each other only if they are isosceles triangles.

Compare the Plane and the Sphere

Three distinct lines

On the plane	On the sphere
If three straight lines have a point of intersection in common, then they create six infinite regions.	If three great circles have a point of intersection in common, then they also have another point of intersection in common, and these two points are opposite poles. In this case the three great circles create six finite biangular regions. Each pair of opposite biangles is congruent.
If each of the straight lines intersects the other two lines, but all three lines do not have a common point of intersection, then the lines create six infinite regions and one finite (triangular) region.	If each of the great circles intersects the other two great circles, but all three great circles do not have a common point of intersection, then they create eight triangles with finite area. The pairs of triangles on opposite sides of the sphere are reflexive (congruent) triangles. The three great circles create four pairs of reflexive (congruent) triangles.
If two of the straight lines are parallel, then the three lines create six infinite regions. If all three straight lines are parallel, then they create four infinite regions.	Great circles cannot be parallel.

Explore More

11. Each of the four triangles has a reflexive mate among the other four triangles. Because two reflexive triangles have the same area, the total area of the first four triangles must be equal to the total area of the second four triangles. However, the eight triangles cover the whole spherical surface without gaps or overlaps, so the total area of the first four triangles must be half of the whole sphere (the area of a hemisphere).

12. **a.** The empty plane has zero lines and one region on it. Imagine that you use a razor blade to cut the plane along a straight line. Now you have one line, and $1 + 1 = 2$ regions. Next, make another cut with the blade along a second straight line. You create a new region when you intersect your cut along the first line. When you go on with the cut after the point of intersection, you make still another region. Now you have two lines, and $1 + 1 + 2 = 4$ regions. Make a third cut so that the three straight lines do not have a common point of intersection. Each time you intersect one of the previous lines, you make a new region and have one more region after the last point of intersection. Now you have three straight lines, and $1 + 1 + 2 + 3 = 7$ regions.

Now you can see the pattern. For n straight lines among which there are no three concurrent lines, the number of distinct regions is $1 + 1 + 2 + 3 + \ldots + (n - 1) + n = 1 + n(n + 1)/2$.

b. The empty sphere has zero great circles and one region on it. Imagine that you use a razor blade to cut the spherical surface into two regions along a great circle. Now you have one great circle, and $1 + 1 = 2$ regions. Next, make another cut with the blade along a second great circle. You do not create a new region when you intersect your cut along the first great circle. You have to go on with the cut to the second point of intersection to create a new region. When you go on after the second point of intersection and arrive at your starting point, then you make still another region. Now you have two great circles, and $1 + 1 + 2 = 4$ regions. At this stage, it looks as if the plane and the sphere behave in the same way! Make a third cut so that the three great circles are not concurrent. The third great circle will have four points of intersection with the other two. You create just as many new regions as there are new points of intersection. Now you have three great circles, and $1 + 1 + 2 \cdot 1 + 2 \cdot 2 = 8$ regions. For four great circles, you have $1 + 1 + 2 \cdot 1 + 2 \cdot 2 + 2 \cdot 3 = 14$ regions.

Now you can see the pattern. For n great circles among which no three are concurrent, there are $1 + 1 + 2[1 + 2 + 3 + \ldots + (n - 1)] = 2 + 2(n - 1)n/2 = 2 + (n - 1)n$ distinct regions.

ADVENTURE 3.3

How many triangles can have the same three vertices?

Suppose you pick three points.

- Investigate how many different triangles you can get by connecting the points with line segments on the plane.
- Investigate how many different triangles you can get by connecting the points with arcs on the sphere.

Construction on the Plane

Draw three **noncollinear** points on the plane. Construct a triangle with these three points as vertices.

Investigate

1. How many different line segments can you draw between two points on the plane?
2. How many different triangles can you draw that have the same three vertices?

Make a Guess

3. How many different ways can you connect three points on a sphere to make a triangle?

Construction on the Sphere

Step 1 Draw three points on your sphere, making sure that all three points are not on the same great circle and that no two of the three points are opposite each other. Label your points A, B, and C.

Step 2 Construct a spherical triangle with points A, B, and C as vertices.

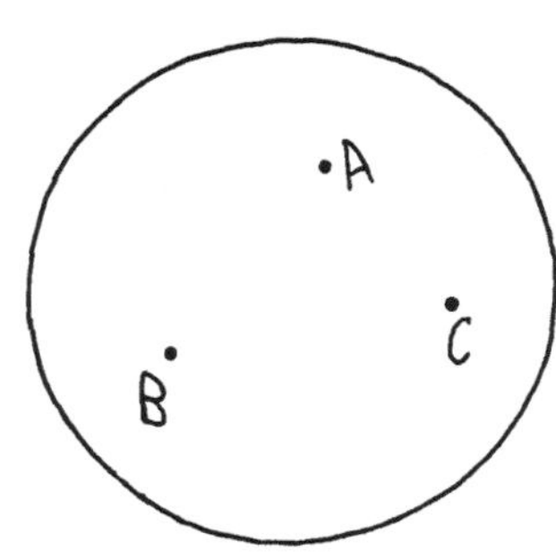

Investigate

4. How many different arcs of a great circle can you draw between two points, assuming the points are not opposite each other?
5. Show that points A, B, and C in your construction do not determine a unique spherical triangle. Use different-colored markers to show some different triangles determined by these three points.
6. **a.** How many different spherical triangles can you draw with points A, B, and C as vertices?

   b. Explain how you determined this number.
7. Two points on a sphere divide the great circle that passes through them into two arcs. Let's decide to always choose the shorter of the two arcs when we construct spherical triangles.

   a. Give an example of a spherical triangle that adheres to this new definition.

   b. Explain how this new definition will simplify your further investigation of triangles on a sphere.

Compare the Plane and the Sphere

8. See how many observations you can make about triangles on the plane and triangles on the sphere. Record them on a comparison chart like the one at right. Add as many rows as you need.

Triangles	
On the plane	On the sphere

9. Do you think triangles are simpler on the plane or on the sphere? Why?

10. Now try to reverse your argument. Give reasons why triangles are simpler on the surface you *didn't* choose above.

Explore More

11. Draw three points on the sphere so that two of them are opposite each other. Explain why these three points do not determine a unique spherical triangle.

12. **a.** Describe a triangle that has all three of its vertices on the same line in the plane.

    b. Describe some different triangles that have all three of their vertices on the same great circle on the sphere.

    c. The triangles you described in parts a and b are called **degenerate** triangles. Explain why this name is appropriate.

How many triangles can have the same three vertices?

Student Audience: Middle School/High School

Prerequisites: Students should know how to draw a great circle through two spherical points.

Class Time: 30–50 minutes

Construction/Investigation on the Plane

1. We can draw only one line segment between any two different points on the plane.

2. We can draw only one line segment between each of the three pairs of points, so the three vertices determine one triangle.

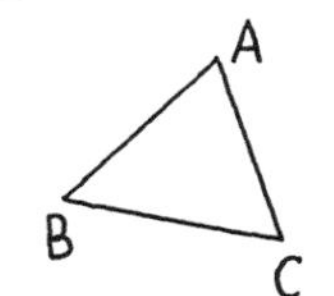

Construction/Investigation on the Sphere

4. Two different points that are not opposite can be connected with exactly two different arcs of a great circle. Thus two vertices determine two different possibilities for the side of the triangle between these two vertices.

6. There are three pairs of vertices in a triangle: *A* and *B*, *B* and *C*, and *C* and *A*. Each of these pairs gives rise to two possible sides, a shorter arc and a longer arc, if the two vertices are not opposite poles. Thus the total number of the triangles with vertices *A*, *B*, and *C* is $2 \times 2 \times 2$, or 8. Students should shade in some of these triangles on their spheres.

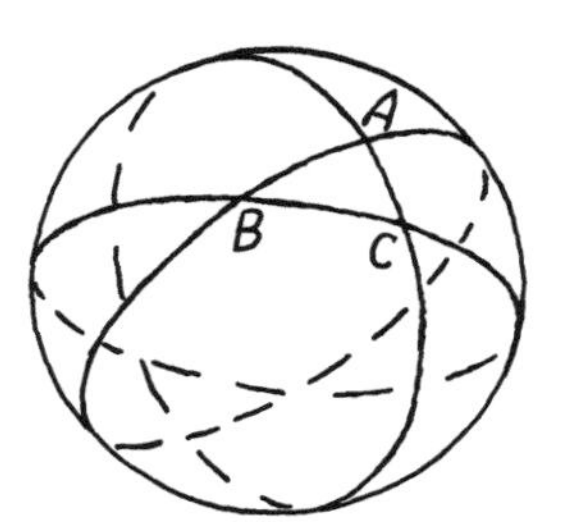

7. If the vertices are not opposite, then they divide the great circle that passes through them into a shorter and a longer arc. We can choose one of these two arcs to be the triangle's side. For consistency, we will always choose the shorter one. In this way we can choose one triangle from the eight possible triangles. Each of the sides of this chosen triangle must measure less than 180°.

   Therefore we define a side of the triangle as the shorter arc between the two vertices. Using this definition, the three vertices do determine only one spherical triangle.

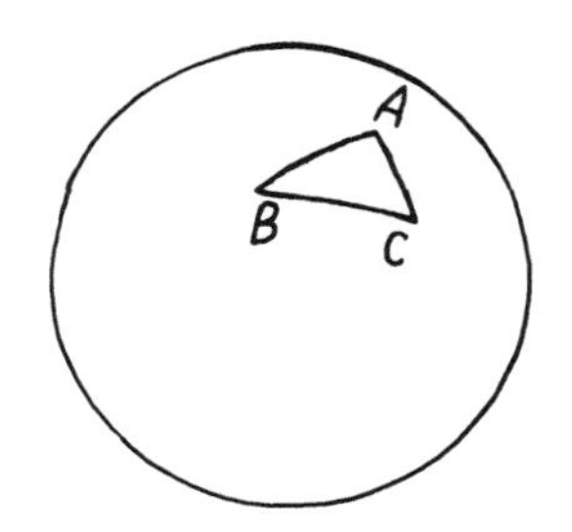

Compare the Plane and the Sphere

Triangles

On the plane	On the sphere
Any pair of points can be connected with exactly one line segment. Thus three noncollinear points determine a unique triangle.	Any pair of points that are not opposite poles can be connected with two different arcs of a great circle. As a result, three noncollinear points that are not opposite determine eight different spherical triangles.
	However if we define a side of a spherical triangle to be the shorter of the two arcs, the situation is a bit simpler. Then three noncollinear points determine a unique spherical triangle as long as no two of the three points are opposite each other.
	Two points on a sphere that are opposite poles do not determine a unique great circle. Therefore if two of the three vertices are pole points, then the three vertices do not determine a unique spherical triangle.

Explore More

11. If the triangle has a pair of opposite vertices, then we can find infinitely many arcs (meridians) measuring 180° that connect the two vertices. Thus, in this case, the three vertices do not determine only one triangle, nor do they determine a finite number of triangles.

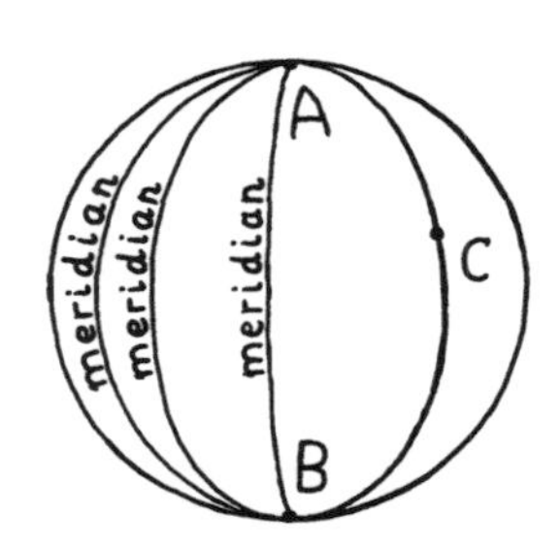

12. b. On the sphere, there are two types of triangles that have all three vertices on the same great circle. In one case, one of the vertices lies on the shorter arc between the other two. This triangle is an arc of a great circle with a point on the arc. In the other case, each of the three vertices lies on the longer arc between the other two. This triangle is an entire great circle with three points on the great circle.

c. These triangles have a number of properties that nondegenerate triangles do not have. On the sphere, the two types of degenerate spherical triangles represent the extremities that nondegenerate triangles never possess. For example, the sum of angle measures in triangles of the first type is $0° + 180° + 0° = 180°$; in the second type, the sum is $180° + 180° + 180° = 540°$. For any nondegenerate triangle, this sum is between these two limits.

What is the sum of the angle measures of a triangle?

If you add the measures of the angles of a triangle, do you always get the same sum?

- Investigate the sum of the angle measures of planar triangles.
- Investigate the sum of the angle measures of spherical triangles.

Construction on the Plane

Draw two triangles, one completely inside the other. Measure the interior angles of each triangle.

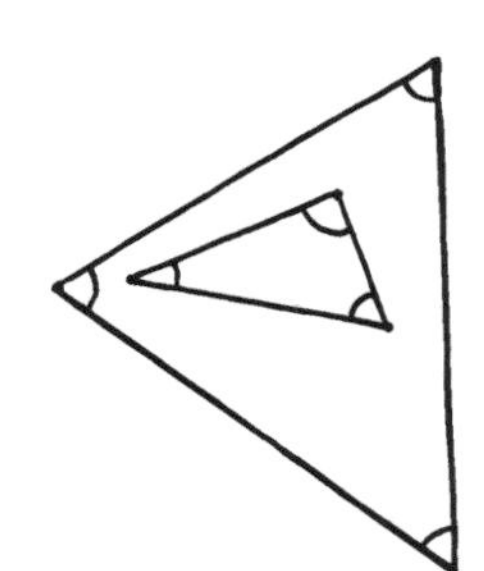

Investigate

1. Explain why the sum of the measures of the interior angles of a planar triangle is always the same.

Make a Guess

2. What is the sum of the measures of the interior angles of a spherical triangle?

Construction on the Sphere

Draw three triangles, the first triangle completely inside the second and the second completely inside the third. Measure the interior angles of each triangle.

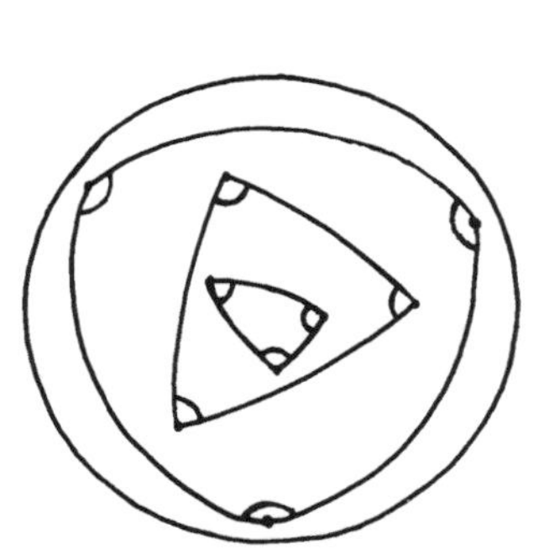

Investigate

3. Find the sum of the measures of the angles of each of your spherical triangles.

4. Explain why you get different answers for different triangles.

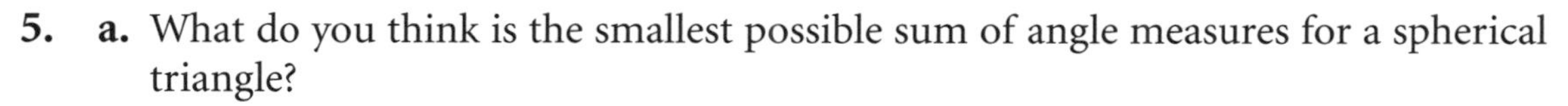

5. **a.** What do you think is the smallest possible sum of angle measures for a spherical triangle?

b. What is the largest? Explain your reasoning.

Compare the Plane and the Sphere

6. See how many observations you can make about the sum of the angle measures of a triangle on the plane and on the sphere. Record them on a comparison chart like the one at right. Add as many rows as you need.

Sum of the angle measures of a triangle

On the plane	On the sphere

7. Do you think the sum of the angle measures of a triangle is simpler on the plane or on the sphere? Why? Which case is more interesting? Which case is the more likely to inspire connections between angle measurement and other properties of triangles?

8. Now try to reverse your argument. Give reasons why the surface you *didn't* choose above is simpler or more interesting.

Explore More

9. Construct a triangle with three right angles. Explain why this is possible.

10. Draw a small triangle on your sphere. Suppose we allowed the interior of a spherical triangle to be the larger triangular region "around the back." Now what is the greatest possible sum of the interior angles of a spherical triangle?

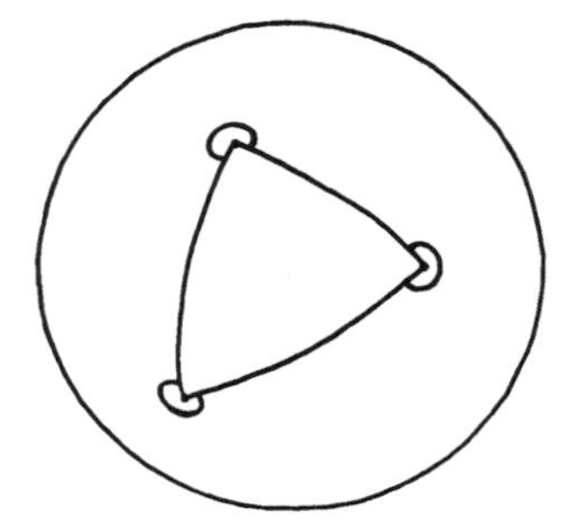

11. Investigate sums of the measures of the angles of quadrilaterals on the sphere.

12. Investigate sums of the measures of the angles of other polygons on the sphere. What is the sum of the measures of the angles of a spherical polygon with n sides?

ADVENTURE 3.4

What is the sum of the angle measures of a triangle?

Student Audience: High School

Prerequisites: Students should know how to measure angles on the sphere.

Class Time: 30–60 minutes

Construction/Investigation on the Sphere

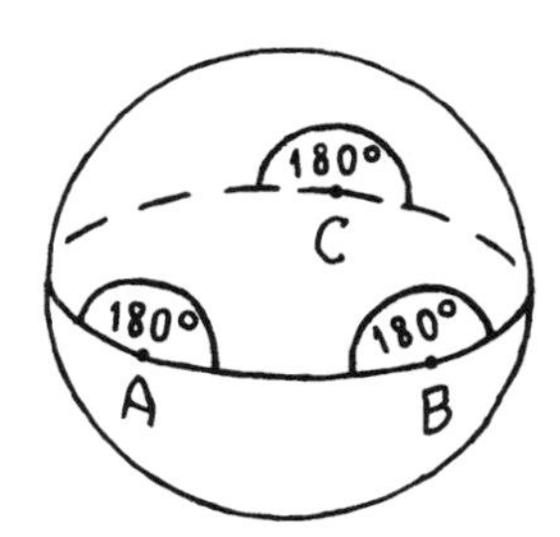

5. The sum of the angle measures is greater than 180° but less than 540°. For degenerate triangles, it can be exactly 180° or 540°.

Only the degenerate triangle with angles of measure 0°, 0°, and 180° has its angle measure sum exactly equal to 180°.

Only the degenerate triangle with angles of measure 360°, 360°, and 360° has its angle measure exactly equal to 540°.

Compare the Plane and the Sphere

Sum of the angle measures of a triangle

On the plane	On the sphere
The measures of the interior angles of a triangle always add up to 180°.	The measures of the interior angles of a triangle add up to different numbers of degrees, depending on the size of the triangle.
	The largest possible triangle has all vertices on the same great circle. This triangle has three 180° angles, so the sum of the angle measures is 540°. This is a degenerate triangle because its three vertices are collinear. The smallest possible triangle has all three vertices on the same great circle and one side that lies on top of the other two. This degenerate triangle has two 0° angles and one 180° angle, so the sum of its angle measures is 180°. Thus the sum of the angle measures of a triangle is greater than or equal to 180° and less than or equal to 540°. For nondegenerate triangles, the sum of the angle measures is greater than 180° and less than 540°.

7. The sum of the angle measures in a spherical triangle is not a constant; rather, it varies from 180° to 540°. A consequence that makes the sphere seem more complicated than the plane is that the sum of the angle measures in a spherical quadrilateral is not a constant. However, a second consequence is that the greater the sum of the angle measures in a spherical triangle, the larger the area of the triangle, which may prove to be very simple and useful.

Explore More

9. Draw a 90° arc and construct two perpendiculars at its endpoints. The three arcs form a triangle with three right angles; thus the sum of the angle measures of this triangle is 270°.

10. The sum of the interior angle measures of the triangular region "around the back" is greater than 540° but less than 900°. The greater this triangular region, the greater the sum of angle measures.

11. For any convex spherical quadrilateral, the sum of the angle measures varies between 360° and 720°.

ADVENTURE 3.5

Can a triangle have more than one right angle?

You may have already learned some special properties of right triangles.

- See if you can construct a triangle with more than one right angle.

Construction on the Plane

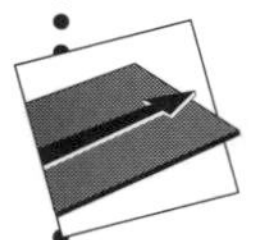

Construct a right triangle on the plane.

Investigate

1. Explain why it is impossible for a triangle on the plane to have more than one right angle.

Make a Guess

2. Is it possible for a triangle on the sphere to have more than one right angle?

Construction on the Sphere

Step 1 Draw a point *P*. Then draw the equatorial great circle that has *P* as a pole point.

Step 2 Draw a perpendicular from point *P* to its equator.

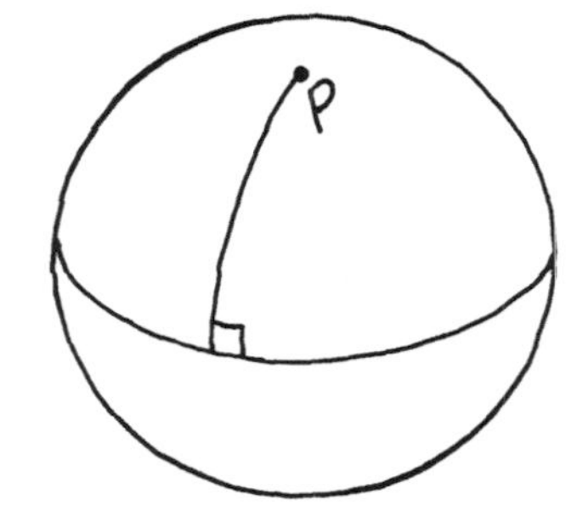

Step 3 Draw three other perpendiculars. Label the points of intersection on the equator *A*, *B*, *C*, and *D*, as shown.

Step 4 Measure the angles of triangles *PAB*, *PAC*, and *PAD*.

Step 5 Measure the sides of triangles *PAB*, *PAC*, and *PAD*.

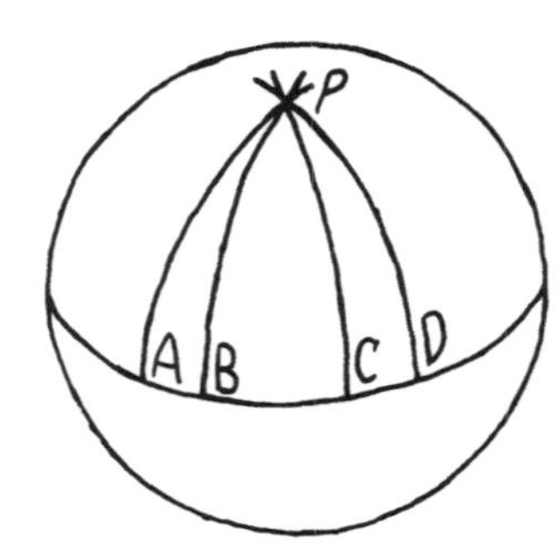

Investigate

3. **a.** Find the sum of the measures of the three angles in each of these triangles. Do the measures of the interior angles of spherical triangles always add up to 180°?

   b. Describe any relationship you observe between the areas of these triangles and the sums of their angle measures.

4. Draw a triangle that has exactly three right angles. Record the lengths of its sides and the sum of its angles.

5. Two triangles satisfy the AAS (Angle-Angle-Side) condition if two pairs of corresponding angles are congruent *and* a pair of corresponding sides not included by these angles is congruent. Any pair of triangles on the plane must be congruent if they satisfy the AAS condition. Use the right triangles you drew in this investigation to explain why the AAS condition does not guarantee congruence for triangles on the sphere.

6. Two triangles satisfy the SSA (Side-Side-Angle) condition if two pairs of corresponding sides are congruent *and* a pair of corresponding angles not included by these sides is congruent. On the plane the SSA condition guarantees congruence only for certain pairs of triangles. For example, if both triangles are right triangles, then the SSA condition guarantees their congruence. Use the right triangles you drew in this investigation to explain why the SSA condition does not guarantee congruence for right triangles on the sphere.

Compare the Plane and the Sphere

7. See how many observations you can make about triangles with right angles on the plane and triangles with right angles on the sphere. Record them on a comparison chart like the one at right. Add as many rows as you need.

Triangles with right angles	
On the plane	On the sphere

8. Do you think triangles with right angles are simpler on the plane or on the sphere? Why?

9. Now try to reverse your argument. Give reasons why the surface you *didn't* choose above is simpler.

Explore More

10. In Chapter 0, you learned a riddle about a wandering bear.

    a. Change the riddle so that the bear's path traces a triangle with three right angles. How far does the bear travel in each of the three directions?

    b. Explain why the bear must be a good swimmer.

11. Decide whether the Pythagorean theorem holds true for right triangles on the sphere.

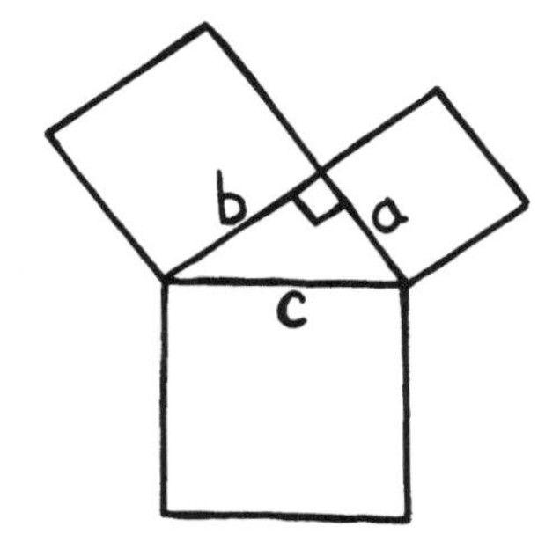

12. Isosceles triangles on the plane have congruent base angles. Determine if this is true for isosceles triangles on the sphere.

13. What is the sum of the angle measures in a spherical triangle with two right angles?

14. Draw a triangle with two right angles and whose third angle measures 180°. What is the sum of the angle measures in this triangle?

Can a triangle have more than one right angle?

Student Audience: Middle School/High School

Prerequisites: Students should know or be introduced to the fact that each point on the sphere has only one equator.

Class Time: 25–45 minutes

Construction/Investigation on the Plane

1. We cannot draw a planar triangle with two right angles because the sum of the angle measures is 180° for these two angles—nothing is left for the third angle. Therefore the two sides are parallel and do not determine a third vertex.

Construction/Investigation on the Sphere

Here's a construction tip: Any great circle that is perpendicular to the equator will pass through the equator's pole point.

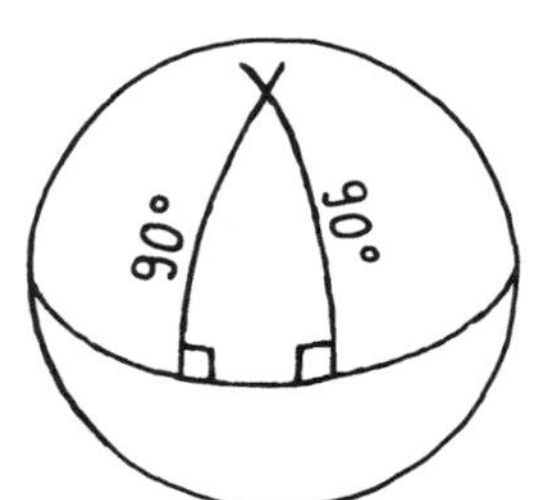

3. Any one of these triangles is an isosceles triangle with two base angles that each measure 90° and two sides that each measure 90°. The sum of the three angle measures is 180° plus the third angle at the pole point. The greater the sum of angles, the greater the area of the triangle.

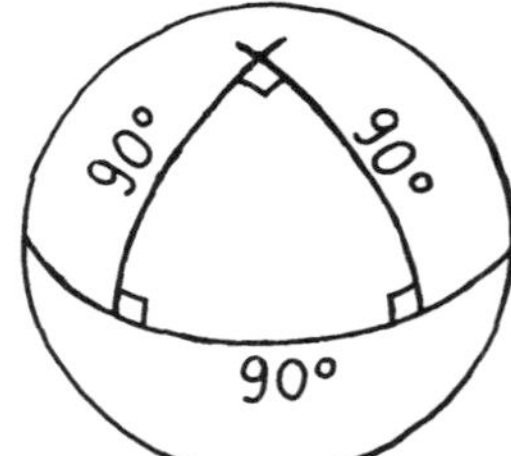

4. If the spherical distance of the base measures 90° exactly, then the triangle is not only an isosceles triangle, but also an equilateral triangle, with each of the sides and the angles measuring 90°. Therefore any of the sides of this triangle are perpendicular to both of the other two sides.
5. The AAS (Angle-Angle-Side) condition guarantees two congruent triangles on the plane but not on the sphere. In any spherical triangle with two right angles, we find two angles that each measure 90° and a side that measures 90°. This means that all these triangles have two angles and one side in common but that these triangles are not congruent.

Compare the Plane and the Sphere

Triangles with right angles

On the plane	On the sphere
A triangle can have at most one right angle.	A triangle can have one, two, or three right angles.
The AAS property guarantees that two triangles are congruent.	The AAS property does not guarantee that two triangles are congruent.
The SSA property guarantees that any two right triangles are congruent.	The SSA property does not guarantee that two triangles are congruent.

Explore More

11. The Pythagorean theorem does not hold true for right triangles on the sphere, as is clearly demonstrated by the triangle with three right angles. This is an equilateral triangle, but whatever units of measurement we use, $a^2 + a^2 = a^2$ always implies that $a = 0$.

12. Yes. The axis of symmetry divides the isosceles triangle into two reflexive right triangles. These reflexive triangles have the same three angles, so the base angles of the isosceles triangle are congruent.

13. The sum is 180° plus the measure of the third angle.

14. If the third angle measure is 180°, then the triangle coincides with a biangle, as shown. The sum of the angle measures in this "biangled" triangle is 360°.

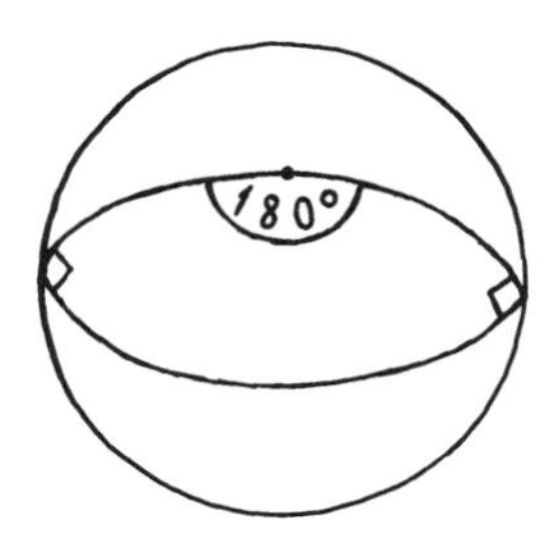

CHAPTER 4
Similarity and Congruence

Chapter 4: Similarity and Congruence

Adventure 4.1: Can you construct similar polygons?

Adventure 4.2: What is special about two triangles whose corresponding angles are congruent?

Adventure 4.3: What conditions guarantee congruence of spherical triangles?

This chapter focuses on determining the criteria that guarantee similarity and congruence of figures. The results reveal more of the remarkable differences between the geometry of the sphere and of the plane. Again, for simplicity, most explorations use triangles.

In Adventure 4.1, students might be surprised when they discover that it is impossible to scale a polygon on a sphere without changing its shape. Essentially, the geometric notion of similarity does not exist on a sphere.

In Adventure 4.2, students construct pairs of triangles that have all three pairs of corresponding angles congruent (often called the Angle-Angle-Angle or AAA condition). This condition guarantees similarity, but not congruence, for a pair of planar triangles. However, this condition has a different consequence for triangles on a sphere.

In Adventure 4.3, students summarize and compare all the possible congruence conditions for triangles on the plane and on the sphere. The Explore More section in Adventure 3.5 addresses the Side-Side-Angle (SSA) and Angle-Angle-Side (AAS) conditions, and Adventure 4.2 addresses the AAA condition. You can begin with these two adventures, but an adventurous class can proceed directly to Adventure 4.3, where they will experiment with all these conditions anyway as they determine all the triangle congruence properties. Adventure 4.1 is not a prerequisite for the other two adventures.

Use the Adventure Cards at the beginning of the chapter for more open-ended lessons. Use the Student's Guides for more structured lessons. The Teacher's Guide that follows each Student's Guide contains solutions and suggestions.

ADVENTURE 4.1

Can you construct similar polygons?

Two polygons are *similar* if their corresponding angles are congruent and their corresponding sides are proportional.

- Decide whether you can draw similar polygons on the plane and on the sphere.

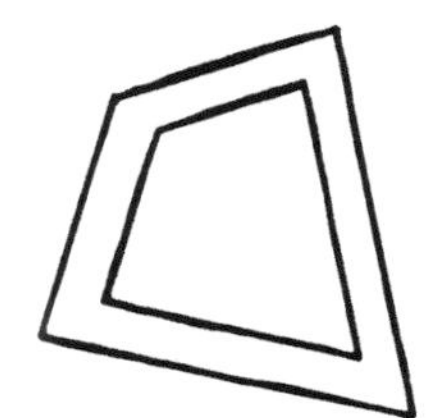

ADVENTURE 4.2

What is special about two triangles whose corresponding angles are congruent?

- Investigate whether two triangles must be similar if their corresponding angles are congruent.
- Investigate whether two triangles must be congruent if their corresponding angles are congruent.

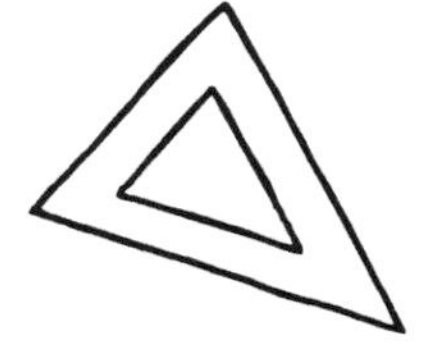

ADVENTURE 4.3

What conditions guarantee congruence of spherical triangles?

Do you recall which combinations of congruent sides and angles guarantee congruence of two triangles on the plane?

- Test these combinations to find which ones also guarantee congruence of spherical triangles.
- Find some combinations of congruent sides and angles that guarantee congruence of spherical triangles but not of planar triangles.

ADVENTURE 4.1

Can you construct similar polygons?

Two polygons are **similar** if their corresponding angles are congruent and their corresponding sides are proportional.

- Decide whether you can draw similar polygons on the plane and on the sphere.

Construction on the Plane

Step 1 Construct a triangle.

Step 2 Construct another triangle with sides half as long as the corresponding sides of your first triangle.

Step 3 Measure and label all the sides and the angles of each triangle.

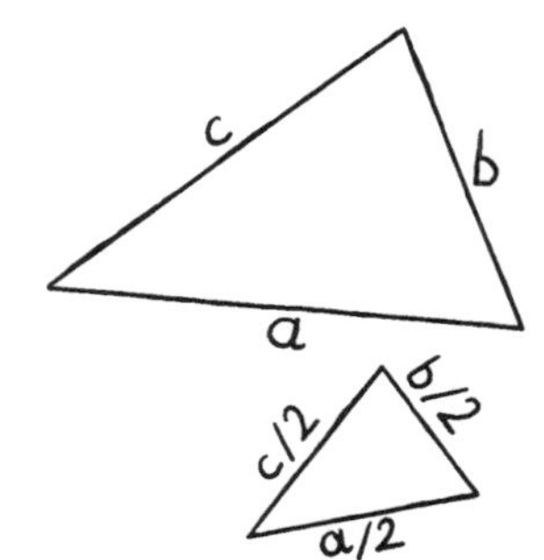

Investigate

1. Explain why your two triangles are similar triangles.

Make a Guess

2. Can you draw a pair of similar triangles on your sphere?

Construction on the Sphere

Follow the same steps that you did in the construction on the plane. Start with a fairly large triangle.

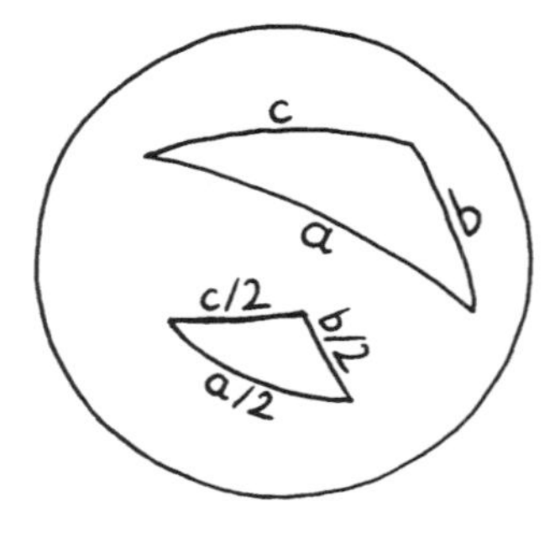

Investigate

3. Are the triangles you drew on your sphere similar triangles? Why or why not?

4. Two polygons are **similar** if and only if (1) all the corresponding angles are equal in measure and (2) all the corresponding sides are proportional.

a. Determine if it is possible to draw a pair of polygons on your sphere that satisfies the first part of this definition. Draw examples.

b. Determine if it is possible to draw a pair of polygons on your sphere that satisfies the second part of this definition. Draw examples.

c. What can you conclude about similar polygons on the sphere?

Compare the Plane and the Sphere

5. See how many observations you can make about similarity on the plane and similarity on the sphere. Record them on a comparison chart like the one at right. Add as many rows as you need.

Similarity

On the plane	On the sphere

6. Do you think similarity is simpler on the plane or on the sphere? Why?

7. Now try to reverse your argument. Give reasons why similarity is simpler on the surface you *didn't* choose above.

Explore More

8. Many professions such as engineering, insurance, design, and architecture require scale drawings of buildings, clothing, and machinery. What is the purpose of a scale drawing?

9. **a.** Imagine you have two spheres of the same size. One sphere has a picture on it. Is it possible to draw a scale drawing of that picture on the other sphere?

   b. What if the two spheres are different sizes?

10. Suppose somewhere on earth you could build a giant scale model of your home state. You want the dimensions of the model to be half the actual dimensions of the streets, buildings, hills, and mountains of your state. Describe the model and determine if it would be possible to build.

Can you construct similar polygons?

Student Audience: Middle School/High School

Prerequisites: Students should know or be introduced to the definition of a polygon on the plane and on the sphere. (On the plane, it is a closed chain of points and the segments connecting every two consecutive points. On the sphere, segments of straight lines are replaced by arcs of great circles.)

Class Time: 25–45 minutes

Construction/Investigation on the Sphere

3. No. The concept of similarity of triangles cannot be transferred to the sphere. On the sphere, three given angles determine a triangle just as three given sides do. If the corresponding sides of two spherical triangles are proportional, but not congruent, then the angles will not be congruent. For example, the corresponding sides of any two noncongruent equilateral triangles are proportional, but the angles in one of the triangles will be different from those in the other triangle. (On the plane, any of these angles is always equal to 60°.)

Students sometimes propose to double the sides of the original triangle instead of halving them. This is okay on the plane but does not always work on the sphere. If one of the sides of the original triangle is longer than 90°, then the triangle with doubled sides can't be constructed on the sphere because no spherical triangle has a side longer than 180°.

4. **a.** For example, students can construct two quadrilaterals with angles that measure 90°, 90°, 90°, and 120°, respectively, but with quite different sides. Here is one way to construct such quadrilaterals: Draw two perpendicular arcs of great circles on the sphere or on a transparency. Cut out a 120° angle from another transparency. Move the cut-out angle over the two perpendiculars so that the sides of the 120° angle are perpendicular to their two respective original perpendiculars. You will find that there are infinitely many solutions, from kite-like shapes to long and skinny quadrangles. Although no two quadrilaterals with corresponding angles congruent can be found with corresponding sides proportional, there is a property that these two quadrangles do have in common: They have the same area. (See Adventure 6.2.)

b. Students can construct two noncongruent quadrilaterals that have corresponding sides proportional, but the corresponding angles of these quadrilaterals will not be congruent.

c. On the sphere it is impossible to draw two noncongruent spherical polygons whose corresponding angles are equal in measure and whose corresponding sides are proportional. The conclusion is that similarity of polygons does not exist on the sphere.

Compare the Plane and the Sphere

Similarity

On the plane	On the sphere
It is possible to scale any polygon on the plane. Scaling produces a similar polygon that has the same shape but is a different size. The corresponding angles of similar polygons are equal in measure and the corresponding sides are proportional.	There are no similar shapes on the sphere that are not congruent. It is impossible to scale a polygon on the sphere. When you change the scale of a figure, you change its shape. If you create two non congruent polygons that have corresponding sides proportional (for example, two noncongruent equilateral triangles), then the corresponding angles will not be congruent.

Explore More

8. A scale drawing provides a plan for the design and the construction of an object, such as a dress, an engine part, or a school. A drawing is easier to make and change than the product itself. Additionally, a scaled drawing allows the designer to work at a size that is convenient, because many products are too large or too small to display and visualize easily on a desk or a computer screen.

9. **a.** The only scale drawing possible on the second sphere is one identical (congruent) to the original picture on the first sphere.

b. If the spheres are different sizes, there is only one possible drawing on the second sphere that is similar to the picture on the first sphere. The scaled drawing and the picture are different sizes: The drawing on the larger sphere will be a larger drawing. The scale factor between the two drawings will be the same as the ratio between the radii of the two spheres.

10. The smaller model will need to maintain a scaled version of the curvature of the earth if it is to be truly similar to the original model. The curvature of the smaller model should match the curvature of a sphere with half the radius of the earth. Some students may argue that this would be impossible to build on the earth because it is difficult to accommodate this sharper curvature. Others may argue that you could adjust for the model somehow, perhaps by propping it up on some mountains. The results are different depending on the size of your home state. Students in Rhode Island will not think their model is as difficult to build as those in Texas. Of course, many students will respond that a project of this scale is impossible because it is so impractical.

ADVENTURE 4.2

What is special about two triangles whose corresponding angles are congruent?

- Investigate whether two triangles must be similar if their corresponding angles are congruent.
- Investigate whether two triangles must be congruent if their corresponding angles are congruent.

Construction on the Plane

Step 1 Draw a triangle on a piece of paper and use scissors to cut it out. Mark each angle near its vertex.

Step 2 Tear each of the three angles off of your triangle.

Step 3 Move the angles to try to create another triangle having the same angles but with sides that have different lengths than the first triangle.

Investigate

1. How many different triangles can you make using these same three angles?

2. If two triangles have all three pairs of their corresponding angles congruent, then we say that the triangles satisfy the **AAA (Angle-Angle-Angle) condition**. What is special about two planar triangles that satisfy the AAA condition?

3. If a pair of planar triangles satisfies the AAA condition, does that guarantee that the two triangles are congruent?

Make a Guess

4. Will the AAA condition guarantee either similarity or congruence of triangles on the sphere?

Construction on the Sphere

You will need to cut up at least one transparency to do this construction.

Step 1 Draw a triangle on your sphere. To keep track of the angles later, mark each angle near its vertex with a different color or mark.

Step 2 Place a transparency over one angle of your triangle so that the angle's vertex is under the edge of the transparency. Trace the angle onto the transparency and extend the sides of the angle until they almost intersect. Then cut out the angle and color it to match the original angle on the sphere.

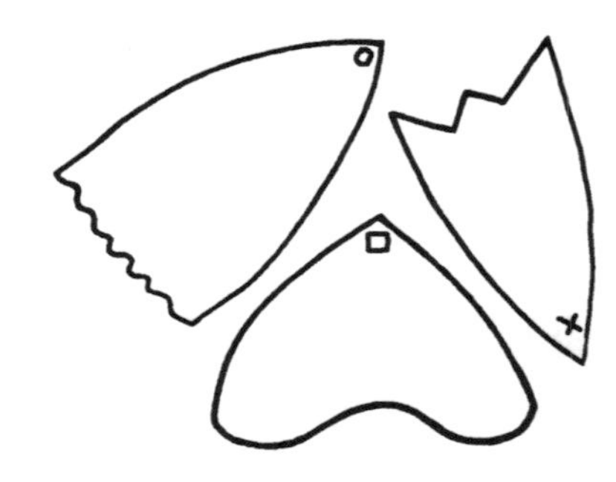

Step 3 Repeat Step 2 for the other two angles.

Step 4 Turn your sphere over so that your original triangle is on the bottom. Stack the three angles on top of your sphere. Move the angles around and try to form a new triangle having these three angles as vertices. You may want to mark the sides of the angles to make them easier to see.

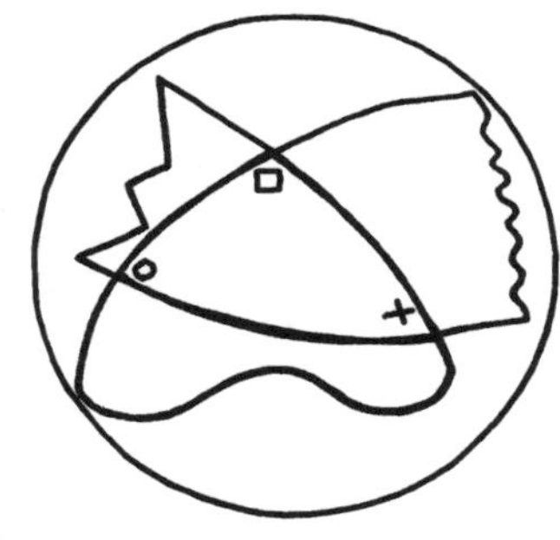

Step 5 When you have formed a triangle, tape the three angles together. Then turn your sphere over again and compare your new triangle to the original triangle.

Investigate

5. How does your triangle made of transparencies compare to the original triangle you drew on the sphere?

6. How many different spherical triangles can you make using the same three angles?

7. What is special about spherical triangles whose corresponding angles are congruent?

8. Mix your spherical angles together with those made by others in your class and then try to form spherical triangles. What do you find?

Compare the Plane and the Sphere

9. See how many observations you can make about planar triangles that satisfy the AAA condition and spherical triangles that satisfy the AAA condition. Record them on a comparison chart like the one at right. Add as many rows as you need.

The AAA condition in triangles

On the plane	On the sphere

10. Do you think the plane or the sphere is simpler in this case? Why?

11. Now try to reverse your argument. Give reasons why the surface you *didn't* choose above is simpler.

Explore More

12. You already know that the sum of the angle measures of a planar triangle is 180°. What would happen if you tried to form a planar triangle out of three angles whose measures did not add up to 180°?

13. You already know that the sum of angle measures in a spherical triangle is not less than 180° and is not greater than 540°.

a. What would happen if you tried to form your spherical triangle out of three angles whose measures added up to exactly 180°?

b. What if the three spherical angles measured 90°, 90°, and 60°?

c. What if each of the three spherical angles measured 180°?

14. Add the three angle measures in the various spherical triangles you constructed. Do you find any connection between the sum of the angle measures and the area of the triangle?

15. Given two spherical quadrilaterals that have corresponding angles congruent, are the quadrilaterals themselves necessarily congruent?

ADVENTURE 4.2

What is special about two triangles whose corresponding angles are congruent?

Student Audience: Middle School/High School

Prerequisites: Students should know how to measure angles on the plane and on the sphere. They need to know or be introduced to the fact that the sum of angle measures in a planar triangle is 180° and that the sum of angle measures in spherical triangles is not less than 180° and not greater than 540°.

Class Time: 35–60 minutes

Construction/Investigation on the Plane

1. The three angle regions can be stacked up so that they form an infinite number of planar triangles with the same angles but with different sides in them. All these triangles are similar to one another.
2. The two triangles are similar to each other.
3. No.

Construction/Investigation on the Sphere

Each of the three spherical angle regions is marked with an angle. If we stack up the three angle regions at random, we usually do not get a spherical triangle. However, by carefully moving them around on top of one another, we can arrive at a position where the sides of the angles exactly form a spherical triangle having the three given angles.

6. In general, we can construct exactly two spherical triangles with the three given angles. These two triangles have the same angles and sides and are reflections of each other.
8. If the measures of the three angles add up to not less than 180° and not more than 540°, then the three given angles determine two spherical triangles that are reflexive to each other. Two reflexive triangles have the same size angles and sides. If the sum of angle measures is less than 180° or more than 540°, then no spherical triangle with the given angles can be found.

Compare the Plane and the Sphere

The AAA condition in triangles

On the plane	On the sphere
AAA does not guarantee that two triangles are congruent.	AAA correspondence guarantees that two triangles are congruent. If the triangles are a reflexive pair, they may not appear congruent at first.
AAA correspondence guarantees that two triangles are similar.	Similar triangles do not exist on a sphere (unless they are congruent).

Three given sides determine two reflexive triangles on both the plane and on the sphere. In this adventure, we have found that three given angles on the sphere determine the spherical triangle, just as three given sides determine the triangle both on plane and sphere.

Explore More

12. If the sum of the three angle measures is not exactly 180°, then we cannot construct a planar triangle with these three angles.
13. **a.** If the three spherical angle measures add up to 180°, then the spherical triangle diminishes into a single spherical point.

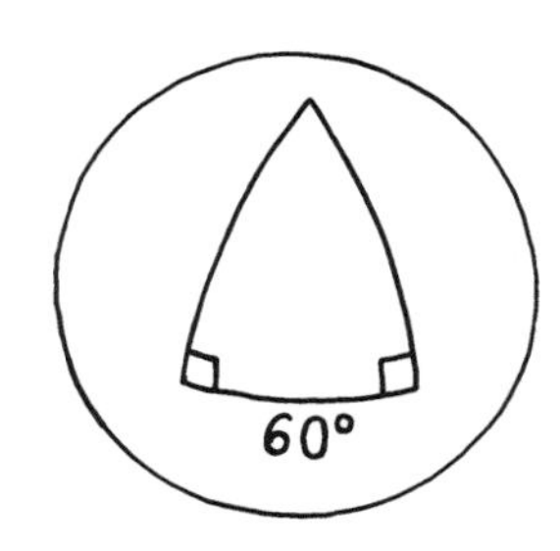

b. In a spherical triangle with two right angles, the measure of the third angle is equal to the measure of the third side. So we draw an arc of a great circle that measures exactly 60° and construct two perpendiculars at its endpoints. We have constructed a spherical triangle with angles that measure 90°, 90°, and 60°.

14. The greater the sum of angles is, the greater the area of the spherical triangle.

15. No. You can construct, for example, two quadrilaterals that both have angles 90°, 90°, 90°, 120°, but they are not congruent. (It is interesting to mention that they have the same area!) At this stage, students can only construct these quadrilaterals by trial-and-error methods. Later, in Adventure 9. 5, you will find a method of drawing a regular quadrilateral with angles of measure 120°.

ADVENTURE 4.3

What conditions guarantee congruence of spherical triangles?

Do you recall which combinations of congruent sides and angles guarantee congruence of two triangles on the plane?

- Test these combinations to find which also guarantee congruence of spherical triangles.
- Find some combinations of congruent sides and angles that guarantee congruence of spherical triangles but not of planar triangles.

Investigate on the Plane

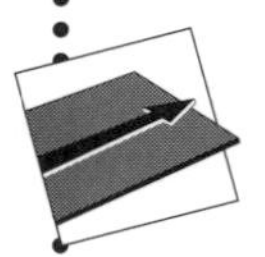

There are many conditions that guarantee that two triangles on the plane are congruent. For example, two triangles satisfy the SSS (Side-Side-Side) condition if all three pairs of corresponding sides of two triangles are congruent. Any pair of triangles that satisfies the SSS condition must be congruent.

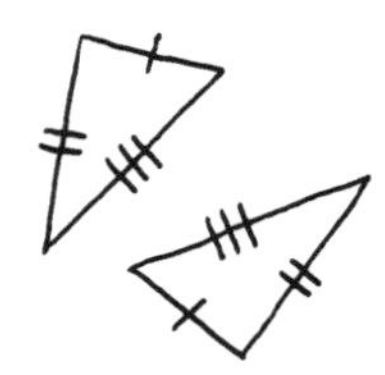

1. Copy the following list of possible congruence conditions. Circle the conditions that guarantee triangle congruence on the plane. Cross out the ones that do not.

SSS AAA AAS SSA ASA SAS

2. For each condition that you crossed out, draw two triangles in which the corresponding parts indicated are congruent but the triangles are not congruent.

Make a Guess

3. Which combinations of congruent angles and sides guarantee congruence of triangles on a sphere?

Investigate on the Sphere

4. Determine which combinations of corresponding congruent parts guarantee congruence of spherical triangles. Make drawings on your sphere that show which conditions work and which do not.

Compare the Plane and the Sphere

5. See how many observations you can make about congruence conditions for triangles on the plane and congruence conditions for triangles on the sphere. Record them on a comparison chart like the one at right. Add as many rows as you need.

Conditions that guarantee congruence of triangles

On the plane	On the sphere

6. Which surface do you think is simpler in this case: the plane or the sphere? Why?

7. Now try to reverse your argument. Give reasons why the surface you *didn't* choose above is simpler.

Explore More

8. Two boats leave different ports. Each boat travels along a great circle for 1000 km. Then each boat changes course by making a 90° turn to the right. After going 50 km in this new direction, each boat changes course again and travels directly to its home port. Did the two boats travel the same distance? Why or why not?

9. Find a pair of spherical triangles that has all of the properties listed below.

   i) The triangles have no right angles.

   ii) The triangles satisfy the SSA condition.

   iii) The triangles are not congruent to each other.

What conditions guarantee congruence of spherical triangles?

Student Audience: High School

Prerequisites: Students should be familiar with the simplest congruence conditions for planar triangles.

Class Time: 25–45 minutes

Compare the Plane and the Sphere

Conditions that guarantee congruence of triangles

On the plane	On the sphere
The following combinations of corresponding congruent sides and angles guarantee congruence of triangles: SSS, AAS, SAS, ASA.	The following combinations of corresponding congruent sides and angles guarantee congruence for triangles: SSS, AAA, SAS, ASA.
The SSA condition guarantees congruence only for right triangles.	The SSA condition does not guarantee congruence for any triangles.
The AAA correspondence guarantees that two triangles are similar.	There are no similar triangles on the sphere (unless they are congruent).

Explore More

8. Both routes determine two right triangles on the sphere with sides of 1000 km and 50 km, respectively. This is the SAS case that guarantees congruence of the two triangles. Thus the third side must also be congruent, and the two routes must be of the same distance.

9. Draw a side with endpoints A and B. Draw a spherical circle with center B and with a radius smaller than spherical distance AB. Draw a great circle through point A so that this great circle has two points of intersection, C_1 and C_2, with the circle. Connect the two points of intersection with point B. The two triangles ABC_1 and ABC_2 have all the three properties.

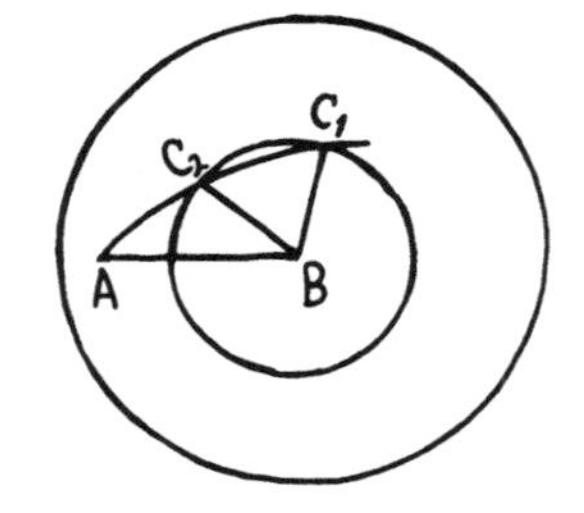

CHAPTER 5
Circles

Photo by Lesley Lovell

Chapter 5: Circles

Adventure 5.1: What are some properties of a circle on a sphere?

Adventure 5.2: What are some relationships in families of concentric circles?

Adventure 5.3: What is the ratio of the circumference of a circle to its diameter?

Your students have already worked with great circles on the sphere and are now ready to use their spherical compass to explore circles of other sizes. In this chapter students will compare spherical circles of all sizes with circles on the plane.

Adventure 5.1 is a simple introduction to the spherical circle and some of the shapes we associate with any circle, such as center, radii, tangents, and chords.

In Adventure 5.2, students construct sets of concentric circles. This construction provides an interesting adventure into the finite nature of the surface of the sphere.

In Adventure 5.3, students rediscover π in circles on the plane, only to find that the ratio of the circumference to the diameter of a circle is not so simple on a sphere.

If students are interested in finding the area of a spherical circle, refer them to Adventure 6.3 in the Chapter 6. In that adventure students use the areas of triangles to approximate the area of a circle.

Use the Adventure Cards at the beginning of the chapter for more open-ended lessons. Use the Student's Guides for more structured lessons. The Teacher's Guide that follows each Student's Guide contains solutions and suggestions. You can easily teach any of these three adventures independently of the other two.

ADVENTURE 5.1

What are some properties of a circle on a sphere?

- Compare circles on the plane with circles on the sphere. What similarities and differences can you find?

ADVENTURE 5.2

What are some relationships in families of concentric circles?

A family of *concentric* circles refers to all circles with the same center.

- Draw a family of concentric circles on the plane and a family of concentric circles on the sphere.
- Compare the two families.

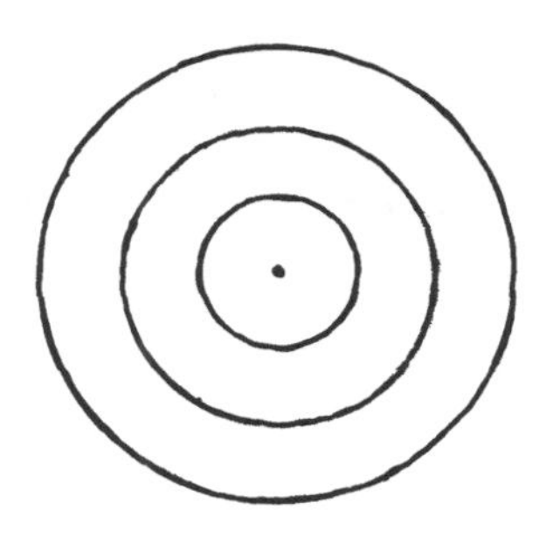

ADVENTURE 5.3

What is the ratio of the circumference of a circle to its diameter?

You may have compared the circumference of a circle to its diameter before.

- Conduct your own experiments to determine the approximate ratio of the circumference to the diameter of a circle on the plane and on the sphere.

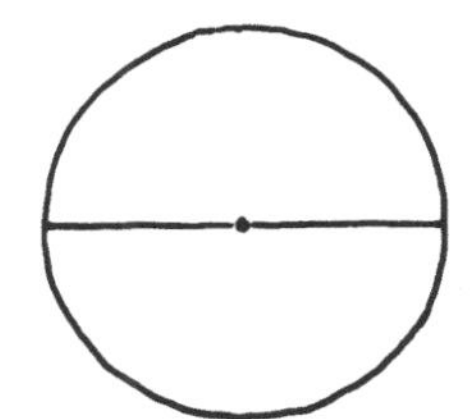

What are some properties of a circle on a sphere?

- Compare circles on the plane with circles on the sphere. What similarities and differences can you find?

Construction on the Plane

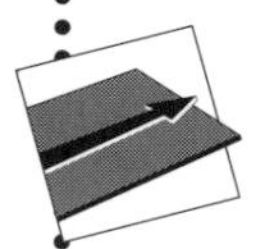

Step 1 Draw a point on the plane, then draw a circle with this point as its **center**. Draw a **radius** of the circle.

Step 2 Draw a **diameter** of the circle, a **chord** of the circle, and a **tangent** to the circle.

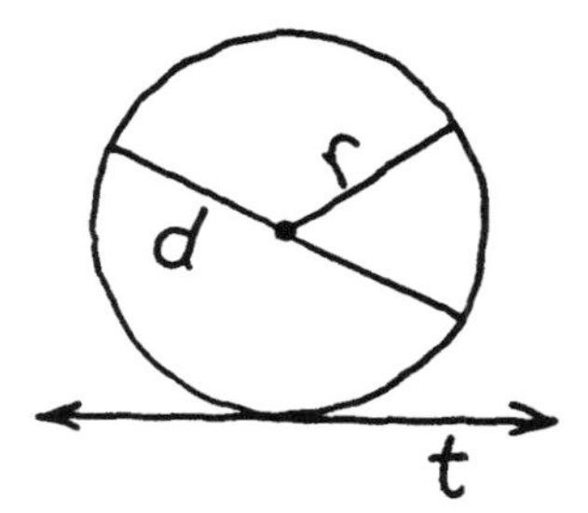

Investigate

1. List some properties that are true for any circle on the plane.
2. Explain why every circle on the plane has only one center.

Make a Guess

3. Which properties of planar circles are true for spherical circles?

Construction on the Sphere

Step 1 Draw a point on your sphere. Label the point *P*. Use your spherical compass to draw a circle with point *P* as its center. Use your spherical ruler to draw a radius of the circle.

Step 2 Use your spherical ruler to draw a diameter of the circle, a chord of the circle, and a tangent to the circle.

Step 3 Draw the point that is opposite point *P*. Label this opposite point *P′*.

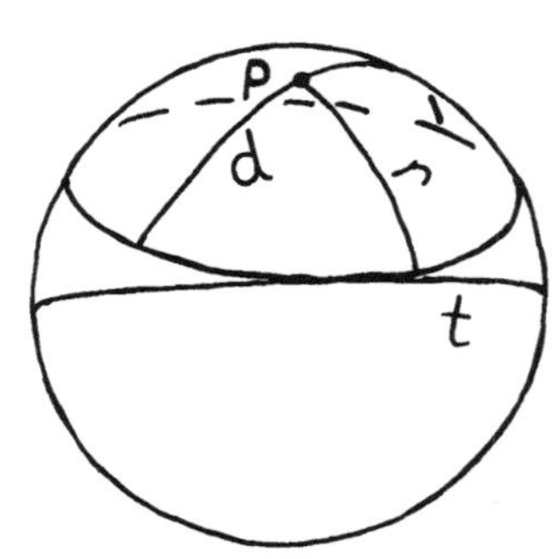

Investigate

4. Draw some points on the circle and measure the distance from each point to *P′*. Is *P′* another center of the circle? Why or why not?
5. Use your spherical ruler to measure the radius of the circle from center *P*, then measure the radius of the same circle from the opposite point *P′*. How do these distances compare?
6. Look at the list you made of properties of circles on the plane. Determine which of these properties are true for circles on the sphere.
7. The spherical compass can only draw circles with radii that measure less than or equal to 90°. Explain how to draw a circle whose radius measures 120°.

Compare the Plane and the Sphere

8. See how many observations you can make about circles on the plane and circles on the sphere. Record them on a comparison chart like the one at right. Add as many rows as you need.

Circles	
On the plane	On the sphere

9. Do you think circles are simpler on the plane or on the sphere? Why?

10. Now try to reverse your argument. Give reasons why circles are simpler on the surface you *didn't* choose above.

Explore More

11. In your Construction on the Sphere, you drew a tangent to a point on a circle. Describe the tangent to a point on a great circle.

12. **a.** Draw an inscribed angle and a central angle, both of which intercept the same arc in a planar circle. How do the measurements of the two angles compare?

    b. Explain the relationship between inscribed angles and central angles on a sphere.

What are some properties of a circle on a sphere?

Student Audience: Middle School/High School

Prerequisites: Students should know the terms **opposite points, circles on the plane,** and **circles on the sphere.**

Class Time: 20–35 minutes. You may want to do this adventure in the same class period that you do Adventure 1.3, "How do you measure distance?"

Construction/Investigation on the Sphere

Students should be careful not to confuse planar radius with spherical radius. The spherical radius of the circle is not segment *a*, nor segment *b*, but arc *r* of a great circle, as shown below.

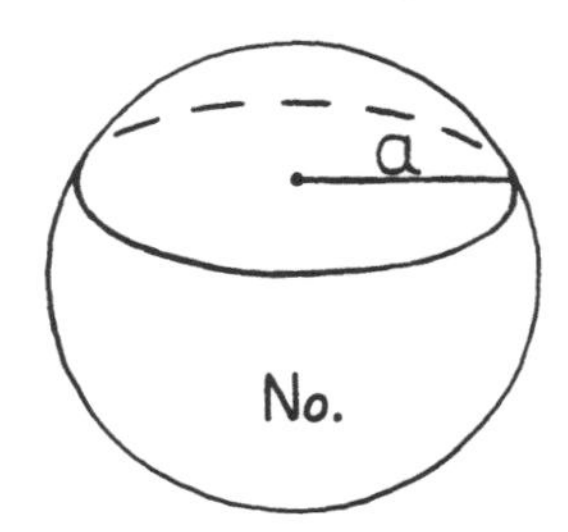

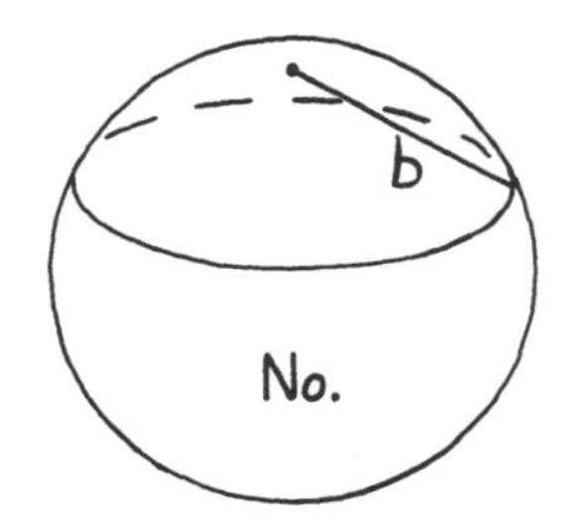

Students may be fascinated by using terms such as *a circle with a radius measure of 60°.*

4. Each spherical circle has two centers on the sphere. These centers are opposite points.

5. If the radius measure of the circle from one of the centers is r, then the radius measure of the same circle from the other center is $180° - r$.

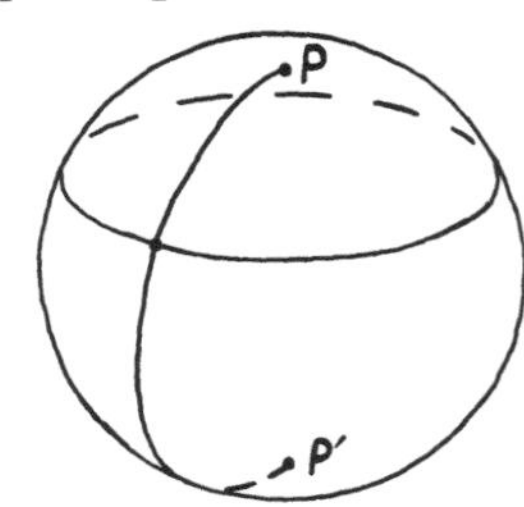

6. The spherical compass can only draw circles on the sphere with radius measures not longer than 90°. To draw a circle with radius measure of 120°, the student has to construct the opposite point of the center first and draw a circle with a radius measure of 180° – 120°, or 60°, from the opposite point as center.

Compare the Plane and the Sphere

Circles

On the plane	On the sphere
Circles have radii, diameters, and chords. Because these shapes are line segments, we measure them in linear units such as centimeters or miles.	Circles have radii, diameters, and chords, which are all arcs of great circles. We can measure them in degrees.
Every circle has exactly one center.	Every circle has exactly two centers. The centers are two opposite pole points.
A radius of a circle is half the length of a diameter.	A radius of a circle is half the length of a diameter.
A tangent to a circle is perpendicular to the radius that meets the circle at the point of tangency.	A tangent to a circle is perpendicular to the radius that meets the circle at the point of tangency.
	Many other properties of planar circles will work on the sphere, but some (like the Inscribed Angle Theorem discussed below) will not.

Explore More

11. The tangent of a great circle at any of its points is the great circle itself.

12. On the plane, the measure of an inscribed angle is half the measure of its central angle. The proof is based on the Triangle Sum Conjecture, which states that the sum of the angle measures of a planar triangle is always 180°. On the sphere, however, we can only state that the sum of the three angle measures of a spherical triangle can't be less than 180°. This implies that the sum of the two inscribed angles of a spherical triangle can't be less than the central angle. For non-degenerate triangles, in which the sum of angle measures is definitely greater than 180°, the sum of the measures of the two inscribed angles cannot be less than the central angle.

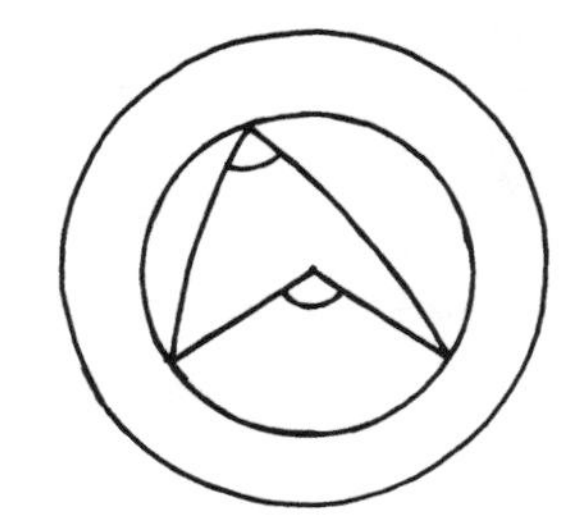

What are some relationships in families of concentric circles?

A family of **concentric** circles refers to all circles with the same center.

- Draw a family of concentric circles on the plane and a family of concentric circles on the sphere.
- Compare the two families.

Construction on the Plane

Step 1 Draw a point on the plane. Label the point P.

Step 2 Draw a circle with center P and a radius of 3 cm.

Step 3 Draw another circle with center P and a radius of 3 + 3 cm, or 6 cm.

Step 4 Draw still another circle with center P and a radius of 3 + 3 + 3 cm, or 9 cm.

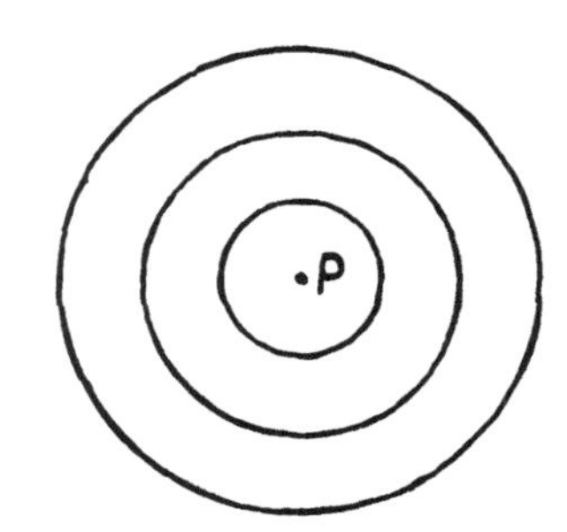

Investigate

1. You just constructed a few members of a family of concentric circles on the plane. Is it possible to continue this construction process forever, assuming you have a large enough compass?
2. As circles get larger, they appear to curve less. Can you find circles in your family of concentric circles that are so big they are straight lines? In other words, if you have a large enough compass, can you open it wide enough to draw a straight line? Explain.
3. Can you construct smaller and smaller concentric circles until you construct one so small that it is just a point?
4. Can you find any two distinct circles in your family of concentric circles that are congruent to each other?

Make a Guess

5. How does a family of concentric circles on the sphere differ from a family of concentric circles on the plane?

Construction on the Sphere

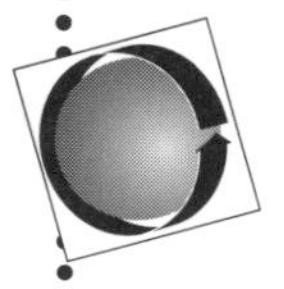

Repeat the same steps on the sphere that you performed on the plane, replacing the radius measure of 3 cm with a radius measure of 30°. The radii of your circles should measure 0°, 30°, 60°, and 90°.

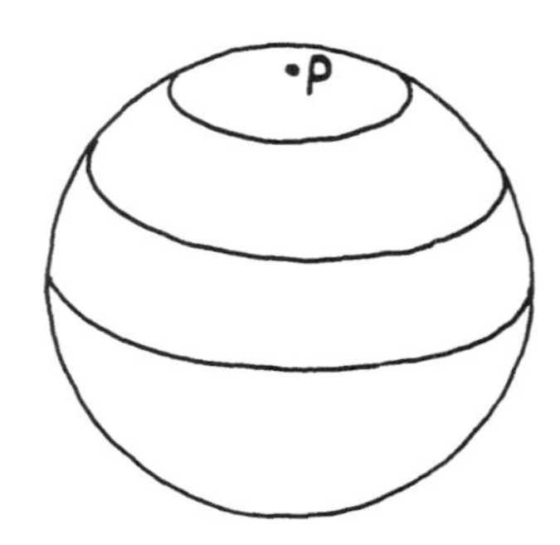

Investigate

6. You just constructed a few members of a family of concentric circles on the sphere. Is it possible to continue this construction process forever, assuming you have a large enough compass?

7. Can you find circles among all these concentric circles that are so big they are great circles? In other words, can you open your spherical compass wide enough to draw the spherical equivalent of a straight line?

8. Can you construct smaller and smaller concentric circles until you construct one so small that it is just a point?

9. Can you find any two distinct circles in your family of concentric circles that are congruent to each other?

Compare the Plane and the Sphere

10. See how many observations you can make about concentric circles on the plane and concentric circles on the sphere. Record them on a comparison chart like the one at right. Add as many rows as you need.

Concentric circles	
On the plane	On the sphere

11. Do you think concentric circles are simpler on the sphere or on the plane? Why? And which of the two is more interesting?

12. Now try to reverse your argument. Give reasons why the surface you *didn't* choose above is simpler or more interesting.

Explore More

13. Draw a circle on your sphere and draw several of its tangents. Find the pole points of these tangents. Describe the figures that all the pole points trace.

14. Illustrate your conclusions about concentric circles on the sphere with terms taken from the earth's geographic coordinate system.

What are some relationships in families of concentric circles?

Student Audience: Middle School/High School

Prerequisites: Students should know the terms **opposite points**, **circles on the plane**, and **circles on the sphere**.

Class Time: 25–40 minutes. You may want to do this adventure in the same class period that you do Adventure 5.1, "What are some properties of a circle on a sphere?"

Construction/Investigation on the Plane

1. This process of drawing greater and greater concentric circles that share the same center can be continued forever.

2. We cannot open our planar compass wide enough to draw a straight line because this would mean that we'd draw a circle with an infinite radius.

3. In this family of concentric circles, the only circle that is both a point and a circle is the center itself.

4. The greater the radius, the greater the circle; therefore no congruent circles with different radii can be found among these circles.

Construction/Investigation on the Sphere

6. The spherical compass can only draw circles with radius measures not longer than 90°. If we want to draw a circle with a radius that measures 120°, we construct the opposite point of the center first, then draw a circle with a radius that measures 180° – 120°, or 60°, from the opposite point as center. This process of drawing greater and greater circles that share the same center cannot be continued forever because the spherical surface is finite.

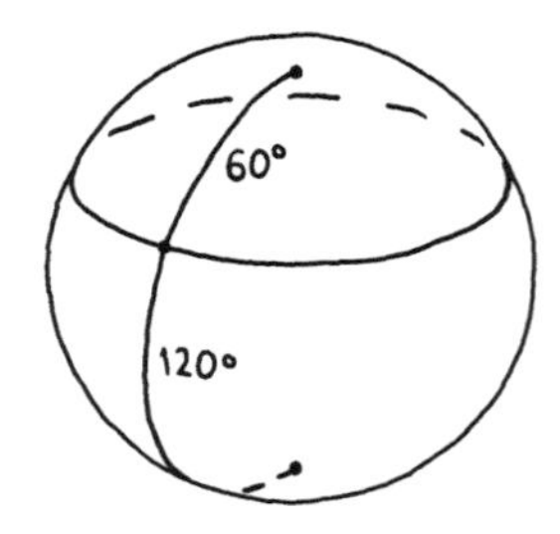

7. There exists one great circle among these circles, halfway between the center and the opposite point. This great circle has a radius that measures 90° when measured from either of its centers.

8. In this family of concentric spherical circles, we find two circles that are points: the point with a radius that measures 0° and the other point with a radius that measures 180°.

9. Any circle with a radius that measures less than 90° has a congruent mate, on the other side of the sphere, with a radius that measures greater than 90°.

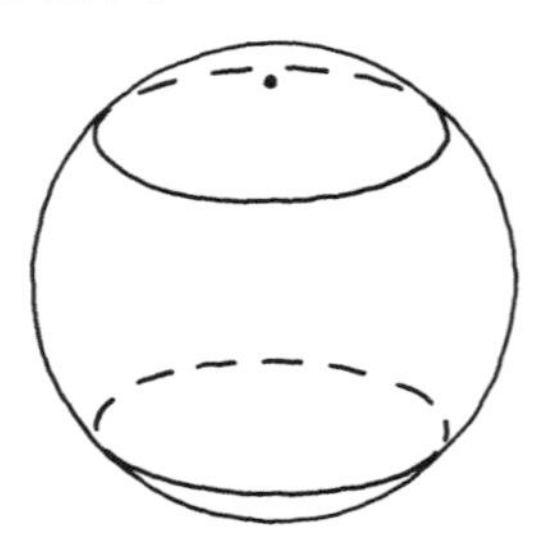

Compare the Plane and the Sphere

Concentric circles

On the plane	On the sphere
The radius of a circle can be as large as you'd like it to be.	The radius of a circle cannot be more than 180°.
Every family of concentric circles has one circle of radius 0. This circle is just the center point.	Every family of concentric circles has one circle of radius 0° and one of radius 180°. These circles are the two center points. The two center points are opposite pole points.
There is no circle so large that it is a straight line.	The circle with a 90° radius is a great circle, the spherical equivalent of a straight line.
In a family of concentric circles, no two distinct circles are congruent.	In a family of concentric circles, every circle has a congruent mate on the other side of the sphere. The only exception is the great circle (which is congruent to itself). If the radius of the first circle has degree measure x, then the radius of its congruent mate has degree measure $180° - x$.

In a family of concentric spherical circles, we found a number of properties unmatched on the plane, such as the opposite point of the center, two centers of a circle, and the great circle with a radius that measures 90°. Thus the sphere seems to be more interesting in this adventure.

Explore More

13. The pole points of the tangents to the circle will trace two circles which are congruent with each other and are concentric with the original circle. The radius of each of these two circles is $90° - r$, measured from the center of the original circle in one case and from the opposite point of this center in the other case.

14. Let the center of the family of concentric circles be the North Pole; then its opposite point is the South Pole. The great circle in this family of concentric circles is the equator. There are infinitely many pairs of congruent circles with different radii. Two examples of these are the Arctic Circle and Antarctic Circle, and the Tropics of Cancer and the Tropic of Capricorn.

ADVENTURE 5.3

What is the ratio of the circumference of a circle to its diameter?

You may have compared the circumference of a circle to its diameter before.

- Conduct your own experiments to determine the approximate ratio of the circumference to the diameter of a circle on the plane and on the sphere.

Construction on the Plane

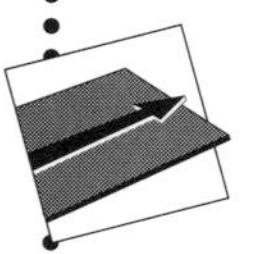

Step 1 Wind a piece of string around the circular edge of a drinking glass, plastic cup, or any round and hollow object. Ask your partner to mark the circumference of the circle on the string.

Step 2 On a flat piece of paper, stretch the string into a straight line. Ask your partner to measure and record the length of the circumference. Express your answer in centimeters.

Step 3 Place your round object on the flat piece of paper, and trace around its circular edge.

Step 4 Measure and record the diameter of the circle in centimeters.

Investigate

1. Find the ratio of the circumference to the diameter.

2. Choose another round object, smaller or larger, and repeat the process. Record your results.

3. Does the ratio of the circumference to the diameter remain the same for smaller and larger circles? Explain what you know about this famous ratio.

Make a Guess

4. Will the circumference to diameter ratio be the same for circles on the sphere?

Construction on the Sphere

Step 1 Wind a piece of string around the circular edge of the same round object you used in your construction on the plane. Ask your partner to mark the circumference of the circle on the string.

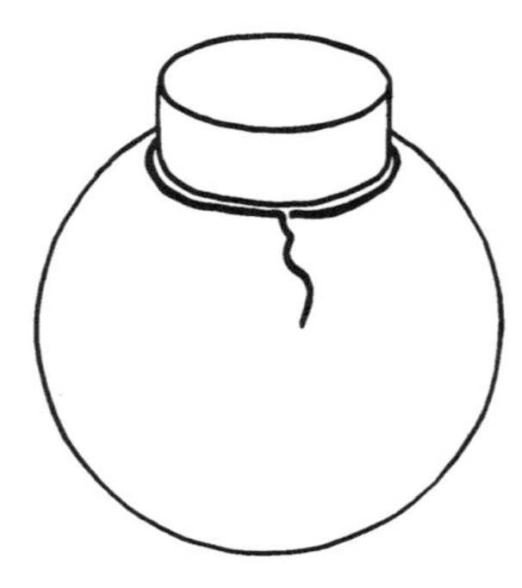

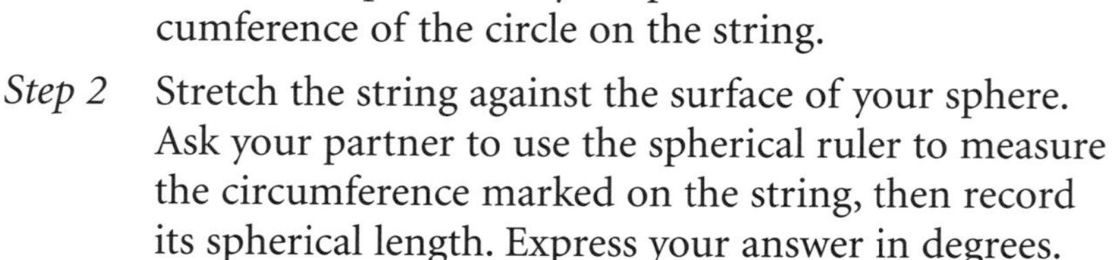

Step 2 Stretch the string against the surface of your sphere. Ask your partner to use the spherical ruler to measure the circumference marked on the string, then record its spherical length. Express your answer in degrees.

Step 3 Place your round object on the surface of your sphere and trace around its circular edge.

Step 4 Use your spherical ruler to measure the spherical diameter of the circle, then record its length. Express your answer in degrees.

Investigate

5. Find the ratio of the circumference to the diameter of your circle.

6. Choose another round object, smaller or larger, and repeat the process. Record your results.

7. Explain what happens to the ratio of the circumference to the diameter as the size of the circle varies.

8. Is it possible to draw a circle whose circumference is double its diameter? Explain why or why not.

Compare the Plane and the Sphere

9. See how many observations you can make about the circumference to diameter ratio in circles on the plane and the same ratio in circles on the sphere. Record your observations on a comparison chart like the one at right. Add as many rows as you need.

Ratio of circumference to diameter in circles

On the plane	On the sphere

10. Which surface do you think is simpler in this case: the plane or the sphere? Why?

11. Now try to reverse your argument. Give reasons why the surface you *didn't* choose above is simpler.

Explore More

12. What is the smallest possible ratio of the circumference to the diameter of a circle on a sphere? What is the largest?

13. Every spherical circle has two centers. Therefore every spherical circle has two possible measurements for its diameter. Find the range of possible circumference to diameter ratios, taking both diameters into consideration.

14. Archimedes (ca 287–212 B.C.) was an inventor in ancient Greece and one of the greatest mathematicians of all time. In his treatise *Measurement of a Circle,* Archimedes used regular polygons to approximate π. He argued that the circumference of a circle is slightly greater than the perimeter of an inscribed regular polygon but slightly less than the perimeter of a regular polygon circumscribed around the circle. Therefore the average of these two perimeters is a good approximation for the circumference of the circle. Archimedes then divided this average by the diameter of the circle to find a value for π. Polygons with more sides have perimeters closer to the circumference of the circle, so these polygons result in better approximations for π.

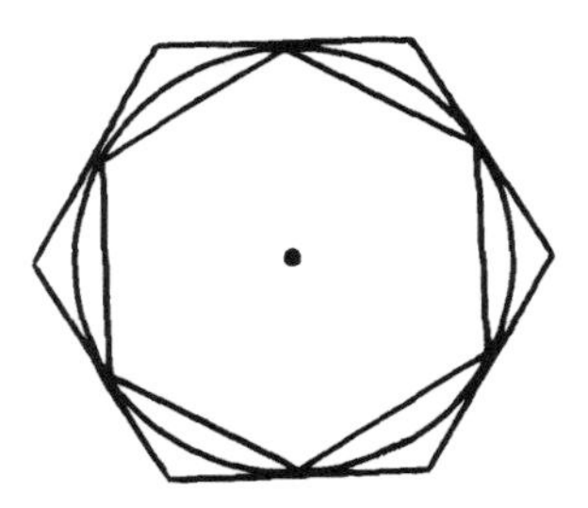

   a. Draw a circle on the plane and a circle on the sphere. Inscribe a regular polygon in each circle and circumscribe a regular polygon around each circle. Pick as many sides as you like for your polygons. Use Archimedes' method to determine the circumference to diameter ratio of each circle.

   b. Roughly estimate the diameter of the spherical circle for which the circumference to diameter ratio is exactly 3. Check your estimate by making a drawing on the sphere.

What is the ratio of the circumference of a circle to its diameter?

Student Audience: High School

Prerequisites: Students should know how to construct the spherical diameter of a circle on the sphere.

Class Time: 35–50 minutes

Construction/Investigation on the Plane

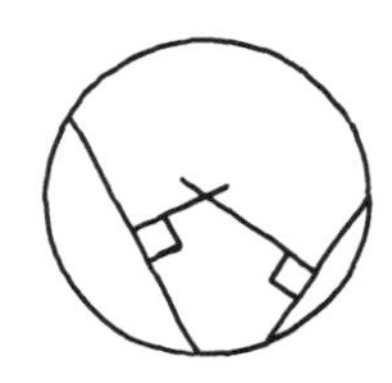

Before measuring the diameter, you may ask students to construct the center of the circle. For example, they can draw two chords with different perpendicular bisectors in the circle. The point of intersection of the two perpendicular bisectors in the circle is the center, as shown. However, students can make a good estimate of the diameter by approximately locating one of the longest chords in the circle and measuring its distance.

3. The ratio of the circumference to the diameter is always equal to π, or approximately 3.14, whether the circle is big or small.

Construction/Investigation on the Sphere

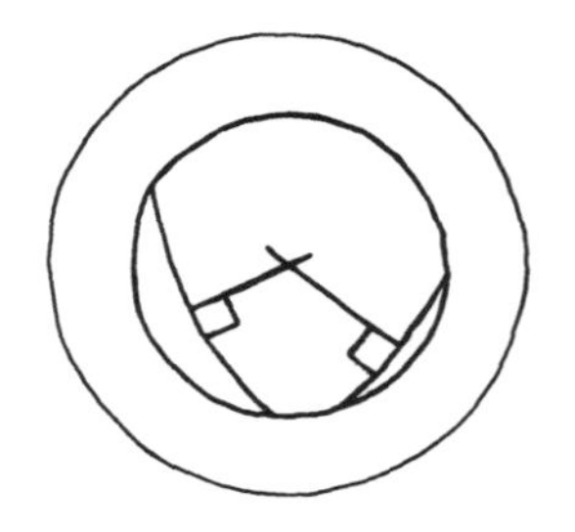

Before measuring the spherical diameter, you may ask students to construct the spherical center of the circle. For example, they can draw two spherical chords with different perpendicular bisectors in the spherical circle. The point of intersection of the two perpendicular bisectors in the circle is one of the circle's spherical centers, as shown. However, students can make a good estimate of the diameter by approximately locating one of the longest chords in the circle and measuring its distance.

7. Here the ratio of the circumference to the diameter is not a constant. For very small spherical circles, the ratio is very near to π. Taking bigger circles around the same center, we find that the bigger the circle, the smaller the ratio. For the great circle, or equator, which is the greatest of all circles possible on the sphere, this ratio is 360°/180°, or exactly 2.

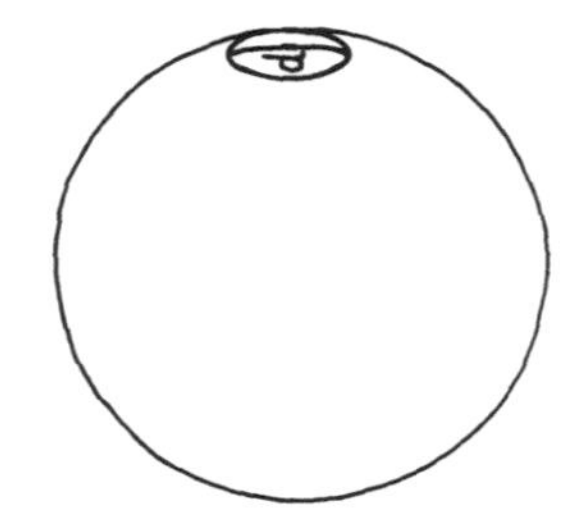

Compare the Plane and the Sphere

Ratio of circumference to diameter in circles

On the plane	On the sphere
The ratio of the circumference to the diameter of any circle is always the same, approximately 3.14. We use the Greek letter pi (π) to denote this constant number.	The ratio of the circumference to the diameter of a circle varies according to the size of the circle. For very small circles, this ratio is close to (but less than) π. The ratio decreases as the circles get larger. For the largest possible circle (the great circle), the ratio is 2.

Explore More

12. If we draw bigger and bigger circles starting from center P until we reach the equator of point P, then the circumference to diameter ratio shrinks from π to 2. If we continue drawing circles on the other side of the equator and measure their radius from the fixed center P, then the circumference to diameter ratio continues to diminish to zero. The figure shows an example of when the ratio is about 1. However, the radius of the spherical circle is usually measured from the center that gives the shorter radius. According to this convention, the radius measure varies from 0° to 90° and the circumference to diameter ratio from π to 2.

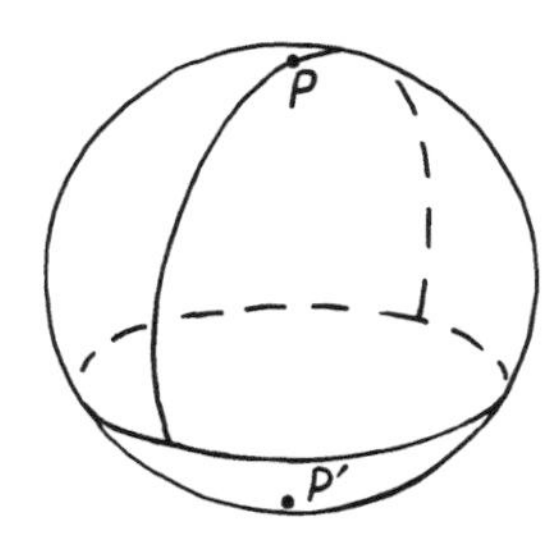

13. Each circle on the sphere has two centers that are opposite each other. Label two opposite points P and P'. If a circle has radius r from center P, then this circle has radius $180° - r$ from the opposite center P'.

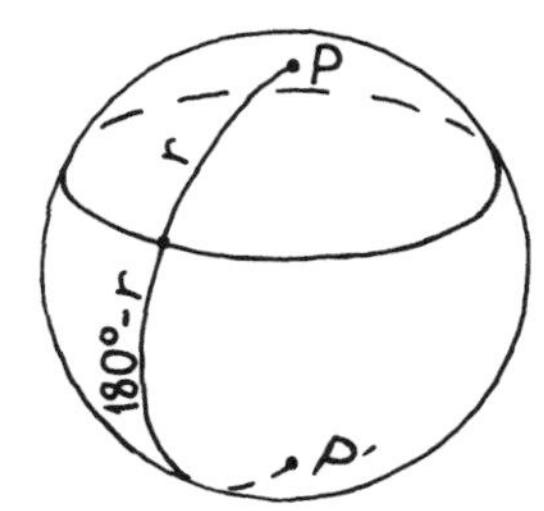

14. **b.** The diameter is 60°, and the radius is 30°.

CHAPTER 6
Area

Chapter 6: Area

Adventure 6.1: Can you always use square units to measure area?

Adventure 6.2: How can you measure the area of a triangle?

Adventure 6.3: How can you approximate the area of a circle?

Perhaps you and your students were surprised to measure distance on a sphere in degrees. You may be even more surprised to find that you can also measure spherical area in degrees. Coming up with a method for measuring area on a sphere is more difficult than students might expect.

In Adventure 6.1, students discover why using traditional square units to measure area is not possible on a sphere.

In Adventure 6.2, students develop a method for measuring the area of a spherical triangle by finding its "spherical excess." This method will make more sense if students have already discovered (in Adventure 3.4, for example) that the sum of the angle measures of a spherical triangle varies according to the size of the triangle. In the Explore More sections of this adventure, students use the areas of spherical triangles to find the areas of other spherical polygons.

In Adventure 6.3, students use the areas of spherical triangles to approximate the area of a spherical circle.

Use the Adventure Cards at the beginning of the chapter for more open-ended lessons. Use the Student's Guides for more structured lessons. You will probably have more success with Adventure 6.2 if you use the Student's Guide. Adventure 6.3 will make more sense to students after they complete Adventure 6.2. Adventure 6.1 works well on its own and is even a good introductory lesson for using some of the spherical tools. The Teacher's Guide that follows each Student's Guide contains solutions and suggestions.

ADVENTURE 6.1

Can you always use square units to measure area?

A *square* is a quadrilateral with four congruent sides and four right angles.

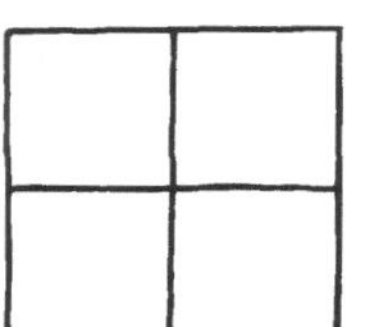

- Construct a square and divide it into smaller congruent squares. Explore this construction on the plane and on the sphere.
- We use square units to measure areas on the plane. Explore what units you can use to measure areas on the sphere.

ADVENTURE 6.2

How can you measure the area of a triangle?

If you divide a finite figure into parts, the area of the whole figure must equal the sum of the areas of the parts.

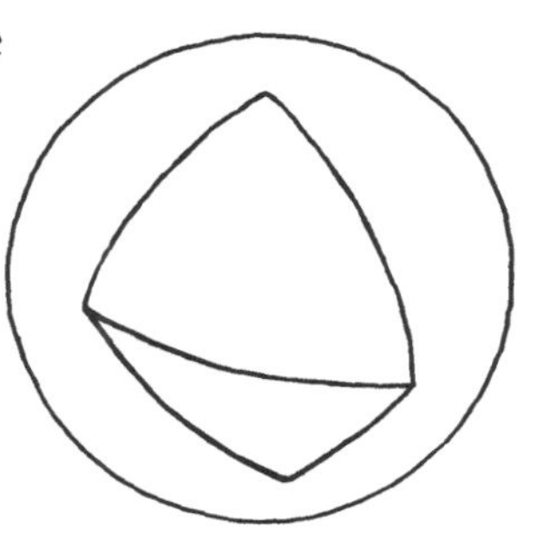

- Show that this is true if you divide a planar triangle into two triangles.
- Find a way to use degrees to measure areas of triangles on the sphere. If necessary, modify your definition of area to ensure that the area of any triangle equals the sum of the areas of its parts.

ADVENTURE 6.3

How can you approximate the area of a circle?

If you *inscribe* a regular polygon in a circle, the area of the polygon is less than the area of the circle. If you *circumscribe* a regular polygon around the circle, then the area of the polygon is greater than the area of the circle.

If you increase the number of sides of either of these regular polygons, the area of the polygon gets closer and closer to the area of the circle.

- Use inscribed and circumscribed polygons to get an approximate value for the area of a planar circle.
- Use the same method to approximate the area of circle on a sphere.

ADVENTURE 6.1

Can you always use square units to measure area?

A **square** is a quadrilateral with four congruent sides and four right angles.

- Construct a square and divide it into smaller congruent squares. Explore this construction on the plane and on the sphere.
- We use square units to measure areas on the plane. Explore what units you can use to measure areas on the sphere.

Construction on the Plane

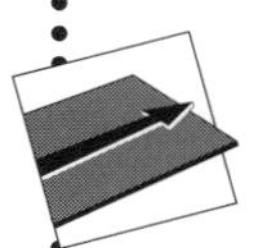

Step 1 Draw a circle with center O.

Step 2 Construct two perpendicular diameters of the circle. Label the points of intersection A, B, C, and D, as shown.

Step 3 Draw segments AB, BC, CD, and DA.

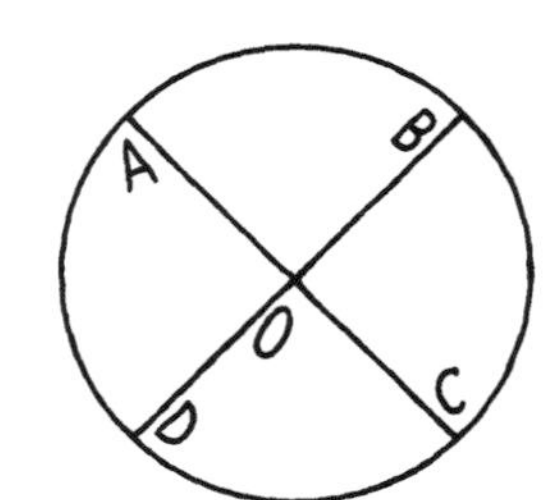

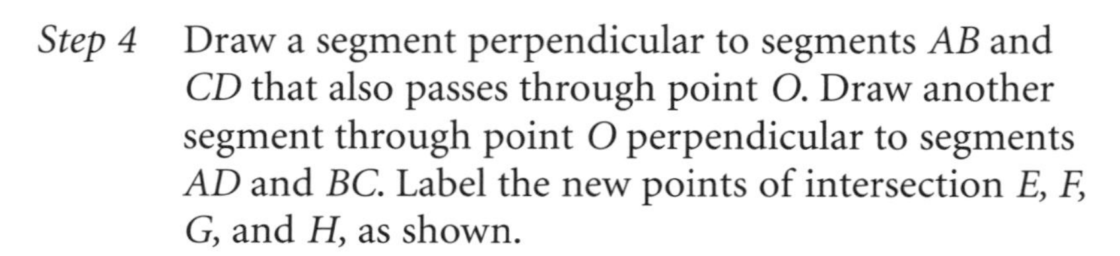

Step 4 Draw a segment perpendicular to segments AB and CD that also passes through point O. Draw another segment through point O perpendicular to segments AD and BC. Label the new points of intersection E, F, G, and H, as shown.

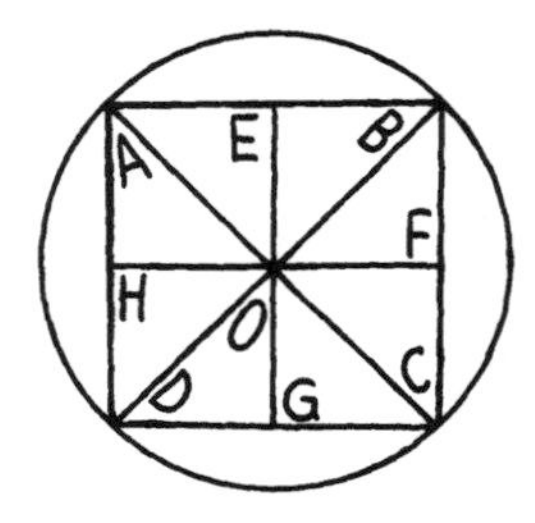

Investigate

1. Compare the sides of quadrilateral $ABCD$.
2. Compare the angles of quadrilateral $ABCD$.
3. Compare the sides and the angles of the four smaller quadrilaterals $OEAH$, $OHDG$, $OGCF$, and $OFBE$.
4. Are these smaller quadrilaterals similar to the big quadrilateral $ABCD$?
5. Which of these quadrilaterals are squares?

Make a Guess

6. Is it possible to construct a square on your sphere?
7. Is it possible to divide a square on the sphere into smaller congruent squares?
8. Is it possible to measure spherical area in square units?

Construction on the Sphere

Repeat the same construction on the sphere that you created on the plane. (Draw arcs of great circles in place of the line segments you drew on the plane.)

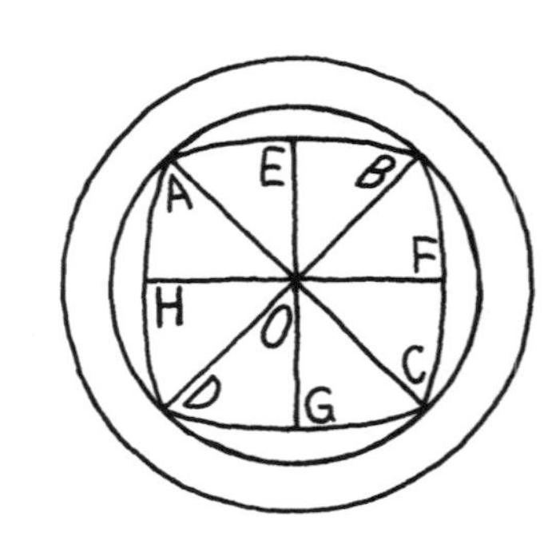

Investigate

9. Compare the sides of spherical quadrilateral $ABCD$.
10. Compare the angles of spherical quadrilateral $ABCD$.

11. Compare the sides and the angles of the four smaller spherical quadrilaterals *OEAH, OHDG, OGCF,* and *OFBE.*

12. Are these smaller quadrilaterals similar to the big quadrilateral *ABCD*?

13. Which of these quadrilaterals are squares?

Compare the Plane and the Sphere

14. See how many observations you can make about dividing a square on the plane and dividing a regular quadrilateral on the sphere. Record them on a comparison chart like the one at right. Add as many rows as you need.

On the plane	On the sphere

15. Do you think dividing a square on the plane is simpler than dividing a regular quadrilateral on the sphere? Why?

Explore More

16. We traditionally use square units to measure the area of a region.

a. Explain why the square is a good shape to use for measuring area on the plane.

b. Explain why it is impossible to use squares to measure area exactly on a sphere.

17. Some authors define a planar "square" as a quadrilateral that is both equilateral and equiangular. If we accept this definition in this single Explore More, can a "square" of this kind exist on the sphere?

Can you always use square units to measure area?

Student Audience: Middle School/High School
Prerequisites: None
Class Time: 25–40 minutes

Construction/Investigation on the Plane

Both the big quadrilateral and all four of the smaller quadrilaterals are regular quadrilaterals, each with four congruent sides and four right angles. In other words, all these quadrilaterals are squares. The four smaller quadrilaterals are congruent to one another and are similar to the big square.

Construction/Investigation on the Sphere

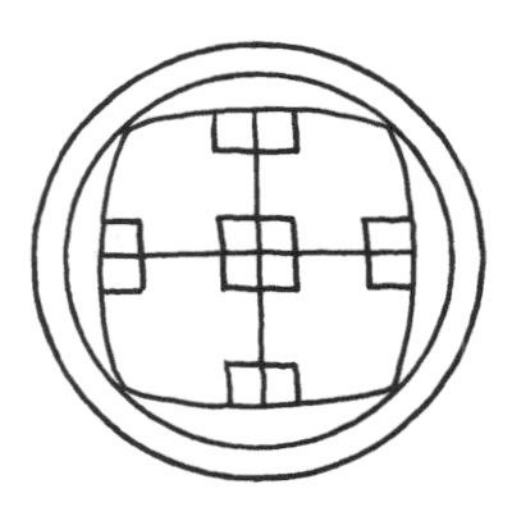

The big quadrilateral *ABCD* is regular, with four congruent angles and four congruent sides. However none of these four angles is a right angle. The four smaller quadrilaterals are congruent to one another, but they are not regular because neither all four sides nor all four angles are congruent. In each of the smaller quadrilaterals there are three right angles, but the fourth angle has measure greater than 90°. Therefore none of the smaller quadrilaterals is similar to the big one.

13. This may be a good opportunity for students to explore on the sphere. Ask students to determine if it is possible to construct a square on the sphere. If yes, they should provide a sketch and a description of their construction. If not, they should explain.

Compare the Plane and the Sphere

Dividing a square

On the plane	On the sphere
It is possible to construct a square.	It is impossible to construct a square. However, you can construct a quadrilateral with four congruent sides and four congruent (but not right) angles.
Any square can be subdivided into smaller squares that are all congruent to each other and similar to the larger square.	The quadrilateral described above can be subdivided into smaller congruent quadrilaterals. However, these smaller quadrilaterals have neither four congruent angles nor four congruent sides. Each has three right angles and one angle with measure greater than 90°. These smaller quadrilaterals are not similar to the large quadrilateral.

Explore More

16. On the plane we can divide a square into smaller squares. On the sphere, however, we cannot divide a regular quadrilateral into smaller regular quadrilaterals that are similar to the first one. Thus we can use the square for measuring any area on the plane, but we cannot find a regular spherical quadrilateral that is suitable for measuring any area in the same way on the sphere.

17. Yes. In this case, the congruent angles of this "square" are greater than 90°. The definition of square as we use it in this book also includes the fact that the regular quadrilateral must have four right angles in it. A quadrilateral with four right angles does not exist on the sphere.

ADVENTURE 6.2

How can you measure the area of a triangle?

If you divide a finite figure into parts, the area of the whole figure must equal the sum of the areas of the parts.

- Show that this is true if you divide a planar triangle into two triangles.
- Find a way to use degrees to measure areas of triangles on the sphere. If necessary, modify your definition of area to ensure that the area of any triangle equals the sum of the areas of its parts.

Construction on the Plane

Step 1 Draw a triangle.

Step 2 Divide your triangle into two smaller triangles by drawing a segment from one vertex to the opposite side.

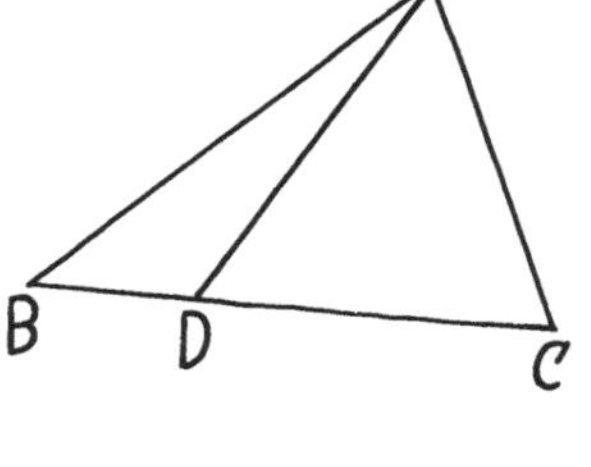

Investigate

1. **a.** Find the area of the large triangle.

b. Find the areas of the two small triangles.

c. Is the area of the large triangle equal to the sum of the areas of the two small triangles?

2. Draw a polygon with more than four sides. Divide the polygon into triangles. Explain why you can find the area of any polygon if you know how to find the area of a triangle.

Make a Guess

3. How can you measure the area of a triangle on the sphere?

Construction on the Sphere

Step 1 Draw a spherical triangle.

Step 2 Divide your triangle into two smaller triangles by drawing an arc of a great circle from one vertex to the opposite side.

Step 3 Find the angle measures in the large triangle and add them up.

Step 4 Find the sum of the angle measures of each of the two small triangles.

Investigate

4. **a.** Add together the sums of the angle measures of the two small triangles. Does this number equal the sum of the angle measures of the large triangle?

b. Explain whether we could define the area of a spherical triangle to be the sum of its angle measures.

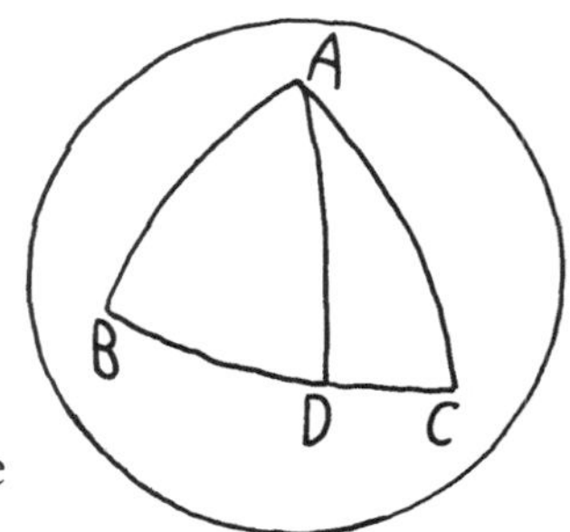

5. We define the **spherical excess** of a triangle as 180° less than the sum of the measures of its angles. Because every triangle on the sphere has angle measures that add up to at least 180°, the spherical excess is always a number greater than or equal to zero. The larger the triangle, the greater its spherical excess.

   a. Use your angle measurements from Construction on the Sphere to find the spherical excesses of your two small triangles and your large triangle.

   b. What is the relationship between these three numbers?

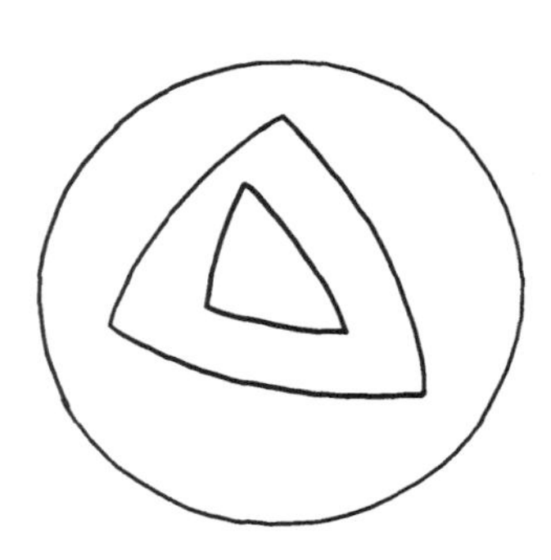

6. **a.** Draw two spherical triangles, one of which is completely inside the other. Find the spherical excess of each triangle. Express your answer in degrees.

   b. How do these two answers compare?

7. Explain why it is reasonable to define the area of a spherical triangle as its spherical excess.

Compare the Plane and the Sphere

8. See how many observations you can make about area measurement on the plane and area measurement on the sphere. Record them on a comparison chart like the one at right. Add as many rows as you need.

Area	
On the plane	On the sphere

9. Which surface do you think is simpler in this case: the plane or the sphere? Why? And which surface is the more interesting?

10. Now try to reverse your argument. Give reasons why the surface you *didn't* choose above is simpler or more interesting.

Explore More

11. **a.** Use the spherical excess of a triangle to find the area of your entire Lénárt Sphere in degrees.

    b. What is the area of the earth in degrees?

    c. What is the area of a tennis ball in degrees?

    d. What are some advantages of measuring spherical area in degrees?

12. **a.** The Lénárt Sphere has a radius of approximately 10 cm. The surface area of a sphere is traditionally measured in square units by the formula $4\pi r^2$, where r is the radius of the sphere. Find the surface area of your sphere in square centimeters.

    b. Draw a triangle on your Lénárt Sphere. Find the area of the triangle in degrees and in square centimeters.

13. The radius of the earth is approximately 6,400 km. Draw a triangle on your sphere and find its area in degrees. Then determine the area of a corresponding land mass on the earth. Show and explain your work.

14. Find a simple way to determine the area of a spherical triangle that has two right angles.

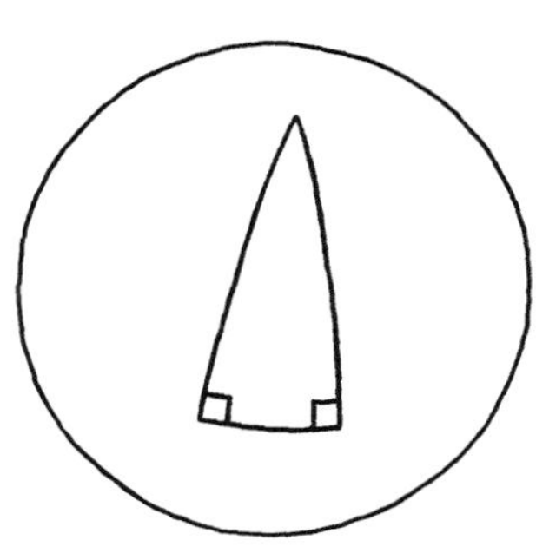

15. Find a spherical triangle that can be used as a unit for measuring area on the sphere.

16. Come up with a way of finding the area of a spherical quadrilateral. Describe your idea. Explain why you think it makes sense. Does your method also apply to concave quadrilaterals?

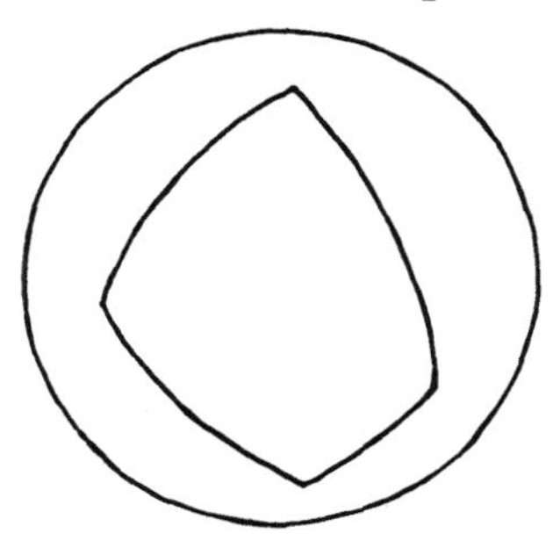

17. On your sphere, draw a polygon with more than four sides. Find the area of the polygon in degrees. Find the area of the polygon in square centimeters. Show and explain your work.

18. Draw a triangle ABC on your sphere, and suppose the measures of the three interior angles at A, B, and C are a, b, and c, respectively. Divide the triangle into two smaller triangles by drawing a segment from one vertex to the opposite side. Use this drawing to prove algebraically that the sum of the areas (spherical excesses) of the small triangles equals the area (spherical excess) of the large triangle.

How can you measure the area of a triangle?

Student Audience: High School

Prerequisites: Students should know how to measure angles on the sphere.

Class Time: 30–60 minutes

Construction/Investigation on the Sphere

4. Students should find that the sum of the sums of the angle measures in the two smaller triangles is 180° greater than the sum of the angle measures in the larger triangle. We cannot define the area of a spherical triangle as the sum of its angle measures because the area of a whole triangle would be less than the sum of the areas of its parts.

5. We can measure the area of a spherical triangle with angles a, b, and c with the expression $a + b + c - 180°$. This expression is called the **spherical excess of the triangle**. In discussion with students, ask them to speculate why this name was given to this quantity. This may help them understand and remember how area is determined on the sphere. This discussion can continue to include quadrilaterals. Don't forget about concave quadrilaterals. (See problem 15 in the Explore More section.)

6. The greater the area of the triangle, the greater the sum of its angle measures.

Compare the Plane and the Sphere

Area

On the plane	On the sphere
You can measure area in square units.	You can measure area in degrees.
To find the area of a triangle you measure the base and height of the triangle, multiply these numbers together, and divide by two.	To find the area of a triangle, you find the sum of the measures of its angles and subtract 180°. This is also called the spherical excess of the triangle.
You can find the area of any polygon by triangulating it and adding together the areas of the triangles.	You can find the area of any polygon by triangulating it and adding together the areas of the triangles.

In this adventure students discover a method for measuring the area of a triangle on the sphere that is different from the more familiar method for measuring area on the plane. The experiment they performed in this adventure is not an exact proof because it only proves one property, the **additivity of the spherical excess for spherical triangles**.

It may be interesting to reverse this finding and ask students: Does the method of spherical excess work for the area of planar triangles, too? The excess for all planar triangles is exactly zero. So additivity does work here because $0 + 0 = 0$. However, this definition is absolutely trivial because all planar triangles have the same area in this way.

Explore More

14. If the third angle is a, then the spherical excess is $90° + 90° + a - 180°$, or a. In other words, the area of a triangle with two right angles is equal to the third angle.

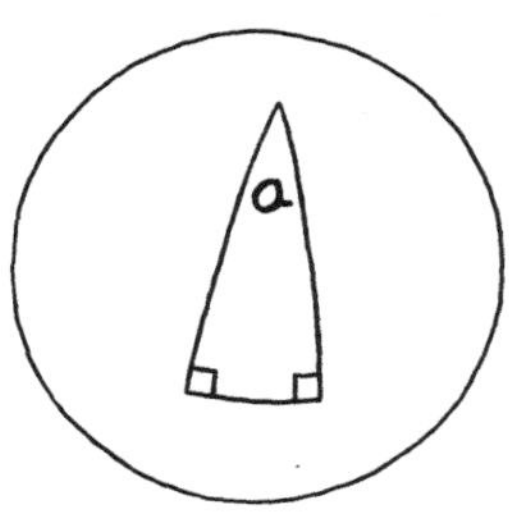

15. The spherical triangle with angles measuring 90°, 90°, and 1° has spherical excess $90° + 90° + 1° - 180° = 1°$. This special spherical triangle can be used as a unit to measure area on the sphere in the same way that we use a unit square to measure area on the plane.

16. Cut the quadrilateral into two triangles with a diagonal and label the angles as shown. Adding the two spherical excesses of the two triangles, we get $a + b + c + d - 360°$ for the area of the spherical quadrilateral.

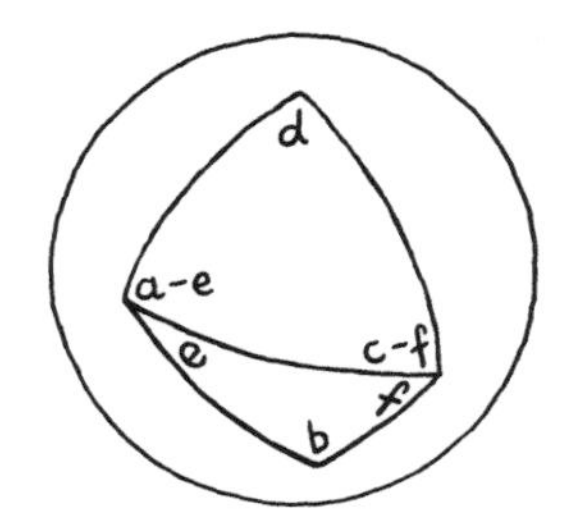

If the quadrilateral is concave, then we can create two triangles so that the area of the quadrilateral will be the excess of the greater triangle less the excess of the smaller triangle.

18. Suppose we draw a segment from vertex A to point D on the opposite side, forming angles of measure d and $180° - d$ at point D and dividing the angle at point A into two angles of measure e and $a - e$. To get the area (spherical excess) of each triangle, we subtract 180° from the sum of its angle measures. In triangle ABC, we get $a + b + c - 180°$; in triangle ABD, we get $e + b + d - 180°$; and in triangle ADC, we get $(a - e) + (180° - d) + c - 180°$. The sum of the areas of the two smaller triangles is $e + b + d - 180° + (a - e) + (180° - d) + c - 180°$, or $a + b + c - 180°$. This is exactly the same area we got for triangle ABC.

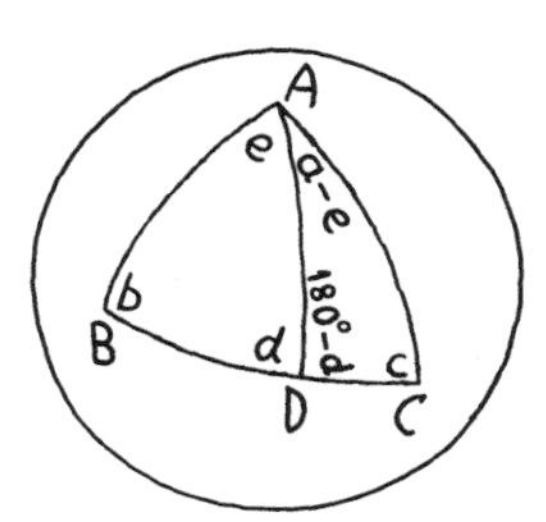

ADVENTURE 6.3

How can you approximate the area of a circle?

If you **inscribe** a regular polygon in a circle, the area of the polygon is less than the area of the circle. If you **circumscribe** a regular polygon around the circle, then the area of the polygon is greater than the area of the circle.

If you increase the number of sides of either of these regular polygons, the area of the polygon gets closer and closer to the area of the circle.

- Use inscribed and circumscribed polygons to get an approximate value for the area of a planar circle.
- Use the same method to approximate the area of circle on a sphere.

Construction on the Plane

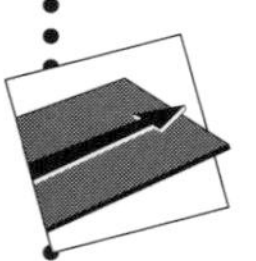

Step 1 Draw a circle and record its radius.

Step 2 Inscribe a 12-sided regular polygon in the circle.

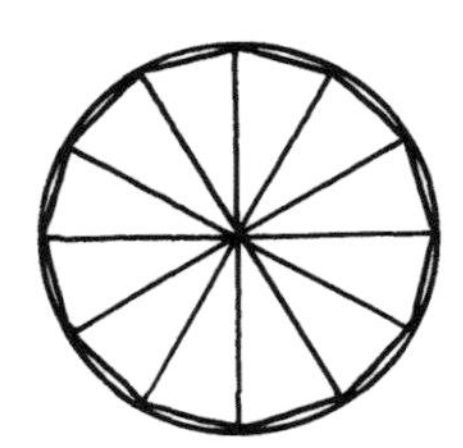

Step 3 Circumscribe a 12-sided regular polygon around the circle.

Investigate

1. Find the area of the inscribed polygon.
2. Find the area of the circumscribed polygon.
3. Average the areas of the inscribed and circumscribed polygons to get a good approximation of the area of your circle.

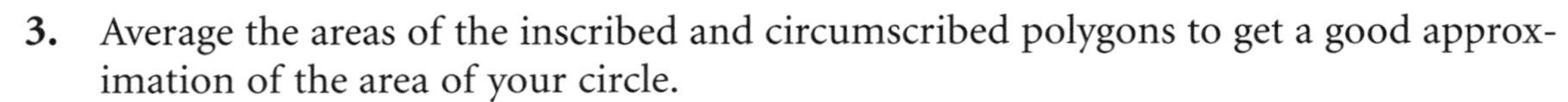

4. Check your approximation by finding the exact area of the circle. How close were you?

Construction on the Sphere

Step 1 Draw a circle and record its radius.

Step 2 Draw 12 radii of the circle so that each pair of adjacent radii forms a 30° angle.

Step 3 Inscribe a 12-sided regular polygon, as shown. Measure the angle labeled *a*.

Step 4 Circumscribe a 12-sided regular polygon, as shown. Measure the angle labeled *b*.

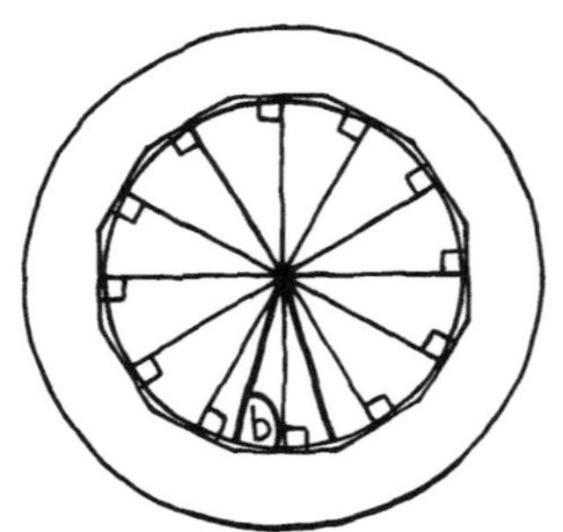

Investigate

5. Find the area of the inscribed polygon, using the fact that the area of a spherical triangle equals its spherical excess. (To find the spherical excess of a triangle, add the measures of the interior angles and subtract 180°.)

6. Find the area of the circumscribed polygon.

7. Average the areas of the inscribed and circumscribed polygons to get a good approximation of the area of your circle.

Explore More

8. The formula for the area of a spherical circle in degrees is $A = (1 - \cos r)$, where r is the spherical radius of the circle. Use this formula to find the exact area of your circle. How close is the exact area to the approximation you made by using regular polygons?

9. The area of a hemisphere is 360°. Find the spherical radius of a spherical circle with half the area of a hemisphere. Construct this circle on your sphere.

How can you approximate the area of a circle?

Student Audience: High School/College

Prerequisites: Students should know or be introduced to the fact that the area of a spherical triangle can be determined by summing its three angle measures and subtracting 180°. This takes into account that the area of a spherical triangle, or of any other region on the sphere, can be measured in degrees.

Class Time: 25–40 minutes. You may want to do this adventure in the same class period that you do Adventure 6.2, "How can you measure the area of a triangle?"

Construction/Investigation on the Plane

Students can achieve greater accuracy by measuring and averaging two or three angles in both the inscribed and circumscribed triangles.

4. The formula for the area of a planar circle with radius r is πr^2.

Construction/Investigation on the Sphere

Again, students can achieve greater accuracy by measuring and averaging two or three angles in both the inscribed and circumscribed triangles.

Advise students to start with a spherical circle with radius somewhere between 30° and 70°. Very small circles are difficult to measure. On the other hand, very large circles that are close to a great circle differ little from their inscribed or circumscribed polygons. (If the circle is a great circle, then all the sides of each inscribed polygon and each circumscribed polygon coincide with the great circle itself.)

5. Answers will vary depending on the size of the circle and the accuracy of students' measurements. Small differences in angle measurement can make a big difference in area calculations, especially for larger circles. It helps to use a fine-point pen to draw the polygons and to use a very accurate protractor to measure the angles. Here are some typical measurements for a circle with radius 50°: Angle a measures about 80°. This means that the other base angle of each of the twelve isosceles triangles measures 80°. The vertex angle of each of these triangles must measure 360°/12, or 30°. Thus the area of each triangle is (80° + 80° + 30°) – 180° = 10°. This means that the polygon consisting of twelve of these triangles has a total area of 12 × 10°, or 120°.

Students might notice that if they choose a circle of radius 90°, they will save themselves all the calculations and the measurement in problems 5, 6, and 7. In this case the inscribed polygon, the circumscribed polygon, and the circle itself are all exactly the same shape; therefore all have the same area. Clearly, these polygons provide excellent approximations for the area of the circle!

6. Answers will vary depending on the size of the circle and the accuracy of students' measurements. For a circle of radius 50°, angle b will measure around 81°. This means that each small right triangle (there are 24 of these) has angles of measures 90°, 81°, and 15°. Thus the area of each of these triangles is (90° + 81° + 15°) – 180° = 6°. Therefore the area of the circumscribed polygon is 24 × 6°, or 144°.

7. Answers will vary depending on the size of the circle and the accuracy of students' measurements. Using the results for a circle with a radius of 50° from problems 5 and 6, we get (144° + 120°)/2 = 132°.

Explore More

8. Answers will vary depending on the size of students' circle. A circle with a 50° radius should have an area of $(1 - \cos 50°)(360°) \approx 128.6°$. This is not too far from the approximate value of 132° that was calculated in problem 7.

9. The area of the required circle is 180°. Substituting this in the formula for the area of a spherical circle, we get

$$\begin{aligned} A &= (1 - \cos r)360° \\ 180° &= (1 - \cos r)360° \\ \tfrac{1}{2} &= 1 - \cos r \\ \cos r &= \tfrac{1}{2} \\ r &= 60° \end{aligned}$$

Thus the spherical radius of the required circle is 60°. If time allows, students can use a hand-held calculator and the formula given in the text to compute the radius for circles with area 1/3, 1/4, 1/5, . . . of a hemisphere. (The approximate radii: for 1/3 of the area of a hemisphere, $r = 48.19$; for 1/4, $r = 41.41$; for 1/5, $r = 36.87$.) Students can construct these circles on the sphere. This activity helps them develop their perception and skill so that they can better estimate area on the sphere.

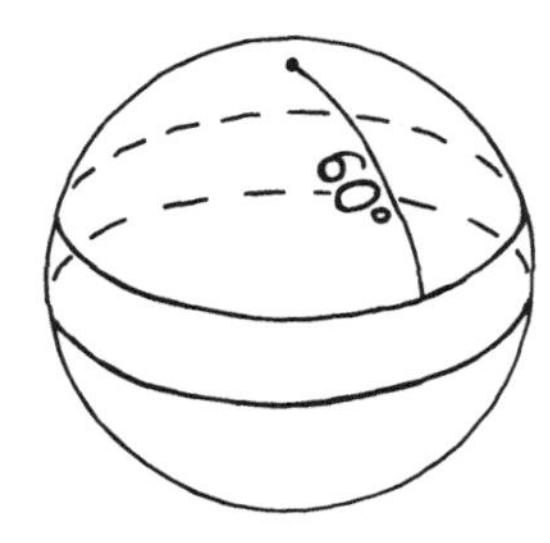

CHAPTER 7

Mapping the Earth

Chapter 7: Mapping the Earth

Adventure 7.1: Can you create a globe from a flat map?

Adventure 7.2: Where in the world are you?

Adventure 7.3: What time is it?

Adventure 7.4: What did Columbus think the world looked like?

Adventure 7.5: What causes earthquakes and volcanoes?

This chapter is devoted entirely to geographical applications and contains less formal mathematics than the previous chapters. The adventures here are excellent examples of how you can integrate mathematics with the social and hard sciences. The constructions in these adventures will take some time if students work carefully, but the results are educational and satisfying. The finished globes are decorative, and you may want to hang them in your classroom.

In Adventure 7.1, students create a spherical map of the earth. The Adventure Card here simply asks students to create an accurate globe, using the information from a flat map. This is quite a challenge. The Student's Guide to this adventure gives more guidance. It contains a projection of the earth with directions for cutting it out, draping it onto a sphere, and tracing this global map onto a pair of transparencies. In each adventure in this chapter, the Adventure Card requires students to do some research, while the Student's Guide provides them with much of the information they need.

Adventures 7.2 through 7.5 all rely on the globe students create in Adventure 7.1. Otherwise, the adventures are independent of one another. You might want to have each group construct the globe in Adventure 7.1, then have different groups explore each of the other adventures.

In Adventure 7.2, students create a coordinate system for their globe.

In Adventure 7.3, students draw time zones for their globe.

In Adventure 7.4, students re-create the skewed map of the world Christopher Columbus used for navigation.

In Adventure 7.5, students cut up their transparencies to represent the tectonic plates of the earth's crust and use these pieces to model earthquakes and the creation of mountain ranges.

The Teacher's Guides provide answers to questions in the Student's Guides and contain helpful suggestions for the teacher.

ADVENTURE 7.1

Can you create a globe from a flat map?

It is fairly easy to draw an exact circle on your sphere with your spherical ruler or compass. But how can you make a more complicated drawing on your sphere, such as a map of the earth?

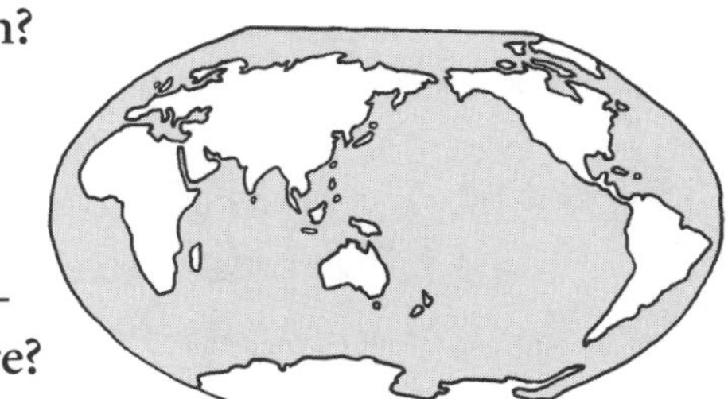

It would be nice to have a map printed on a flat sheet of paper that you could somehow bend onto the sphere. Then you could cover the map with a hemispherical transparency and trace it. Is it possible to exactly bend a flat sheet onto a curved sphere?

- Use a flat, planar map to make an accurate globe of the earth on your sphere. Describe your method and results.

ADVENTURE 7.2

Where in the world are you?

We can use the Cartesian coordinate system to locate points on a plane. How can we locate places on the earth?

- Construct the earth's geographic coordinate system on your globe.
- Use this system to locate points on the earth.

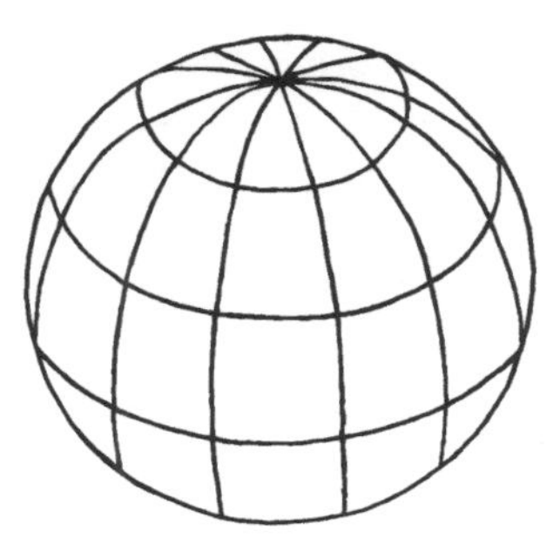

ADVENTURE 7.3

What time is it?

What time is it where you are right now? What time is it in other parts of the world?

- Make a globe that shows the time zones of the earth.

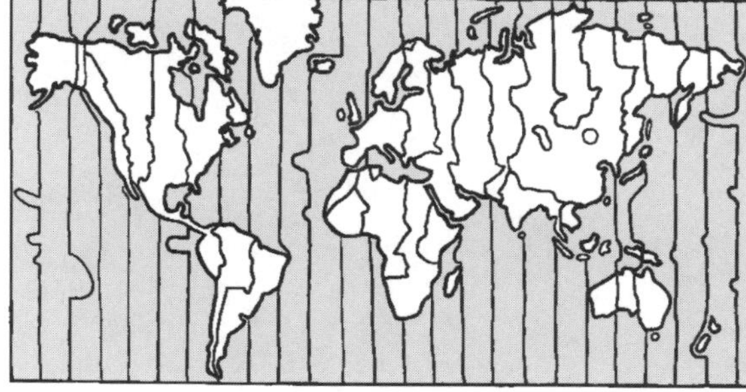

ADVENTURE 7.4

What did Columbus think the world looked like?

Many discoveries have arisen from errors and misunderstandings. The accidental arrival of explorer Christopher Columbus (ca 1446–1506) in the Americas is a famous example. He wanted to reach the East by sailing westward. He thought he could reach the Island of Cipangu (Japan) more easily by sailing westward from Spain across the Atlantic than by traveling eastward through Europe and Asia.

- Make a map of the world Columbus thought he was sailing around and compare it with the actual world.

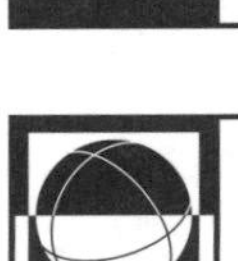

ADVENTURE 7.5

What causes earthquakes and volcanoes?

Our earth's crust consists of *tectonic plates* of solid rock that are continually moving, colliding, and spreading apart. These interactions set off earthquakes, fire up volcanoes, and wrinkle the earth's crust into mountains, valleys, and deep-sea trenches. In most cases, the boundaries of the tectonic plates do not coincide with the coastlines of the dry lands.

- Make a model of the present location of these moving plates.

ADVENTURE 7.1

Can you create a globe from a flat map?

It is fairly easy to draw an exact circle on your sphere with your spherical ruler or compass. How can you make a more complicated drawing on your sphere, such as a map of the earth?

It would be nice to have a map printed on a flat sheet of paper that you could somehow bend onto the sphere. Then you could cover the map with a hemispherical transparency and trace it. Is it possible to exactly bend a flat sheet onto a curved sphere?

- Use a flat, planar map to make an accurate globe of the earth on your sphere. Describe your method and results.

Make a Guess

1. On a planar surface, is it possible to correctly represent a map of the earth?

Two Experiments

2. Cut out a piece of paper or aluminum foil about as big as your open hand. Try to smooth it out on your sphere without making any wrinkles or creases. Describe your results.

3. Put some egg shells on a table and try to break them into pieces so small that they lie perfectly flat on the surface of the table. Describe your results.

Creating Your Own Globe

It is impossible to transform a planar surface into a spherical surface without stretching or altering some distances on the plane. It is also impossible to transform a spherical surface into a planar surface. This problem is of particular importance to geographers. Although the real earth is not a precise sphere, we can approximate it more accurately with a sphere than with a plane. Thus, when geographers draw a global map, they usually assume the shape of the earth is a perfect sphere.

But how can you draw this spherical model on a flat sheet of paper? Geographers have developed methods for approximating spherical surfaces on flat sheets by using different projections. In this adventure you will make use of one of these projections to make a globe of the earth from a flat planar map. Remember that this is not an exact method—just a useful approximation.

Step 1 On the following pages, you'll find eight **polar polyconic map projections** of different sections of the earth's surface. Use scissors to carefully cut out the four projections that make up the northern hemisphere, extending the slit between each pair of **gores** to the end of the dotted line. The more carefully you do your cutting, the better the projections will fit on your sphere.

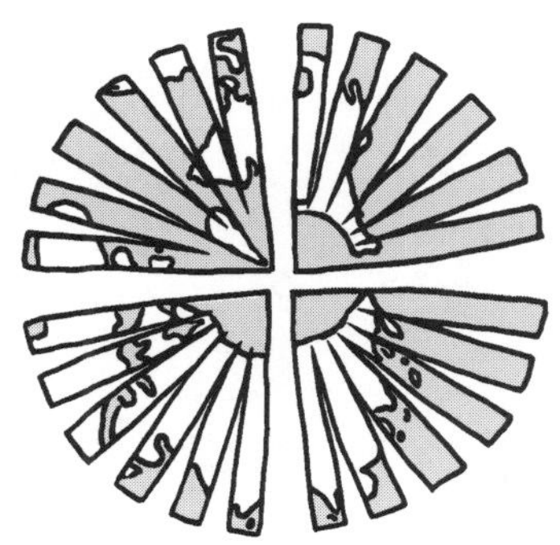

Step 2 Carefully arrange these four cutouts into a flat, circular projection of the northern hemisphere and tape them together near the pole. Drape the projection over the top of your sphere.

Step 3 Next gently rest a clean transparency on top of the projection so that the transparency's hole is directly over the pole. At this point the end of each gore should be sticking out of the transparency.

Step 4 Straighten out one end of a paper clip and use this as a tool to adjust each gore so that it lines up against the adjacent gore.

Step 5 When the gores are all in place, push the transparency down tightly to hold the projection in position.

Step 6 Repeat Steps 1 through 5 for the southern hemisphere, being careful to line up the appropriate parts of the two hemispheres.

Step 7 Use a black *permanent* marker to carefully trace your own map of the earth onto the two transparencies.

Step 8 Carefully take the transparencies off the sphere. Remove the paper projections and put them away for future use. Then line up and replace the transparencies on your sphere. You have created your own globe! You will use your globe in other investigations.

Investigate

4. Find the North Pole, the South Pole, and the equator on your globe.

5. Use an atlas to help you identify the continents, the oceans, the lakes, and the rivers on your globe.

6. Mark the location of your hometown on your globe. Find and mark the point on the opposite side of the earth from your hometown. Is this point where you expected it to be?

7. Describe a polyconic projection that would create a more accurate map on your globe. Describe one that would create a less accurate map.

Explore More

8. How can you use colored markers to fill in your globe with figures relating to geography, biology, world history, and mathematics?

9. Describe different types of map projections that are used on wall maps and in atlases and textbooks. What are the advantages and disadvantages of each?

Can you create a globe from a flat map?

Student Audience: Middle School/High School

Prerequisites: None

Class Time: 45–70 minutes

Two Experiments

Neither of the two methods works. The paper or foil gets wrinkled, either in the middle or by the edges. The egg shells, unless they are pulverized, will not lie flat on the surface of the table.

Creating Your Own Globe

Warning: To make the polar polyconic map projections in this adventure, each student or group of students will need photocopies of the blackline master projections on the following four pages. Before making these photocopies for your students, test to be sure that your copy machine can reproduce pages at exactly 100% of their original size. If not, then locate another copy machine. Students will not be able to fit the projections onto the sphere correctly if they have been even slightly enlarged or reduced in size. Carefully adjust the position of each blackline master on the copy machine so that all edges of the projections are copied clearly.

Students should create and use their globes, but they should not think that the flat paper can be cut and bent into a perfect sphere. Stress that this method of making a globe is practically useful but theoretically incorrect. They can trace the printed map onto the covering transparency with the accuracy that they want and with the time allowed. They should use permanent markers for copying and should keep the drawn transparencies for further adventures. When students remove the paper projections from the sphere, they should carefully put them away for future use.

Explore More

8. Here are some applications for completing the globe with figures.
    - From geography: Plot the location of several major cities; show the distribution of mineral deposits, water, forests, and wasteland; show the world's climatic features, air masses, and ocean currents.
    - From biology: Show the distribution of crops, aquatic and terrestrial flora and fauna, animal habitats, and the migration of birds and sea animals.
    - From world history: Organize areas by cultures and civilizations, or by noted women and men in a given historical period; show economic, political, and commercial relationships of the past and present.
    - From mathematics: Measure the distance between two given geographic spots in degrees and convert your measurement into kilometers or miles; estimate the area of a land mass or an ocean by approximating it with a spherical polygon; plan a route.

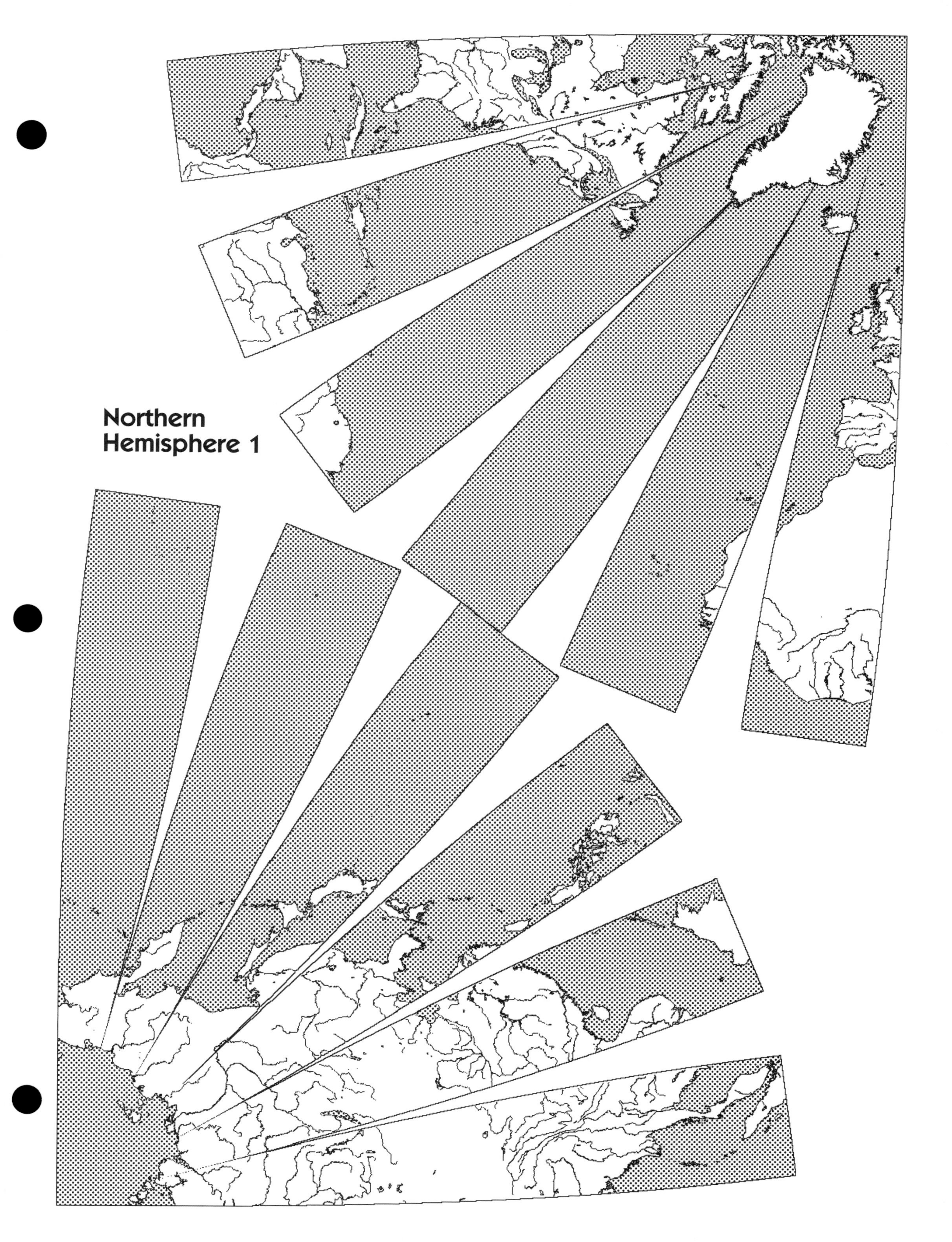
Northern
Hemisphere 1

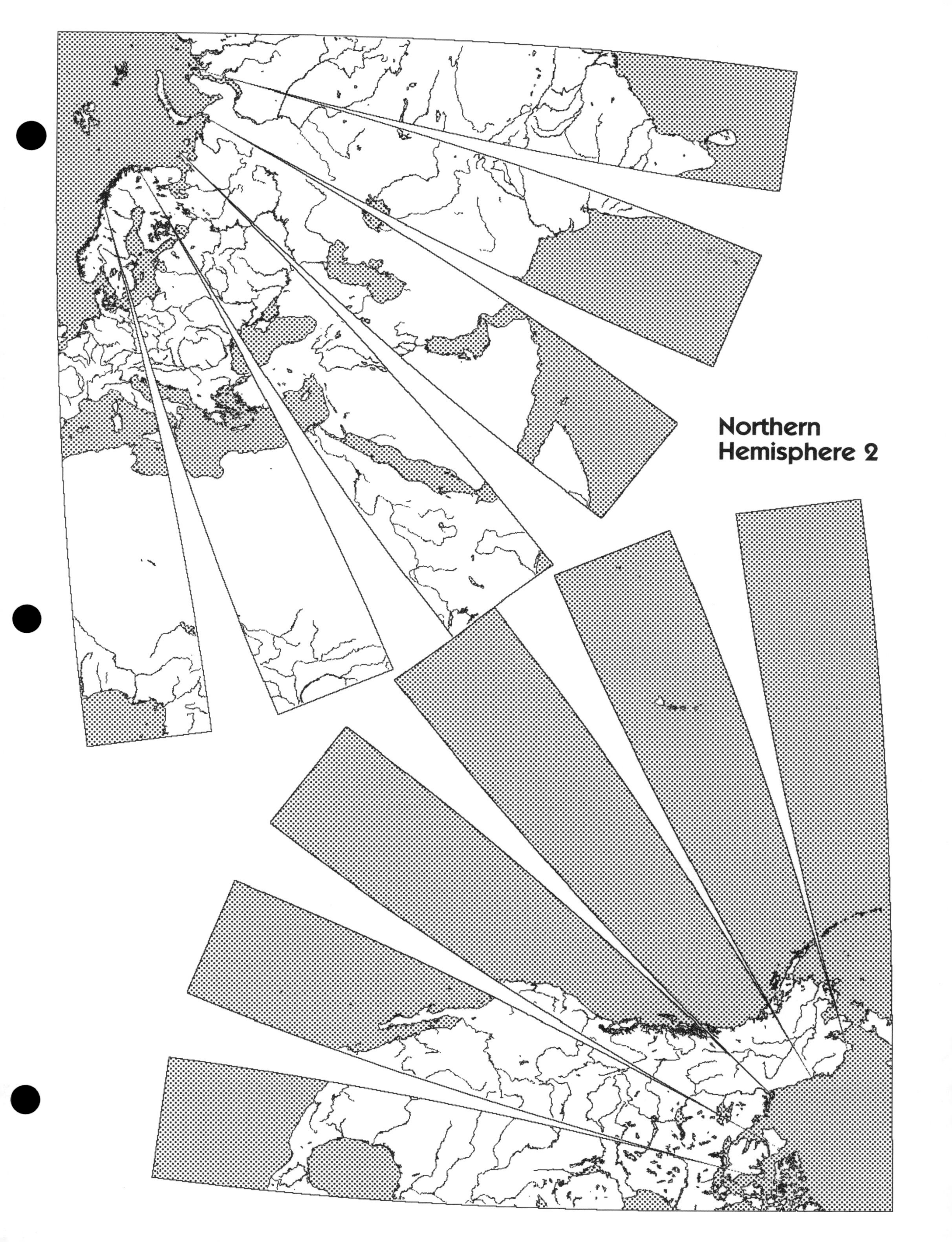
Northern
Hemisphere 2

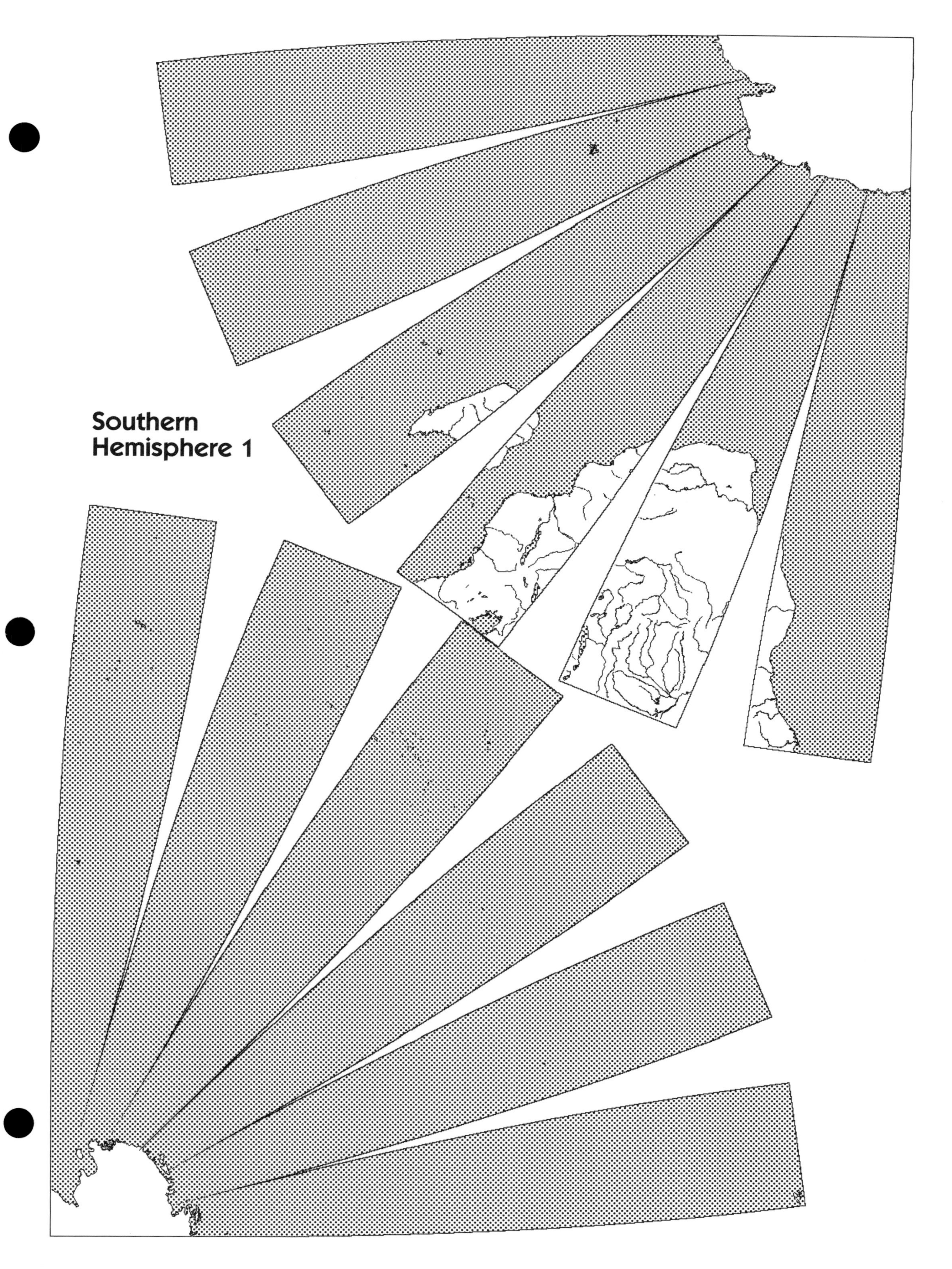
Southern
Hemisphere 1

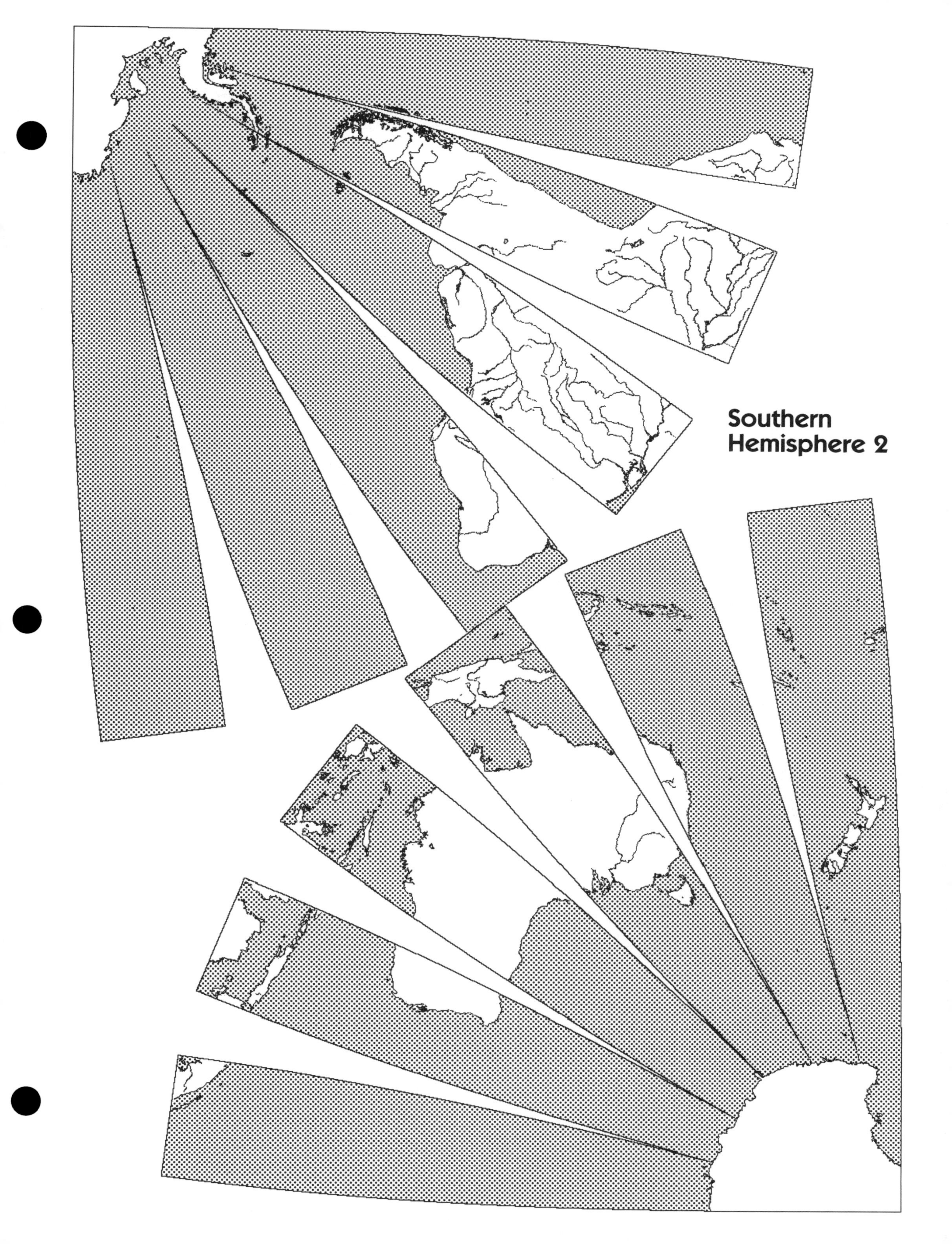
Southern
Hemisphere 2

ADVENTURE 7.2

Where in the world are you?

We can use the Cartesian coordinate system to locate points on a plane. How can we locate places on the earth?

- Construct the earth's **geographic coordinate system** on your globe.
- Use this system to locate points on the earth.

Constructing a Coordinate System on Your Globe

Step 1 Make a globe of the earth by placing the transparencies you created in Adventure 7.1 on your sphere. Wipe off all markings except the permanent map. Use a non-permanent marker to mark and label the **North Pole** and the **South Pole**.

Step 2 Using the North Pole as the center, draw circles with radii that measure 30°, 60°, and 90°. Repeat, using the South Pole as the center. Label the **equator**.

Step 3 Look up Greenwich, England (a suburb of London), in an atlas and mark its location on your globe. Draw the great circle that passes through Greenwich, the North Pole, and the South Pole. Label the arc between the poles which passes through Greenwich the **Greenwich meridian**. Label the arc opposite the Greenwich meridian the **International Date Line**.

Step 4 Beginning at its intersection with the Greenwich meridian, divide the equator into 30° arcs. Then, through each point of division, draw an arc of a great circle from the North Pole to the South Pole.

Step 5 Using the North Pole as the center, draw a dashed circle with a radius that measures 23.5°. Label it the **Arctic Circle**. Repeat, using the South Pole as the center, and label this circle the **Antarctic Circle**. Using the North Pole as the center again, draw another dashed circle with a radius that measures 66.5° and label it the **tropic of Cancer**. Repeat with the South Pole and label this circle the **tropic of Capricorn**.

Investigate

1. **a.** The circles on your globe that are parallel to the equator are called **latitudes** or **parallels**. The name of a latitude is the number of degrees it lies north or south of the equator. Label each latitude on your globe with its degree measurement. Write these labels along the International Date Line. Begin by labeling the equator 0°. Don't forget to label the Arctic and Antarctic circles and the tropics of Cancer and Capricorn.

   b. What is the latitude of the North Pole? The South Pole?

2. a. The lines that you drew connecting the North Pole to the South Pole are called **longitudes** or **meridians**. The name of a longitude is the number of degrees it lies east or west of Greenwich, England. Label each longitude on your globe with its degree measurement. Write these labels along the equator.

   b. What is the longitude of the Greenwich meridian?

   c. What is the longitude of the International Date Line?

   d. What can you say about the longitude of the North Pole and the South Pole?

3. Many globes and maps show longitudes and latitudes every 15°. Draw and label these on your globe.

4. The globe's latitudes and longitudes form a **geographic coordinate system**. Every point on the globe (except the North and South poles) is matched with a pair of degree measurements. The latitude and the longitude are the point's coordinates. Find and mark the locations of ten cities on different parts of your globe. Use the labels you wrote along the equator and the International Date Line to estimate the latitude and longitude of each of your cities.

5. a. Mark the location of your hometown on your globe. What is the latitude and the longitude of your hometown?

   b. Mark the point on the opposite side of the earth from your hometown. What is its latitude and longitude?

Explore More

6. In reality, the International Date Line does not exactly follow a meridian. Find a map or a globe that shows the actual International Date Line. Can you account for the difference between the date line you drew on your globe and the world's actual date line?

7. Use an atlas to help you locate Sydney, Australia, and Cairo, Egypt, on your globe. Mark the position of each city. Determine the distance, in degrees, between them. Convert this degree measure to kilometers. Remember that the equator measures 360° and is approximately 40,000 km long. Describe your method.

8. Locate New York City on your geographic coordinate system. Determine its approximate distance, in degrees, from the equator. Locate some other geographic spots on the northern hemisphere that lie at the same latitude. Repeat the same on the southern hemisphere. Determine if there is a connection between latitude and climate.

9. The moon can be coordinatized in the same way that the earth is. On the moon, the crater Archimedes is approximately at 0° longitude and 30° N latitude; the crater Ptolemaeus is approximately at 0° longitude and 10° S latitude. What is the distance between them in degrees and in kilometers? The equator of the moon is about 11,000 km long.

10. In some planar maps, latitude and longitude lines form a rectangular grid. Why are these maps inaccurate?

11. Compare the geographic coordinate system on the globe with the Cartesian coordinate system on the plane.

Where in the world are you?

Student Audience: Middle School/High School

Prerequisites: Students should know or be introduced to the geographic terms **North Pole, South Pole,** and **equator**. This may be some students first experience with latitude and longitude. Begin with a brief discussion of these terms, mentioning that the lines perpendicular to the equator and 30° apart from one another are called **meridians** and are used to measure longitude. The circles with centers at the North and South poles are **parallels** and are used to measure latitude. Students will need access to globes, atlases, and the transparencies they made in Adventure 7.1 to complete this adventure.

Class Time: 20–45 minutes

Constructing a Coordinate System on Your Globe

2. c. The continuation of the Greenwich meridian is called the International Date Line and has longitude 180°.

Explore More

7. Location of Sydney: 33° 52′ S latitude, 151° 13′ E longitude.

Location of Cairo: 30° 3′ N latitude, 31° 15′ E longitude.

The distance between the two cities is approximately 130° ≈ 14,400 km ≈ 8949 mi. (One degree on the earth equals approximately 40,000 km/360° ≈ 111 km.)

8. New York is about 40° distance from the equator, that is, about 40° N latitude. Near this latitude are Philadelphia, Pennsylvania; Columbus, Ohio; Denver, Colorado; Beijing, China; Baku, Azerbaijan; Ankara, Turkey; and Madrid, Spain. Along 40° S latitude are far fewer cities, including Wellington, New Zealand; Melbourne, Australia; and Bahia Blanca, Argentina. The climatic features of these locales vary widely according to altitude, ocean currents, and other factors.

9. The distance between the two craters is approximately 40° ≈ 1220 km ≈ 76 mi. (One degree on the moon equals approximately 11,000 km/360° ≈ 31 km.)

10. The maps are inaccurate because no quadrangle with four right angles exists on the sphere. Therefore planar maps unavoidably distort the actual geographic configuration. (Here, again, we must be careful about stating anything about "absolute accuracy." As we know, the real earth is neither an exact plane nor an exact sphere, so distortion must happen on a perfect globe, too. The difference lies in the order of magnitude of the inaccuracy.)

11. A similarity between the two coordinate systems is that you can locate any place on the globe by its latitude and longitude. Similarly, you can locate any place on the Cartesian plane by its x and y coordinates.

Here is an important difference: The Cartesian coordinate system only makes use of straight lines on the plane; but the geographic coordinate system makes use of great circles and smaller circles as well. Exactly two straight lines of the coordinate system pass through any point on the plane, but infinitely many longitudes pass through the North and South poles. (Some very intriguing results can be found when we try to describe the sphere with three-dimensional coordinate triplets, but these results are a bit beyond the scope of this book.)

ADVENTURE 7.3

What time is it?

What time is it where you are right now? What time is it in other parts of the world?

- Make a globe that shows the **time zones** of the earth.

Constructing the Time Zones on Your Globe

Step 1 Place the transparencies you made in Adventure 7.1 on your sphere to make a globe of the earth. Wipe off all markings except the permanent map. Look up Greenwich, England (a suburb of London), in an atlas and mark a dot at its location on your globe.

Step 2 Use a colored non-permanent marker to draw a great circle that passes through Greenwich and the North and South poles. Write **Greenwich meridian** along the arc that has the North and South poles as endpoints and that passes through Greenwich.

Step 3 Place your ruler around the equator so that the Greenwich meridian passes exactly halfway between two adjacent 5° marks on the ruler. Use a different-colored non-permanent marker to divide the equator into 15° arcs, beginning 7.5° to the right of the Greenwich meridian. Then draw a meridian connecting the North and South poles through each point of division.

Step 4 Label the equatorial arc below Greenwich, England, as $\pm 0h$. Label the equatorial arcs to the east of $\pm 0h$ as $+1h$, $+2h$, . . . , $+11h$ and $\pm 12h$, as shown in the figure below. Label the equatorial arcs to the west of $\pm 0h$ as $-1h$, $-2h$, . . . , $-11h$.

Step 5 To complete your globe of the time zones, write **International Date Line** along the meridian opposite the Greenwich meridian.

Investigate

1. Why do 15° arcs create time zones?
2. What do the labels you wrote along the equator stand for? How can you use these labels to help you find the time difference between any two places on the earth?

3. a. What time is it where you are right now?

   b. Where in the world are people sleeping right now?

   c. Where are they eating breakfast? Eating lunch? Eating dinner?

4. Find the following spots on your map: Washington, D.C.; Rio de Janeiro, Brazil; Copenhagen, Denmark; Bangkok, Thailand. What time is it in these cities when it is noon in Greenwich, England?

5. a. What time is it in the cities listed above when it is noon in Washington?

   b. What time is it in these cities when it is noon in Rio de Janeiro?

   c. And what time is it when it is noon in Copenhagen?

   d. And what time is it when it is noon in Bangkok?

Explore More

6. Your representation of time zones is not quite correct because the actual time zone boundaries do not exactly follow lines of longitude. Find a map that shows the actual time zones of the world. How can you account for the differences between your time zones and the actual time zones of the world?

7. a. How could a plane leave Hong Kong on Thursday and arrive in San Francisco on Wednesday?

   b. What happens with times and dates when you cross the International Date Line?

   c. Explain why the International Date Line is necessary.

What time is it?

Student Audience: Middle School/High School

Prerequisites: Students will need maps, atlases, and the transparencies they made in Adventure 7.1.

Class Time: 20–45 minutes

Constructing the Time Zones on Your Globe

2. The labels express the adjustment that one needs to make to Greenwich Mean Time to obtain the local time. To find the time difference between any two places, subtract the smaller value from the larger one, taking into account the signs of the labels. For example, Alexandria, Egypt, is in the zone labeled +2; Guatemala City, Guatemala, is in the zone –6; so the time difference between the two is $2 - (-6) = 8$ hours.

5. When it is noon in Washington, it is 10 a.m. in Rio, 6 a.m. in Copenhagen, and midnight in Bangkok.

Explore More

6. If time allows, students can mark the most striking differences from the simple 15° grid, especially with respect to their local time zone.

7. If you cross the International Date Line from west to east (from China to North America, for example), then you have to change the date a day back (from Thursday to Wednesday, for example). When you cross it from east to west, you change the date ahead.

ADVENTURE 7.4

What did Columbus think the world looked like?

Many discoveries have arisen from errors and misunderstandings. The accidental arrival of explorer Christopher Columbus (ca 1446–1506) in the Americas is a famous example. He wanted to reach the East by sailing westward. He thought he could reach the Island of Cipangu (Japan) more easily by sailing westward from Spain across the Atlantic than by traveling eastward through Europe and Asia.

- Make a map of the world Columbus thought he was sailing around and compare it with the actual world.

Creating Columbus's World

Step 1 Place the transparencies you made in Adventure 7.1 on your sphere to make a globe of the earth. Wipe off all markings except the permanent map.

Step 2 Use the first map shown here to locate the town of Palos in southern Spain. This is the seaport where Columbus started his voyage. Use a colored non-permanent marker to mark Palos on your globe. Use the second map to locate the island of San Salvador (formerly Watling or Guanahani) in the Bahamas, the place where Columbus ended his voyage. Mark San Salvador on your globe. Columbus believed all his life that this island was not far from Japan.

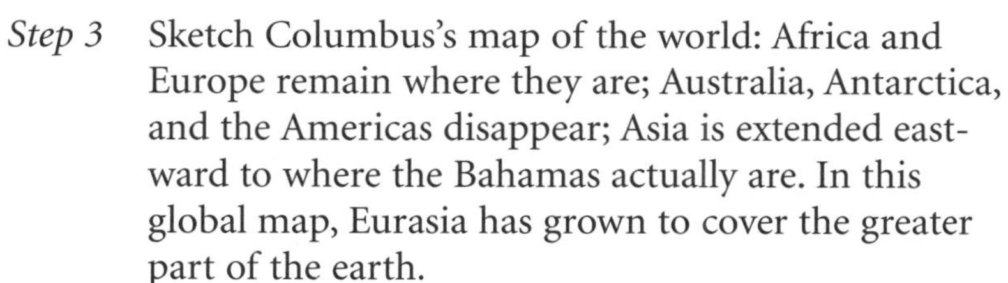

Step 3 Sketch Columbus's map of the world: Africa and Europe remain where they are; Australia, Antarctica, and the Americas disappear; Asia is extended eastward to where the Bahamas actually are. In this global map, Eurasia has grown to cover the greater part of the earth.

Step 4 Mark Columbus's route from Palos to San Salvador. Measure, in degrees, the distance between Palos and San Salvador.

Investigate

1. The equator measures 360° or approximately 40,000 km. Find how many kilometers correspond to one degree. What is the distance from Palos to San Salvador in kilometers?

2. Columbus thought the Bahamas were Japan and computed that one degree on the equator corresponded to 84 km. Using his assumptions, what is the circumference of the equator?

3. Look at Columbus's global map.

   a. What is the approximate ratio of the dry lands to the seas?

   b. Compare this ratio to the same ratio on a contemporary global map.

Explore More

4. Draw the routes of some other great discoverers and travelers, such as Ibn Battuta (ca 1304–1369), Ferdinand Magellan (ca 1480–1521), and Captain James Cook (1728–1779).

5. From ancient times, the seafaring peoples of the Pacific Ocean traveled and discovered many islands and sea routes. Read about their travels and mark some of their discoveries on your globe. What kinds of navigational methods helped them find their way on the sea?

6. a. Create a globe, using the polyconic projection on the *Living Earth* poster that came with your Lénárt Sphere. This projection was composed from hundreds of satellite images of the earth. Explain why it is impossible for it to be sunny everywhere on the earth at the same time.

   b. Assume that the diameter of your globe is 8.00 inches and the earth has a diameter of 12,742,000 meters. Calculate the scale of your *Living Earth* globe in relation to the real earth. Calculate how many kilometers are represented by one centimeter on your globe. Calculate how many miles are represented by one inch.

What did Columbus think the world looked like?

Student Audience: Middle School/High School

Prerequisites: Students will need maps, atlases, and the transparencies they made in Adventure 7.1.

Class Time: 20–45 minutes

Investigate

1. 40,000 km/360° ≈ 111 km/degree

2. If 1 degree equals 84 km, the circumference of the whole equator is about 30,000 km, or about one quarter too small.

3. It is not easy to estimate the ratio of dry land to sea on a global map. Naturally, we do not expect an exact answer, just a rough estimate of Columbus's error in computing the dry land to sea ratio. The real earth is made up of about three parts dry land to seven parts sea. Columbus's global map is made up of about six parts dry land to one part sea. This same error in estimating the ratio of dry land to sea led several travelers to search for a huge dry land in the southern hemisphere. Instead they discovered Australia and the South Sea Islands.

Explore More

4. Many interesting articles on this topic can be found in National Geographic magazine. For more information on Ibn Battuta, see *The Adventures of Ibn Battuta: A Muslim Traveler of the 14th Century,* Ross E. Dunn, University of California Press, Berkeley, 1989.

5. Among other methods, Polynesians studied the constellation of the stars and the interference of sea waves. Their maps were made of the leaves of cocoa palms.

6. **a.** The sun can only light up one hemisphere at a time. Additionally, there are always clouds somewhere between the earth and the sun because of the water in the atmosphere. For this reason, the completely sunny, cloudless day pictured on the *Living Earth* poster that comes with your Lénárt Sphere set can never really exist.

b. The scale of the globe in relation to the earth is 8.00 inches : 12,742,000 m. Since 1 inch = 2.54 cm, it follows that 8 inches = 20.32 cm = 0.2032 m. So the scale can be expressed as 0.2032 : 12,742,000. Dividing both numbers by 0.2032, we get 1 : 62,706,692.

Using this scale, we can calculate the distance represented by 1 cm as follows:

$$\begin{aligned} 1 \text{ cm} &= 62{,}706{,}692 \text{ cm} \\ &= 627{,}067 \text{ m} \\ &= 627 \text{ km} \end{aligned}$$

We can calculate the distance represented by 1 inch as follows:

$$\begin{aligned} 1 \text{ inch} &= 62{,}706{,}692 \text{ inches} \\ &= 5{,}225{,}557 \text{ feet} \\ &= 989.7 \text{ mi} \end{aligned}$$

ADVENTURE 7.5

What causes earthquakes and volcanoes?

Our earth's crust consists of **tectonic plates** of solid rock that are continually moving, colliding, and spreading apart. These interactions set off earthquakes, fire up volcanoes, and wrinkle the earth's crust into mountains, valleys, and deep-sea trenches. In most cases, the boundaries of the tectonic plates do not coincide with the coastlines of the dry lands.

- Make a model of the present location of these moving plates.

Creating a Globe of Tectonic Plates

You will need to cut up two transparencies to complete this adventure.

Step 1 Place the transparencies you made in Adventure 7.1 on your sphere to make a globe of the earth. Wipe off all markings except the permanent map.

Step 2 Use a different-colored marker to copy the earth's main tectonic plates onto your globe from the map shown at right. Take into account each plate's relative position to the continents.

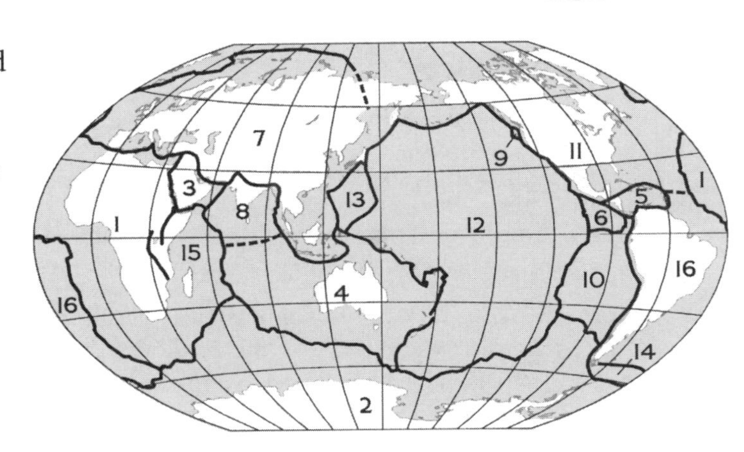

Step 3 Label each tectonic plate with its name.

1. African
2. Antarctic
3. Arabian
4. Australian
5. Caribbean
6. Cocos
7. Eurasian
8. Indian
9. Juan de Fuca
10. Nazca
11. North American
12. Pacific
13. Philippine
14. Scotia
15. Somali
16. South American

Step 4 Use scissors to cut the tectonic plates out of the transparencies. Use clear tape to join the pieces of any plates that cross over the equator.

Investigate

1. When colliding, a rock plate can submerge under and lift up one side of another plate. In this way, high mountain ranges emerge along the boundaries of the colliding plates. These zones of collision, called **subduction zones**, are the most turbulent parts of the earth's crust and are where earthquakes are most likely to occur. Use the National Geographic Society's map of *The Earth's Fractured Surface* to locate these subduction zones on your model.

2. Demonstrate the action of the subduction zones by pushing one plate a few millimeters under an adjacent plate and attaching the two plates to your sphere in this position. For example, the Nazca plate is pushed under the South American coastline of the South American plate, which causes the puckering of the Andes.

3. The radius of the earth is about 6370 km long, and the highest mountains are about 8 or 9 km high. Measure the radius of your globe and the approximate thickness of the transparencies. Does your model accurately portray the ratio of the height of mountains to the radius of the earth? For example, can the thickness of the transparency represent the high peaks of the Andes?

Explore More

4. Study the coastlines of Africa and South America. Compare them with the borderline between the African and South American tectonic plates. What do you observe?

5. Reconstruct the world of the dinosaurs on your globe. In other words, draw the relative position of the continents in the geographic age of the dinosaurs. Use maps and atlases that show where the continents have moved throughout history.

What causes earthquakes and volcanoes?

Student Audience: Middle School/High School

Prerequisites: You will need calipers capable of measuring the thickness of transparencies. (If you have no access to such equipment, then students should consider the thickness of the transparencies to be between 0.3 mm and 0.5 mm.) You will also need a copy of the National Geographic Society's map, *The Earth's Fractured Surface*. Students will need the transparencies they made in Adventure 7.1.

Class Time: 30–60 minutes

Creating a Globe of Tectonic Plates

The map figure in this investigation is adapted from the National Geographic Society's 22″x 36″ map, *The Earth's Fractured Surface*, copyright April 1995 and used with permission. Copies of *The Earth's Fractured Surface* may be ordered by calling toll free 1-800-NGS-LINE or by writing to the National Geographic Society, 1145 Seventeenth Street NW, Washington, DC 20036-4688.

Investigate

1. Subduction zones are indicated on *The Earth's Fractured Surface* by triangular points showing the direction of plate movement.

2. Pushing the transparency plates under each other creates gaps between the plates at other places of the globe. This causes no problem, because these gaps represent the deep sea troughs in the earth's crust.

3. If the surface of the sphere represents the sea level of the earth, then the ratio of the height of the highest peaks to the radius of the earth is about 1 to 700 or 800. The radius of our sphere is approximately 100 mm, so the highest peaks on the model should be about $100/800 \approx 0.12$ mm. The transparencies are between 0.30 mm and 0.50 mm in thickness, so they actually represent much higher mountains on our model than those existing on the real earth! If the thickness of the transparencies correctly represented the highest peaks on the model, then the Himalayas would be more than 20,000 m high.

   One can also argue that the surface of the sphere must represent the ocean floor on which the movement of the continental plates takes place. The average depth of the oceans is about 5 km, so the difference between the average depth of the oceans and the peaks of the highest mountains is about $8 + 5 = 13$ km. The ratio of this difference to the radius of the earth is about 1 to 500, so on a sphere with a radius of about 100 mm, the highest peaks should be about $100/500 = 0.20$ mm. If the transparencies are between 0.30 mm and 0.50 mm in thickness, then the Himalayas would correspond to mountains that are about 15,000 m or 20,000 m high. Even in this case we can say that the transparencies represent much higher mountains on our model than the mountains on the real earth—the figures just need to be corrected a bit.

Explore More

4. The shapes of the coastlines and the borderline are very similar to each other. This is because Africa and South America once constituted one piece of dry land. The striking resemblance between these coastlines inspired the theory of moving plates, developed in the nineteenth and twentieth centuries.

5. If time allows, students can sketch on the map some dinosaurs in their habitats.

CHAPTER 8

Surprises on the Sphere

Chapter 8: Surprises on the Sphere

Adventure 8.1: What is special about triangles inscribed on a diameter of a circle?

Adventure 8.2: What are some properties of a triangle inscribed in an octant?

Adventure 8.3: How can you construct Napier's pentagon?

The adventures in this chapter result in some surprising discoveries in spherical geometry. The only prerequisite for any of these adventures is the knowledge that the shortest path between two points on a sphere is an arc of a great circle. If you have only a little time to spend with the sphere and you want to demonstrate how surprisingly different spherical geometry is from what we are familiar with on the plane, any of these three adventures is ideal.

These adventures also make good projects for advanced students who can try to prove the surprising results of each construction.

In Adventure 8.1, students construct a special triangle inside a circle. In Adventure 8.2, they construct a special triangle inside an octant. Adventure 8.3 contains instructions for constructing the spherical pentagon discovered by Scottish mathematician John Napier. Each of these adventures is independent of the other two.

The Teacher's Guides contain answers to questions in the Student's Guides and some basic ideas about how to prove these surprising conjectures.

ADVENTURE 8.1

What is special about triangles inscribed on a diameter of a circle?

- Inscribe a triangle in a circle so that one side of the triangle is a diameter of the circle. Then measure the angles of the triangle.
- What special properties do triangles of this type have on the plane?
- Determine if these properties also hold for spherical triangles inscribed in a circle.

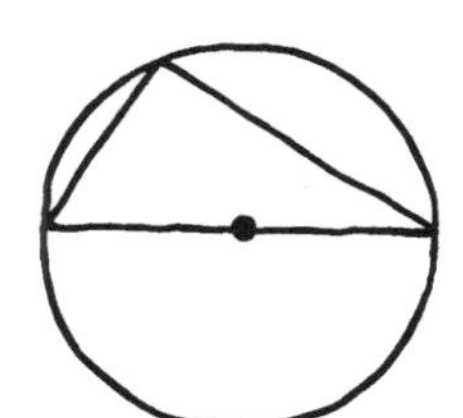

ADVENTURE 8.2

What are some properties of a triangle inscribed in an octant?

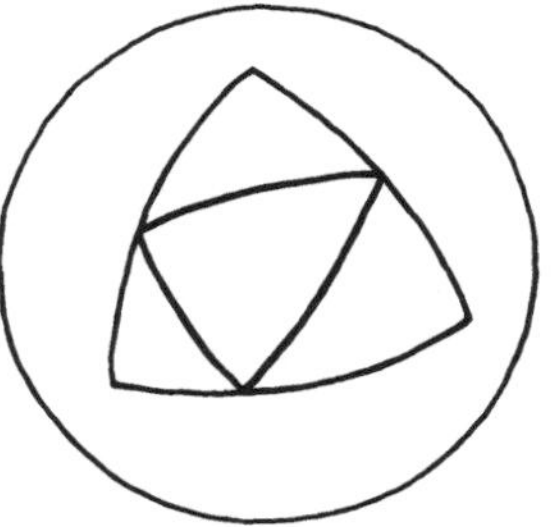

The spherical triangle with three right angles is called an *octant* because eight of these triangles cover the whole sphere without gaps or overlaps.

Construct an octant and choose a point in it. Connect this point with the vertices and find the three points of intersection on the opposite sides. Connect these three points to inscribe a triangle in the octant.

- Measure the sides of the inscribed triangle. What do you find about the sum of these measures?
- Can you possibly prove your findings?

ADVENTURE 8.3

How can you construct Napier's pentagon?

There are five nonadjacent pairs of sides in pentagon *PQRST: PQ* and *RS*, *QR* and *ST*, *RS* and *TP*, *ST* and *PQ*, *TP* and *QR*.

- Draw a planar pentagon so that one of these pairs consists of two perpendicular sides (say, *PQ* and *RS* are perpendicular to each other).
- Show whether you can draw a pentagon on the plane with all these pairs consisting of perpendicular sides.
- Show whether you can draw a pentagon on the sphere with all these pairs consisting of perpendicular sides.

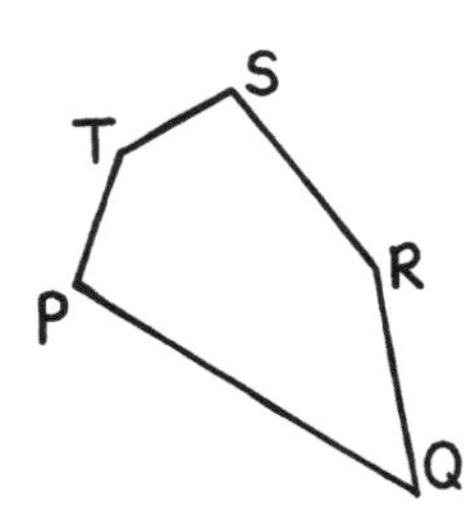

ADVENTURE 8.1

What is special about triangles inscribed on a diameter of a circle?

- Inscribe a triangle in a circle so that one side of the triangle is a diameter of the circle. Then measure the angles of the triangle.
- What special properties do triangles of this type have on the plane?
- Determine if these properties also hold for spherical triangles inscribed in a circle.

Construction on the Plane

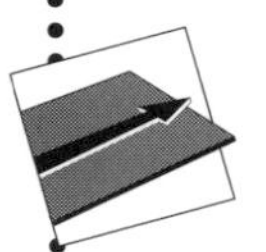

Step 1 Construct a circle with center *O*. Construct a diameter with endpoints *A* and *B*.

Step 2 Choose another point *C* on the circle and draw chords *CA* and *CB*.

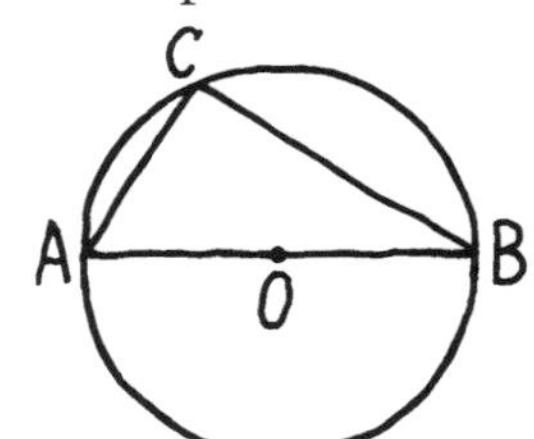

Step 3 Measure angle *ACB*. Measure angles *CAB* and *CBA* and add their measures.

Step 4 Choose another point *D* on the circle and repeat the process.

Investigate

1. Repeat for other points on the circle. What do you observe about the angles of this type of inscribed triangle?

Make a Guess

2. Will the same properties hold on the sphere?

Construction on the Sphere

Step 1 Construct a circle with center *O*. Construct a diameter with endpoints *A* and *B*.

Step 2 Choose another point *C* on the circle and draw chords *CA* and *CB*.

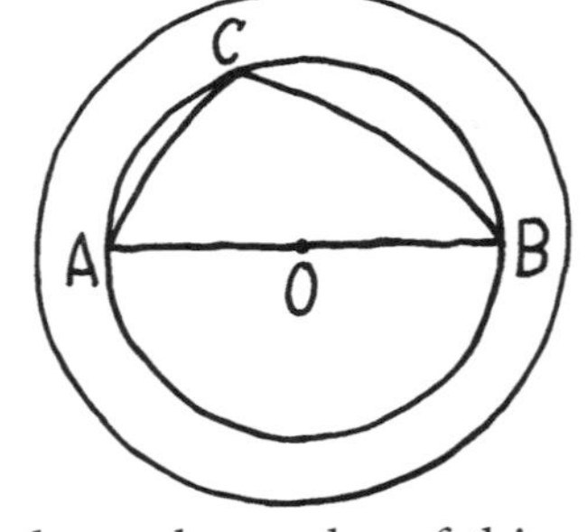

Step 3 Measure spherical angle *ACB*. Measure spherical angles *CAB* and *CBA* and add their measures.

Step 4 Choose two more points *D* and *E* on the circle and repeat Steps 2 and 3 for each point.

Investigate

3. Repeat for other points on the circle. What do you observe about the angles of this type of inscribed triangle?

Compare the Plane and the Sphere

4. See how many observations you can make about this type of triangle on the plane and on the sphere. Record them on a comparison chart like the one at right. Add as many rows as you need.

Triangles inscribed in a circle with one side on a diameter

On the plane	On the sphere

5. Which surface do you think is simpler in this case: the plane or the sphere? Why?

6. Now try to reverse your argument. Give reasons why the surface you *didn't* choose above is simpler.

Explore More

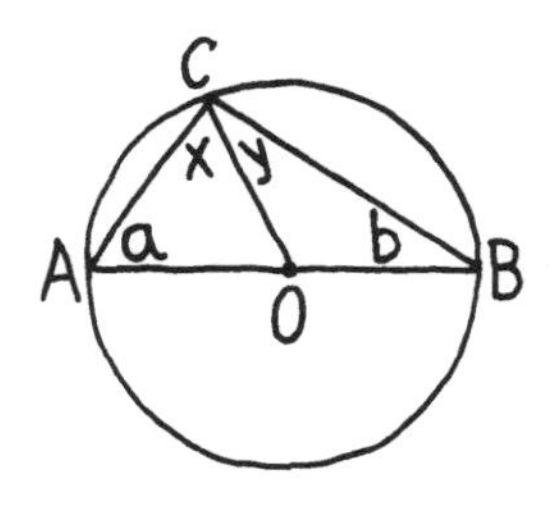

7. **a.** Connect center O with point C in your Construction on the Plane. You now have two smaller triangles AOC and COB. Suppose the angle at point A has measure a and the angle at point B has measure b, as shown. How do these angles compare to the angles labeled x and y? What can you say about the angles in triangle ABC? List as many properties as possible.

   b. Repeat problem 7a on the sphere. Which properties of triangle ABC hold true on the sphere? Which properties fail?

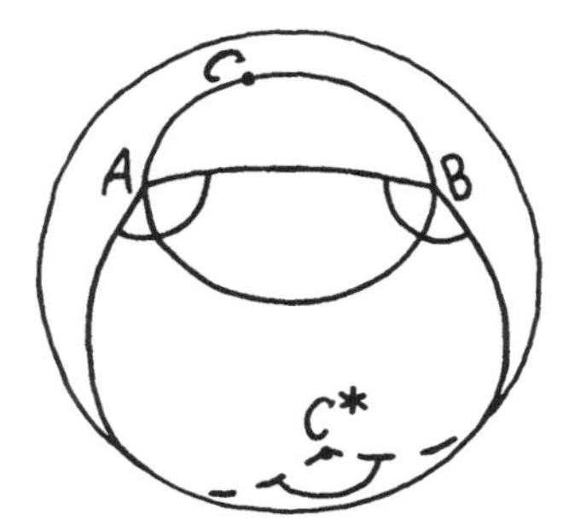

8. **a.** Begin again with a fresh Construction on the Sphere. Draw the opposite pole point of point C and label it C^*. Connect point C^* with points A and B to form triangle ABC^* "on the other side" of diameter AB. Measure the angles in triangle ABC^* and add up these measures.

   b. Repeat for points D and E. Make a conjecture about the sums of the angle measures in these spherical triangles "on the other side" of the diameter.

   c. Prove your conjecture.

ADVENTURE 8.1

What is special about triangles inscribed on a diameter of a circle?

Student Audience: High School/College

Prerequisites: Students should know that the spherical diameter of a circle on the sphere is the smaller arc of the great circle that passes through the circle's center and has endpoints on the circle.

Class Time: 20–40 minutes

Construction/Investigation on the Plane

1. The measure of the angle at vertex *C* always equals 90°; thus triangle *ABC* is a right triangle. The sum of the measures of the other two angles also equals 90°. Thus the measure of the angle at *C* always equals the sum of the measures of the other two angles.

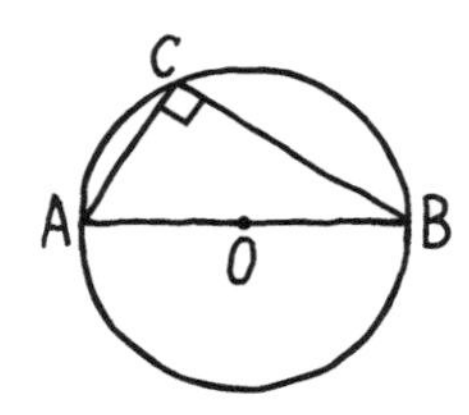

Construction/Investigation on the Sphere

3. The measure of the angle at vertex *C* does not equal 90°; thus triangle *ABC* is not a right triangle. However, it remains true that the measure of the angle at vertex *C* always equals the sum of the measures of the other two angles. The measure of the angle at *C* varies according to the choice of point *C*.

Compare the Plane and the Sphere

Triangles inscribed in a circle with one side on a diameter

On the plane	On the sphere
The triangle is a right triangle with the diameter as its hypotenuse.	The triangle is not a right triangle. The measure of the angle opposite the hypotenuse is greater than 90°.
The measures of the two smaller angles add up to the measure of the largest (right) angle.	The measures of the two smaller angles add up to the measure of the largest angle.
The measures of the two smaller angles add up to 90°.	The measures of the two smaller angles add up to more than 90°.
The measure of the largest angle is a constant.	The measure of the largest angle is not a constant.
If you connect the center of the circle with the opposite vertex of the triangle, you get two isosceles triangles.	If you connect the center of the circle with the opposite vertex of the triangle, you get two isosceles triangles.

Explore More

7. a. Both the triangles *AOC* and *COB* are isosceles triangles because the sides measure *r*, as shown. Therefore the base angles are congruent to each other in triangles *AOC* and *COB*. The two angles on side *AB* of triangle *ABC* add up to the third angle at vertex *C*. This is all valid on both the plane and the sphere. However, on the plane we also know that the sum of the three angle measures must be equal to 180°; thus the angle at *C* must measure 90°.

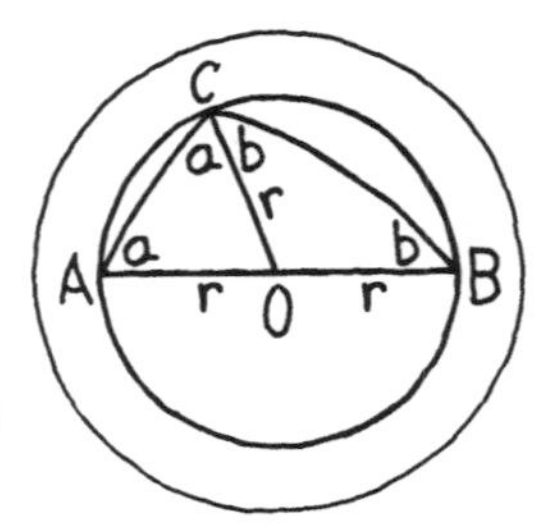

   b. On the sphere, all we can say for sure is that the measure of the angle at *C* is $a + b$, which is the sum of the measures of the other two angles in triangle *ABC*.

8. **a.** The sum of the three angle measures in triangle ABC^* is 360°.

b. The same goes for triangles ABD^* and ABE^*, wherever points D and E are drawn on the circle.

c. Label the angles in triangle ABC as shown. The spherical shape CAC^*BC is a biangle. The two angles of a biangle are always congruent; thus the angles at points C and C^* are congruent. In triangle AC^*B we find an angle supplementary to angle a and an angle supplementary to angle b. Therefore the sum of the three angle measures in triangle AC^*B is $(a + b) + (180° - a) + (180° - b)$, or 360°. If students are already familiar with area measurement on the sphere (Adventure 6.2), then they can calculate that the area of this spherical triangle is $360° - 180° = 180°$, that is, a quarter of the area of a sphere (whether the original circle is large or small).

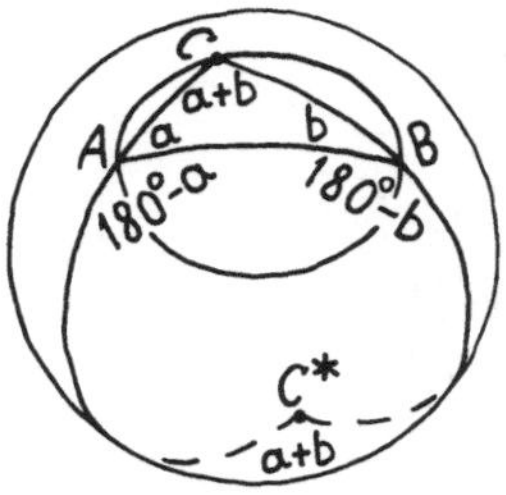

ADVENTURE 8.2

What are some properties of a triangle inscribed in an octant?

The spherical triangle with three right angles is called an *octant* because eight of these triangles cover the whole sphere without gaps or overlaps. The octant has some unusual features. In this adventure you'll investigate a special kind of triangle inscribed in an octant.

- Perform the construction below. Then make conjectures about your construction.
- Try to prove your conjectures.

Construction on the Sphere

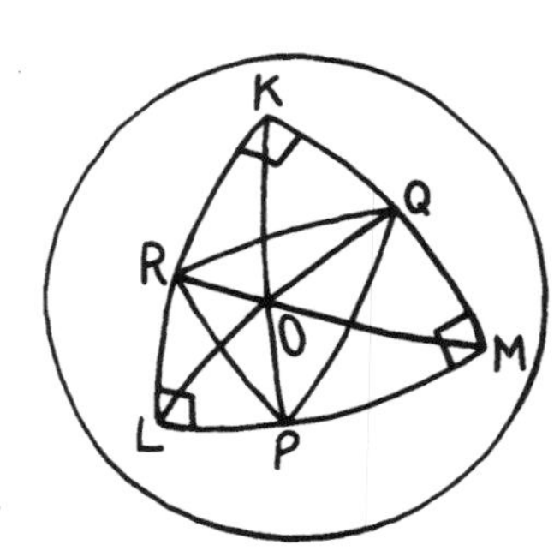

Step 1 Construct an octant. Label its vertices *K*, *L*, and *M*.

Step 2 Draw any point *O* inside triangle *KLM* and connect this point with the three vertices. Extend each new arc beyond point *O* until it intersects the opposite side of triangle *KLM*. Label the points of intersection *P*, *Q*, and *R*, as shown.

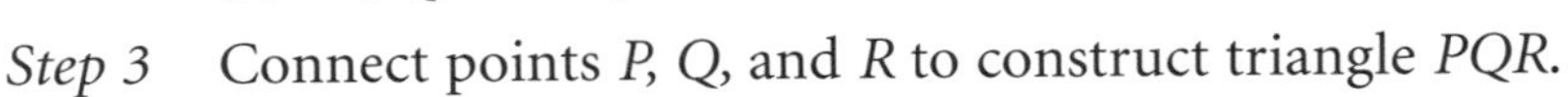

Step 3 Connect points *P*, *Q*, and *R* to construct triangle *PQR*.

Investigate

1. **a.** Measure the three sides of triangle *PQR* and add their measures.

   b. Record any conjecture you can make about the sides of triangle *PQR*.

2. **a.** Measure all the angles at points *P*, *Q*, and *R*.

   b. What can you say about great circles *KP*, *LQ*, and *MR* in triangle *PQR*?

Explore More

3. Try to prove any of the conjectures you made in this adventure.

What are some properties of a triangle inscribed in an octant?

Student Audience: Middle School/High School/College

Prerequisites: Students should know how to measure angles on the sphere.

Class Time: 20–40 minutes

Construction/Investigation on the Sphere

1. The three side measures of triangle *PQR* add up to 180°.

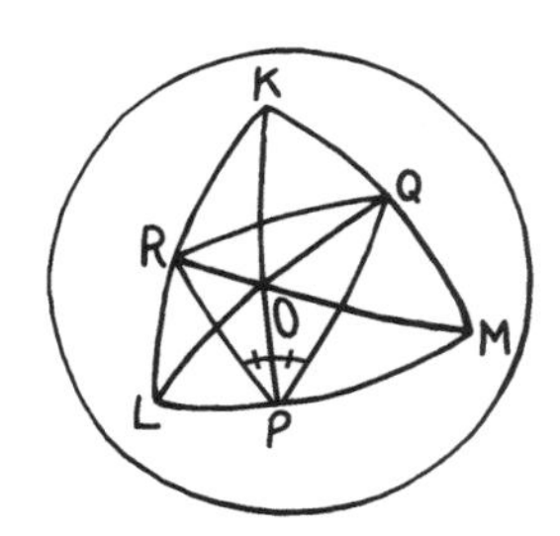

2. The great circles *KP*, *LQ*, and *MR* are the three angle bisectors of triangle *PQR*.

   If the three points *P*, *Q*, and *R* are not on the same great circle, then the sum of angle measures in triangle *PQR* is never equal to, but always greater than, 180°.

   (Because spherical distance and spherical angle are both measured in degrees, students may confuse the sides of a spherical triangle with its angles. This experiment demonstrates the difference between the two. Students should understand that it is the sum of side measures that is equal to 180° in these triangles. However, the sum of angle measures always exceeds 180°.)

Explore More

3. The basic idea is to extend side *RQ* to intersect great circle *LM* in two opposite points, labeled *U* and *V*. It can be proved that the measure of arc *UR* is equal to the measure of side *PR*. Likewise, the measure of *VQ* is equal to the measure of side *PQ*. We straighten out the three sides of triangle *PQR* into one 180°-long arc, that is, into a meridian.

   The exact proof is a bit beyond the degree of difficulty of this book. The central point of this adventure is to clarify the difference between the sum of side measures and the sum of angle measures.

ADVENTURE 8.3

How can you construct Napier's pentagon?

There are five nonadjacent pairs of sides in pentagon *PQRST*: *PQ* and *RS*, *QR* and *ST*, *RS* and *TP*, *ST* and *PQ*, *TP* and *QR*.

- Draw a planar pentagon so that one of these pairs consists of two perpendicular sides (say, *PQ* and *RS* are perpendicular to each other).
- Show whether you can draw a pentagon on the plane with all these pairs consisting of perpendicular sides.
- Show whether you can draw a pentagon on the sphere with all these pairs consisting of perpendicular sides.

Construction/Investigation on the Plane

1. Draw a pentagon *PQRST* with nonadjacent sides *PQ* and *RS* perpendicular to each other.
2. Show whether you can draw a pentagon *PQRST* with all the following pairs of nonadjacent sides perpendicular: *PQ* and *RS*, *QR* and *ST*, *RS* and *TP*, *ST* and *PQ*, *TP* and *QR*.

Construction on the Sphere

Step 1 Draw a triangle *APQ* with exactly one right angle at point *A*, as shown.

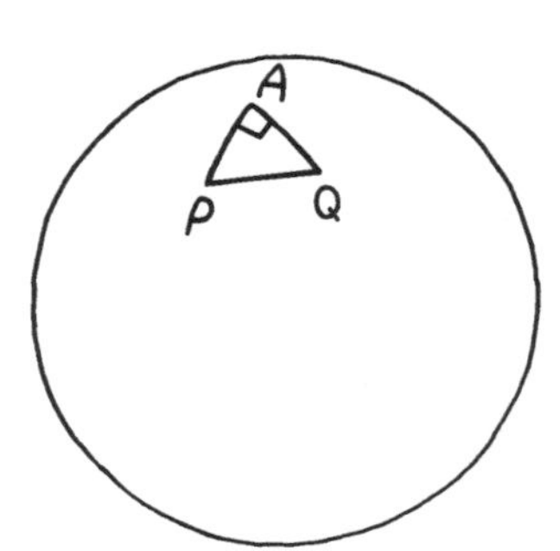

Step 2 Extend hypotenuse *PQ* beyond point *Q* so that the new endpoint's distance from point *P* is 90°. Label this new endpoint *B*.

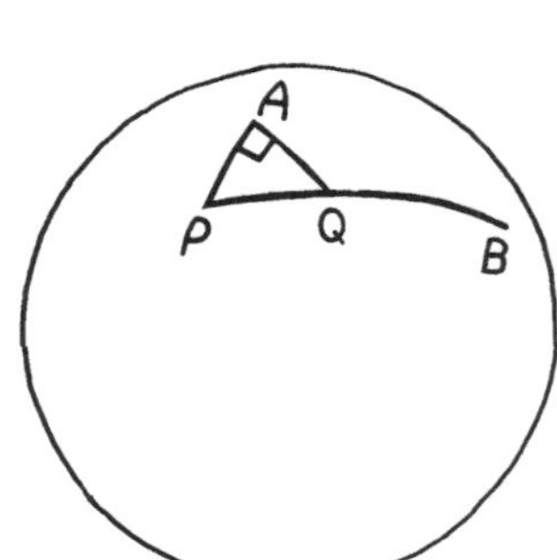

Step 3 Extend side *AQ* beyond point *Q*. Then draw a perpendicular to great circle *PB* at point *B* so that it intersects the extended side *AQ* at point *R*. You now have a new right triangle labeled *BQR*.

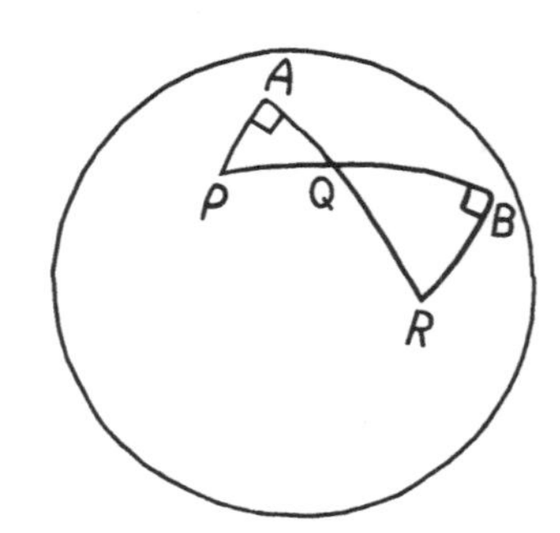

Step 4 Repeat Steps 1 through 3 for triangle *BQR*. You now have another right triangle labeled *CRS*.

Step 5 Repeat Steps 1 through 3 for triangle *CRS*.

Step 6 Continue this process of creating new right triangles.

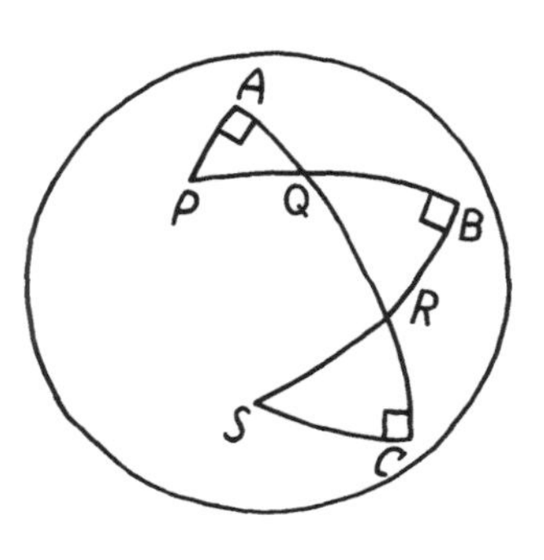

Investigate

3. Describe what happens as you continue this process of constructing new right triangles.

4. How many right triangles did you construct, starting from triangle *APQ*?

5. What can you say about the pairs of nonadjacent sides of spherical pentagon *PQRST*?

Explore More

6. **a.** A pentagram is a five-pointed star. Find and describe the pentagram in your construction.

   b. John Napier (1550–1617) was a well-known Scottish mathematician and inventor. In his explorations in spherical geometry, he discovered this unusual shape. He called it *Pentagramma Mirificium,* which is Latin for "five-pointed star made miraculously." What is miraculous about this construction?

   c. Name some other famous persons who lived about the same time as Napier.

7. Can you find points in the pentagram that are the pole points of great circles in the pentagram?

How can you construct Napier's pentagon?

Student Audience: High School/College

Prerequisites: Students should know how to draw a perpendicular and how to measure distance on the sphere. You may want to do this adventure directly after doing Adventure 3.5, "Can a triangle have more than one right angle?"

Class Time: 20–40 minutes

Construction/Investigation on the Plane

2. This construction cannot be performed on the plane. Why? If straight lines *a* and *b* are perpendicular, *b* and *c* are perpendicular, and *c* and *d* are perpendicular, then you cannot draw a straight line that is perpendicular to both *d* and *a*. That is why a planar pentagon can't have the property described in the introduction to this activity.

Construction/Investigation on the Sphere

For your first attempt at this construction, start with a small right triangle to get a more understandable figure.

3. This construction is "miraculous" because we get back to the first triangle.

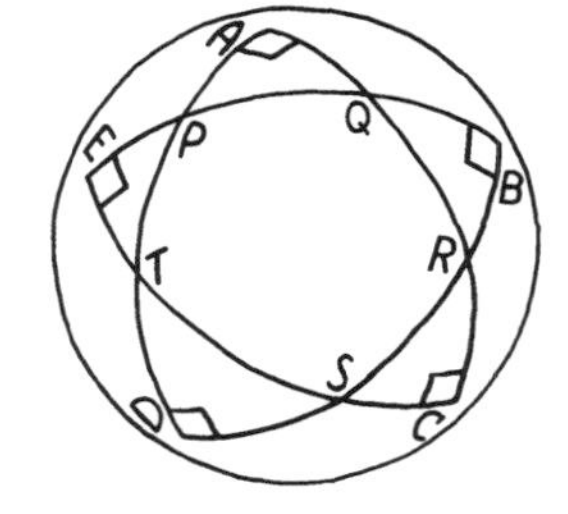

4. We construct a closed chain of five right-angled triangles, each of which is connected to the next one by a common vertex and by two sides lying on the same great circles, respectively.

5. Each pair of nonadjacent sides of the spherical pentagon is perpendicular. Note that this pentagon is not necessarily a regular one.

   This adventure is partly aimed at showing a property of spherical right triangles unmatched on the plane, and so balances the adventures that have focused on properties of planar right triangles unmatched on the sphere—the Pythagorean Theorem, for example.

Explore More

6. **b.** One of its "miraculous" properties is that the construction can be performed on the sphere but not on the plane—see the Construction/Investigation on the Plane above. Another interesting property is the special role of the number 5 in this geometric construction.

   c. Here are some famous contemporaries of Napier: Elizabeth I (1533–1603), Queen of England; Tokugawa Ieyasu (1543–1616), Japanese statesman; Miguel de Cervantes (1547–1616), Spanish writer; William Shakespeare (1564–1616), English dramatist and poet; and Galileo Galilei (1564–1642), Italian astronomer and physicist.

7. Yes, we can find poles and equators in this construction. Each vertex of the pentagon within the *Pentagramma Mirificium* is in pole-equator relation to its opposite side. Thus point *P* is a pole of great circle *RS*, point *Q* a pole of great circle *ST*, point *R* a pole of great circle *TP*, point *S* a pole of great circle *PQ*, and point *T* a pole of great circle *QR*. Why? Consider great circle *PQ*. On this great circle, we find two perpendiculars at points *B* and *E*. The two perpendiculars *BR* and *ET* meet at point *S*. Thus point *S* must be a pole of equator *PQ*.

CHAPTER 9
Tessellations

Chapter 9: Tessellations

Adventure 9.1: What are some tessellations on the sphere?

Adventure 9.2: How can you construct a soccer ball?

Adventure 9.3: How can you tile the sphere with three different types of regular polygons?

Adventure 9.4: How can you inscribe the Platonic solids in a sphere?

Adventure 9.5: How can you "blow up" the Platonic solids to tile a sphere?

The study of tessellations provides an opportunity to integrate art and mathematics. This is as true on a sphere as it is on the plane. Completed spherical tessellations make attractive hanging decorations.

Adventure 9.1 introduces tessellations and compares spherical and planar tilings. The Student's Guide contains instructions for a simple but interesting spherical tiling. The Explore More questions should generate some especially good mathematical discussions.

Each of the other four adventures involves detailed constructions that take a great deal of time. You might have the entire class do Adventure 9.1 and then let each group of students pick one of the other four adventures to complete. You might also assign Adventures 9.2 through 9.5 as long-term projects so that students have time to work slowly and carefully. Although these tessellations require a lot of careful work, the results can be very attractive and satisfying.

In Adventure 9.2, students construct the soccer ball tiling (also known as the buckyball). Adventure 9.3 contains directions for a spherical tessellation using three different regular polygons as tiles. In Adventure 9.4, students build models of the five Platonic solids. The size of each solid allows it to fit exactly inside a pair of hemispherical transparencies. These solids inscribed in spheres are excellent decorations for any geometry classroom. In Adventure 9.5, students create five tilings of the sphere. Each tiling uses exactly one kind of regular polygon as a tile. These tilings are also known as the spherical Platonic solids because they look like the five famous Platonic solids inflated into spherical shapes.

The Adventure Cards in this chapter are truly challenging. In Adventure 9.4, for example, students who figure out the correct sizes for the edges of each of the five inscribed Platonic solids without hints from the Student's Guide have learned a great deal of geometry! If you choose to use the Adventure Cards, remember that you always have the Student's Guides and Teacher's Guides to use as resources.

ADVENTURE 9.1

What are some tessellations on the sphere?

Closed shapes form a *tessellation* or *tiling* of a surface if the shapes cover the entire surface without gaps or overlaps. We call these closed shapes *tiles.* A tessellation is pure if all its tiles are congruent. A tessellation is *semipure* if it has tiles that are not congruent but still has a finite number of different shapes of tiles.

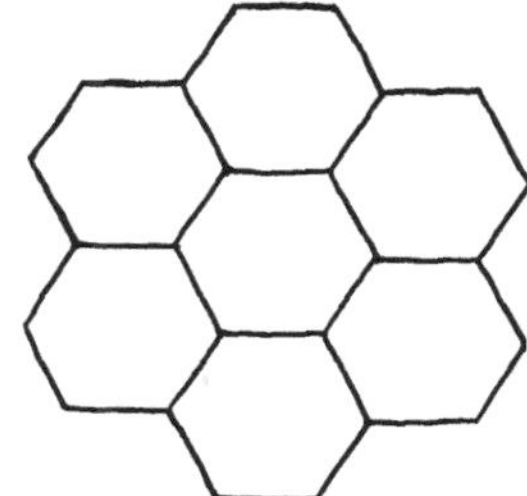

- Using only regular polygons, construct examples of pure and semipure tessellations on the plane and on the sphere. Describe each tessellation.

9.2

How can you construct a soccer ball?

Look at a soccer ball. It's tiled with regular pentagons and hexagons.

- Construct the soccer ball tessellation on your sphere.

ADVENTURE 9.3

How can you tile the sphere with three different types of regular polygons?

The soccer ball is a spherical tessellation that uses two different regular polygons as its tiles. Can you make a spherical tessellation that uses more?

- Using three different types of regular polygons as tiles, construct a spherical tessellation.

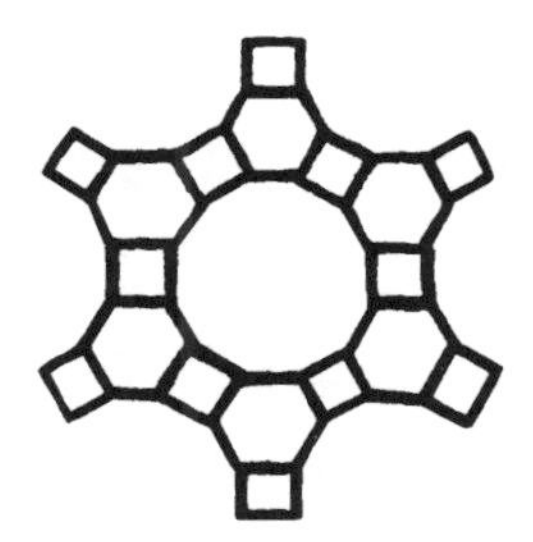

ADVENTURE 9.4

How can you inscribe the Platonic solids in a sphere?

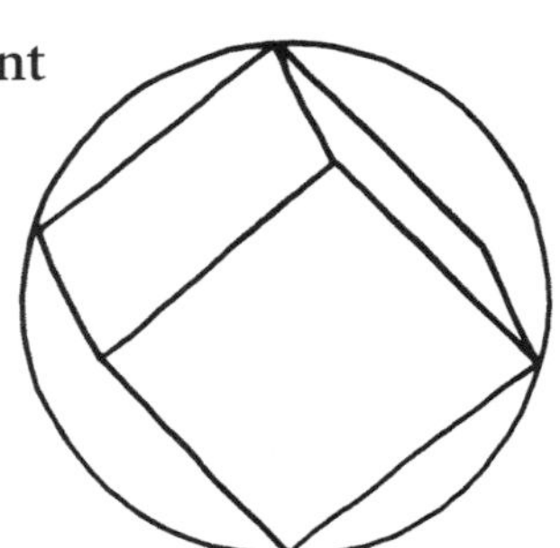

The *Platonic solids* are polyhedra whose faces are all congruent regular polygons meeting at each vertex in the same way. A solid is *inscribed* in a sphere if each of its vertices lies on the surface of the sphere.

- Build the five Platonic solids so they fit exactly inside a sphere made of two transparencies and a hanger.
- Hang up your inscribed Platonic solids to decorate your classroom.

ADVENTURE 9.5

How can you "blow up" the Platonic solids to tile a sphere?

In Adventure 9.1, you drew every possible tiling of the plane that used exactly one type of regular polygon as a tile. In this investigation you will construct such tessellations on the sphere. If you imagine inflating the Platonic solids until they are spherical, you will get an idea of what these five tessellations look like. We name each tessellation after its corresponding solid: the spherical octahedron; the spherical hexahedron, or cube; the spherical tetrahedron; the spherical dodecahedron; and the spherical icosahedron.

- Construct all five spherical Platonic solids on your sphere.

ADVENTURE 9.1

What are some tessellations on the sphere?

Closed shapes form a **tessellation** or **tiling** of a surface if the shapes cover the entire surface without gaps or overlaps. We call these closed shapes **tiles.** A tessellation is **pure** if all its tiles are congruent. A tessellation is **semipure** if it has tiles that are not congruent but still has a finite number of different shapes of tiles.

- Using only regular polygons, construct examples of pure and semipure tessellations on the plane and on the sphere. Describe each tessellation.

Construction on the Plane

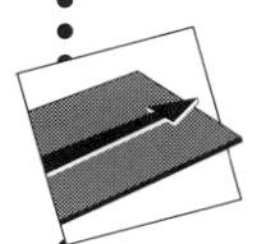

Step 1 There are three types of pure tessellations on the plane that use regular polygons as tiles. Sketch an example of each type.

Step 2 There are many types of semipure tessellations on the plane that use only regular polygons as tiles. Sketch two types.

Step 3 Sketch a tessellation that doesn't use polygons as tiles.

Investigate

1. For each of the six tessellations you constructed, decide how many tiles it would take to tile the entire plane.

2. Explain whether the size of the tiles is important in a tessellation on the plane.

Make A Guess

3. How do tessellations on the sphere differ from tessellations on the plane?

Construction on the Sphere

Step 1 Draw an arc *OA* that measures 70.5°. Draw a circle with center *O* and radius *OA*.

Step 2 Draw two more radii *OB* and *OC* of the circle so that the angles between each pair of radii measure 120°.

Step 3 Construct the opposite point of center *O* and label it *D*. Erase everything on your sphere except points *A, B, C,* and *D*.

Step 4 Consider point *A* a pole point and draw its equator. Repeat with points *B, C,* and *D*. The polygons created by these four equators form a tessellation on the sphere.

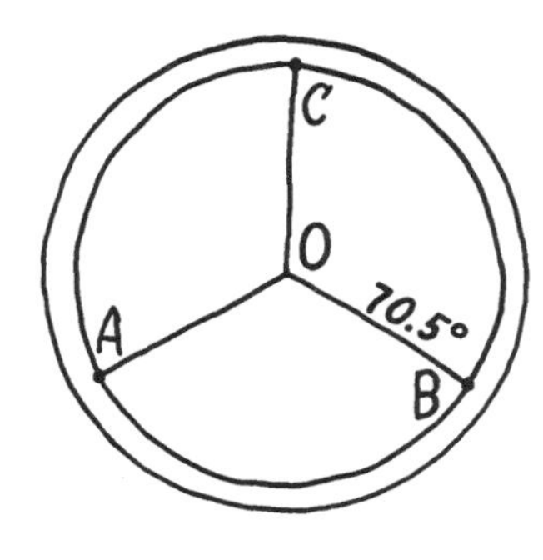

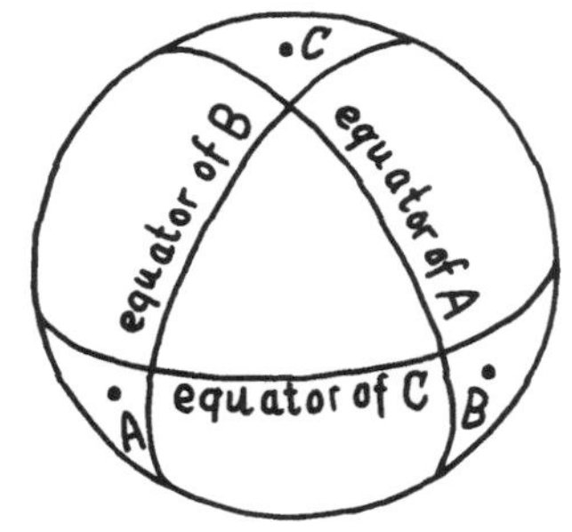

Investigate

4. a. Describe the tessellation formed by the four equators.

   b. What kind of regular spherical polygons do you find in this tessellation?

   c. How many of each kind of regular polygon are in your tessellation?

   d. Without actually measuring them, can you determine the measure of the sides of these polygons?

5. Measure some sides of the tiles. What do you find?

6. Explain whether the number of tiles is important in a tessellation on the sphere.

7. Explain whether the size of the tiles is important in a tessellation on the sphere.

Compare the Plane and the Sphere

8. See how many observations you can make about tessellations on the plane and tessellations on the sphere. Record them on a comparison chart like the one at right. Add as many rows as you need.

Tessellations

On the plane	On the sphere

9. Do you think tessellations are simpler on the plane or on the sphere? Why?

10. Now try to reverse your argument. Give reasons why tessellations are simpler on the surface you *didn't* choose above.

Explore More

11. a. Verify that the four points *A*, *B*, *C*, and *D* in your Construction on the Sphere are all the same distance from one another. Use a colored marker to join each point with the others to form a spherical tetrahedron.

    b. Can you draw four points on the plane with the same property?

12. Invent and construct three other tessellations on the sphere. Be creative! Determine which are pure and which are semipure. Describe the tiles in each tessellation and record the number of each type you needed.

13. The first tessellation you constructed on the sphere was made entirely of equilateral triangles and regular quadrilaterals. Determine if it is possible to tile the plane using these same two types of tiles.

What are some tessellations on the sphere?

Student Audience: Middle School/High School

Prerequisites: Students should know the definition of a regular polygon on the plane and on the sphere.

Class Time: 30–50 minutes

Construction/Investigation on the Plane

The three regular polygons that can be used to form pure tessellations on the plane are equilateral triangles, squares, and regular hexagons.

Construction/Investigation on the Sphere

If you want to construct the 70.5° arc rather than just measuring it, follow Steps 1–3 of Adventure 9.5. The trigonometric formula that explains the calculations leading to the 70.5° arc is beyond the scope of this book, but the argument goes as follows:

Take the four faces of the spherical tetrahedron you constructed in Adventure 9.5. Three equilateral triangles meet at each vertex, so each angle in each of the four triangles must be equal to 360°/3 = 120°. The three medians divide each of these triangles into six smaller right-angled triangles, with each of their other two angles measuring 60°. Label the hypotenuse of such a smaller triangle r. It can be proved that $\cos r = (\cos 60°/\sin 60°)^2 = 1/3$. From this we get $r \approx 70.5°$. You can find the proof in any reference book on spherical geometry.

4. This tessellation consists of six regular spherical quadrilaterals and eight equilateral spherical triangles with each side exactly 60° long.

60°
60°
60°

Compare the Plane and the Sphere

Tessellations

On the plane	On the sphere
It takes an infinite number of tiles to tile the plane with a pure or semipure tessellation.	It takes a finite number of tiles to tile the sphere with a pure or semipure tessellation. The number of tiles required varies according to the tessellation.
If a shape tiles the plane, any shape that is geometrically similar to it will also tile the plane. Both tilings require infinitely many tiles.	There are no similar shapes on the sphere that are not congruent. So we cannot speak about a tessellation with tiles that are similar to the tiles of another tessellation. However, we can speak about tiles of the same type. For example, if a pure tessellation of equilateral congruent triangles exists on the sphere, it does not follow that equilateral congruent triangles of a different measure will also produce a pure tessellation.
Two-sided polygons do not exist on the plane, so there is no tiling of the plane that uses two-sided polygons.	You can tile the sphere with congruent biangles (two-sided polygons) as long as the angle of the biangle divides evenly into 360°.

Explore More

11. b. No. You can construct three points on the plane that are all the same distance from one another. These points are the vertices of an equilateral triangle. To construct a fourth point so that all the four points are the same distance from one another, you have to leave the plane and enter three-dimensional space.

ADVENTURE 9.2

How can you construct a soccer ball?

Look at a soccer ball. It's tiled with regular pentagons and hexagons.

- Construct the soccer ball tessellation on your sphere.

This remarkable tiling is used for more than covering soccer balls. United States architect Buckminster Fuller (1895-1983) used this shape to construct geodesic domes. In 1985 chemists discovered the C_{60} molecule, suggested that it had the structure of a soccer ball, and proposed the name buckminsterfullerene—or buckyball, for short—in recognition of the architect and his domes. Later, when C_{60} was crystallized, the proposed structure was confirmed and buckminsterfullerene became the third form of crystalline carbon (diamond and graphite being the other two).

Construction on the Sphere

This construction can take a long time. Make use of any shortcuts you find along the way. Using a marker with an extra fine point can help you work more accurately.

Step 1 Construct an equilateral triangle with sides that each measure 63.4°. Cover the whole sphere with triangles of this kind, making sure the triangles don't overlap and that there are no gaps between them. (A possible shortcut is to cut a template out of a piece of transparency and then trace the outline of the template until you have covered the entire sphere.) You have constructed a spherical icosahedron.

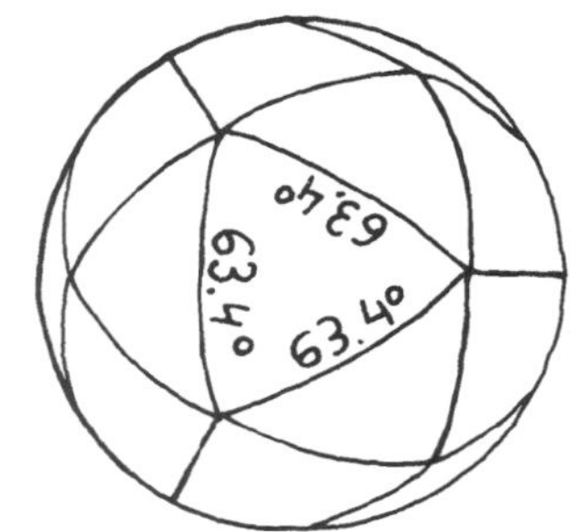

Step 2 Pick one of these triangles and construct the perpendicular bisector of each side. This divides the triangle into six smaller triangles, each with one right angle.

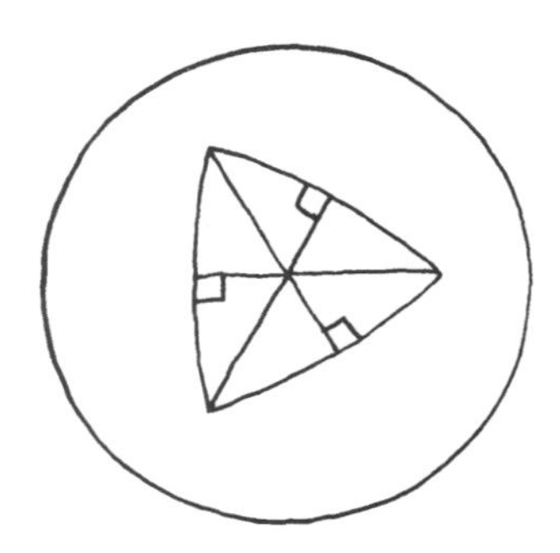

Step 3 Construct the angle bisectors of the six central angles in the equilateral triangle. Mark the points where the angle bisectors intersect the opposite sides.

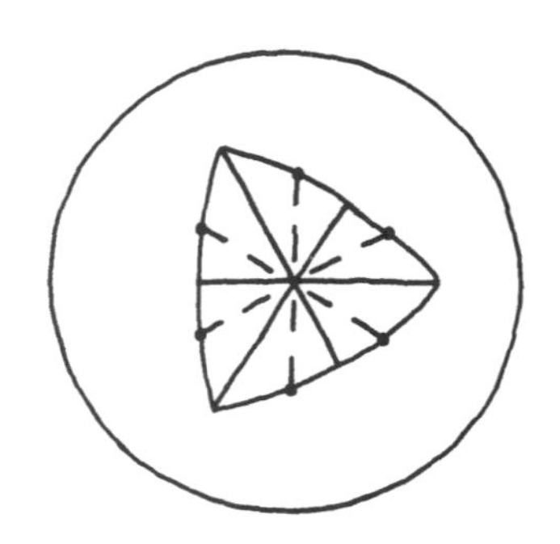

Step 4 Perform Steps 2 and 3 in all twenty equilateral triangles.

Step 5 Use a brightly colored marker to connect the points of intersection nearest to each other. Make your tessellation look like a real soccer ball by coloring some of the regions.

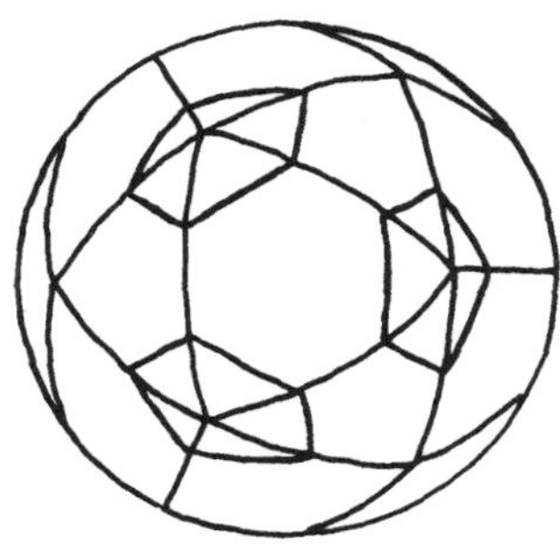

Explore More

1. Record the number of pentagons and the number of hexagons in your tiling.
2. **a.** A soccer ball is usually made of leather, with black pentagons and white hexagons. You can measure the area of a spherical triangle by subtracting 180° from the sum of its angles. Use this information to determine the approximate ratio of black leather to white leather in a soccer ball.

   b. Explain how it is possible to calculate this ratio by making only one angle measurement in your tessellation.
3. If you measured one angle of a hexagon, how could you compute one angle of a pentagon?
4. A tessellation that uses more than one type of regular polygon is either **semiregular** or **demiregular**. A semiregular tessellation has the same arrangement of polygons (whether clockwise or counterclockwise) around each vertex. A demiregular tessellation does not have the same arrangement of polygons around each vertex. Determine whether the buckyball is semiregular or demiregular.

How can you construct a soccer ball?

Student Audience: High School

Prerequisites: Students should know or be introduced to the fact that the angle bisector of a spherical triangle can be constructed just as the angle bisector of a planar triangle is constructed.

Class Time: 45–80 minutes. You may want to do this adventure in the same class period that you do Adventure 9.5, "How can you 'blow up' the Platonic solids to tile a sphere?"

Construction on the Sphere

Perform the first four steps with an extra-fine-point marker to make the final tessellation in Step 5 predominate.

Explore More

1. The tiling consists of 12 pentagons and 20 hexagons. Each pentagon is surrounded by five hexagons, and each hexagon is surrounded by three pentagons and three hexagons.

2. The buckyball consists of 12 pentagons and 20 hexagons. Measure one angle of one hexagon. It is approximately 124.4°. The angle bisector of this angle connects the vertex with the center of the hexagon. The whole hexagon consists of six isosceles triangles with angles that measure 62.2°, 62.2°, and 60°. Thus the area of such a triangle is $62.2° + 62.2° + 60° - 180° = 4.4°$. The area of the whole hexagon is $6 \times 4.4° = 26.4°$. We have 20 hexagons in all, so the total area of hexagons is $20 \times 26.4° = 528°$. The whole surface of the sphere measures 720°, so there is 192° left for the pentagons. The ratio of the area of pentagons to hexagons is approximately $192°/528° = 0.36$. We need about three times as much white leather as black leather.
3. Two hexagons and one pentagon meet at each vertex, so one angle of the pentagon must be $360° - (2 \times 124.4°) = 111.2°$.
4. The buckyball is semiregular because one regular spherical pentagon and two congruent regular spherical hexagons meet at each of its vertices. This arrangement is identical at every vertex.

ADVENTURE 9.3

How can you tile the sphere with three different types of regular polygons?

The soccer ball is a spherical tessellation that uses two different regular polygons as its tiles. Can you make a spherical tessellation that uses more?

- Using three different types of regular polygons as tiles, construct a spherical tessellation.

Construction on the Sphere

This construction has many steps. Find shortcuts along the way and use them! You may want to use different-colored markers for the successive steps of this construction, saving your brightest color for last.

Step 1 Construct three great circles so that each is perpendicular to the other two. You have created eight equilateral triangles that tile the sphere. Each of these triangles has three right angles.

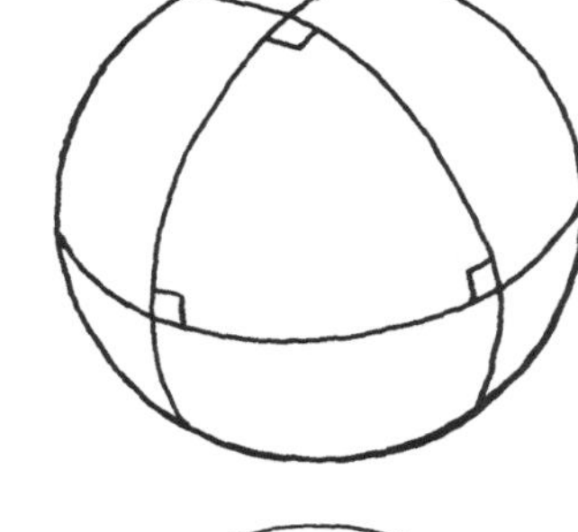

Step 2 Find the midpoints of the sides of the triangles. Connect the midpoint of each side with its opposite vertex. You now have six right triangles in each of the equilateral triangles.

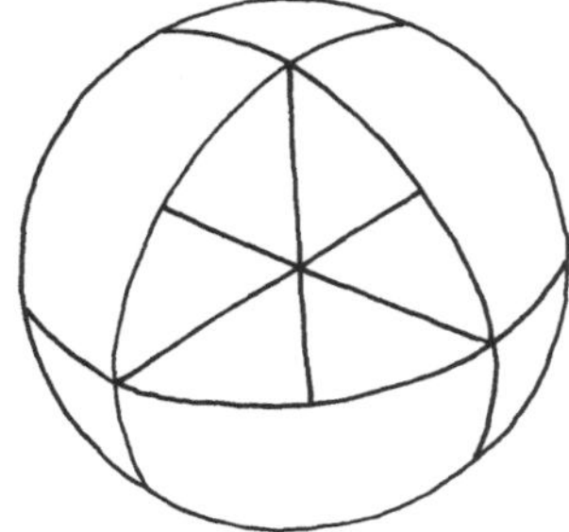

Step 3 In each right triangle, construct the incenter by drawing the angle bisectors and marking their point of concurrency.

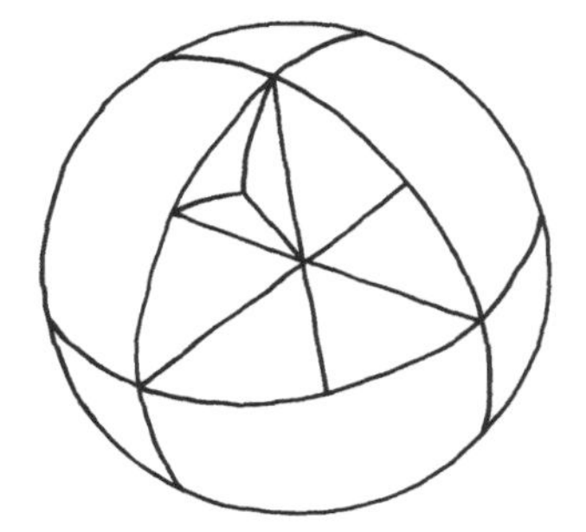

Step 4 Use a bright marker to connect every pair of adjacent incenters. Connect each incenter with three other incenters. Your tessellation is finished!

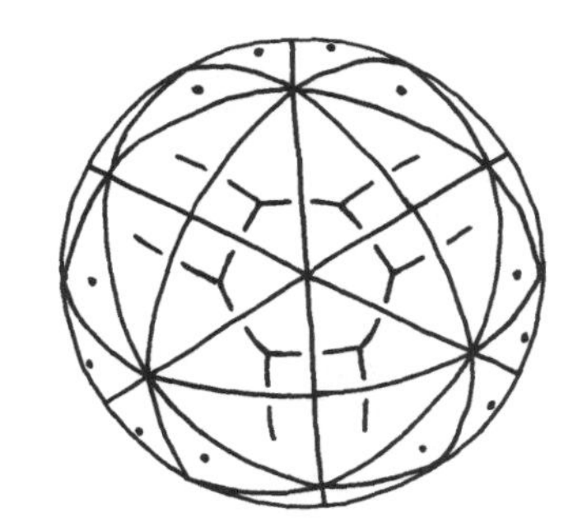

Investigate

1. What types of spherical polygons do you find in your final tessellation?
2. How many of each kind of polygon did you use to tile the sphere?
3. What kinds of polygons meet at each vertex of the tessellation? How many?

Explore More

4. The spherical tessellation you constructed uses three different regular polygons as tiles. Determine whether it is possible to tile the plane by using these three regular polygons.
5. A tessellation that uses more than one type of regular polygon is either **semiregular** or **demiregular**. A semiregular tessellation has the same arrangement of polygons (whether clockwise or counterclockwise) around each vertex. A demiregular tessellation does not have the same arrangement of polygons around each vertex. Determine which type of tessellation you constructed in this adventure.

How can you tile the sphere with three different types of regular polygons?

Student Audience: High School

Prerequisites: Students should know how to construct a triangle's incenter on the plane or the sphere by constructing the point of intersection of the triangle's two angle bisectors.

Class Time: 45–80 minutes

Construction/Investigation on the Sphere

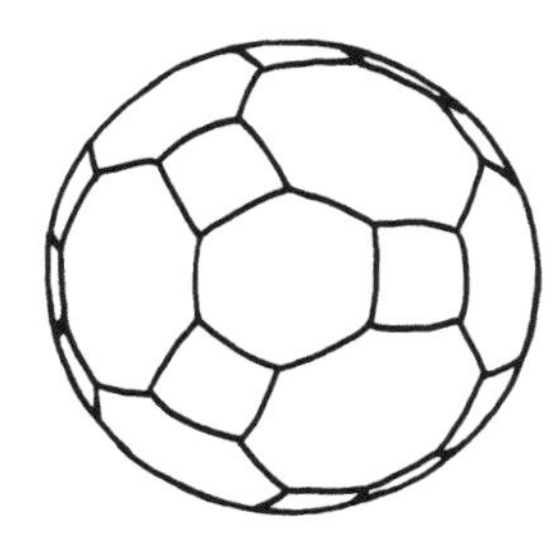

1. The final tessellation is composed of regular octagons, regular hexagons, and regular quadrilaterals.
2. The tessellation uses six regular octagons, eight regular hexagons, and twelve regular quadrilaterals. All these polygon's sides are congruent with one another.
3. We find one octagon, one hexagon, and one quadrilateral at each vertex of the tessellation.

Explore More

4. It is impossible to tile the plane with exactly the same combination of regular octagons, hexagons, and quadrilaterals at each vertex. However, if we start with a tessellation of regular and congruent triangles on the plane, we can perform the same steps we already performed on the sphere. The result is a tessellation on the plane that contains dodecagons rather than the octagons of the spherical tessellation.

ADVENTURE 9.4

How can you inscribe the Platonic solids in a sphere?

The **Platonic solids** are polyhedra whose faces are all congruent regular polygons meeting at each vertex in the same way. A solid is **inscribed** in a sphere if each of its vertices lies on the surface of the sphere.

- Build the five Platonic solids so that they fit exactly inside a sphere made of two transparencies and a hanger.
- Decorate your classroom by hanging up your inscribed Platonic solids.

The nets in the following constructions should be made on heavy paper. They can be constructed by hand, but it is much easier and faster to construct them by using a computer program such as The Geometer's Sketchpad.

Constructing the Tetrahedron

Step 1 Make a net for a tetrahedron with each edge approximately $6\frac{17}{32}$ in. (16.59 cm) long.

Step 2 Cut out the net and assemble it. Use a hanger to enclose your tetrahedron between two hemispherical transparencies of radius 4 in. (10.16 cm). Then hang up your inscribed tetrahedron.

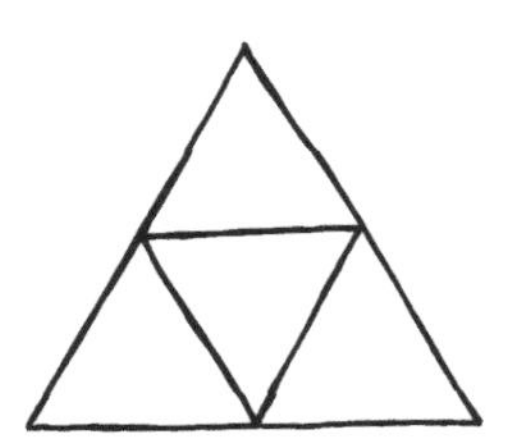

Constructing the Hexahedron or Cube

Step 1 Make a net for a cube with each edge approximately $4\frac{5}{8}$ in. (11.73 cm) long.

Step 2 Cut out the net and assemble it. Use a hanger to enclose your cube between two transparencies. Then hang up your inscribed cube.

Constructing the Octahedron

Step 1 Make a net for an octahedron with each edge approximately $5\frac{21}{32}$ in. (14.38 cm) long.

Step 2 Cut out the net and assemble it. Use a hanger to enclose your octahedron between two transparencies. Then hang up your inscribed octahedron.

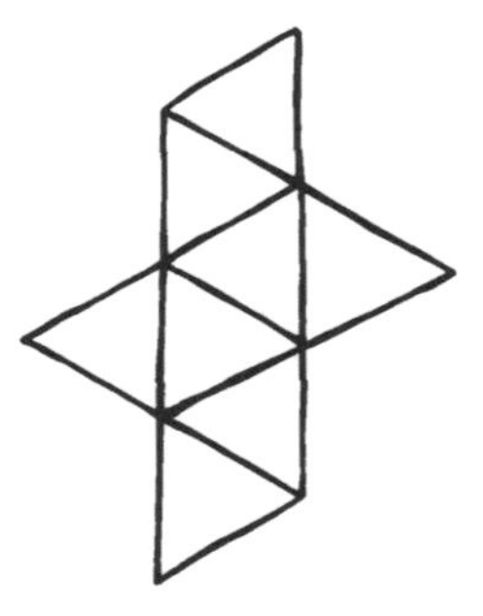

Constructing the Dodecahedron

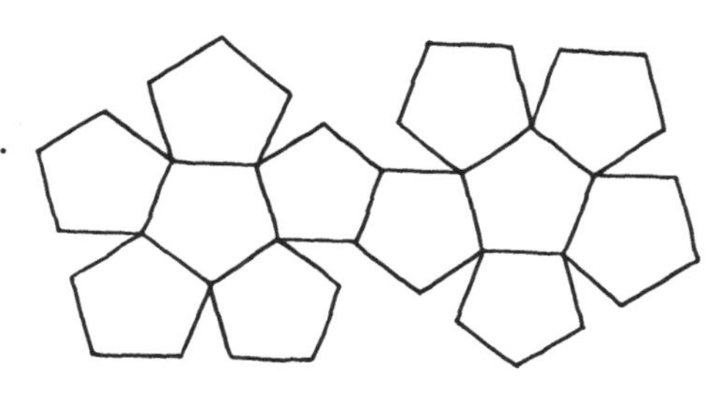

Step 1 Make a net for a dodecahedron with each edge approximately $2\frac{27}{32}$ in. (7.24 cm) long.

Step 2 Cut out the net and assemble it. Use a hanger to enclose your dodecahedron between two transparencies. Then hang up your inscribed dodecahedron.

Constructing the Icosahedron

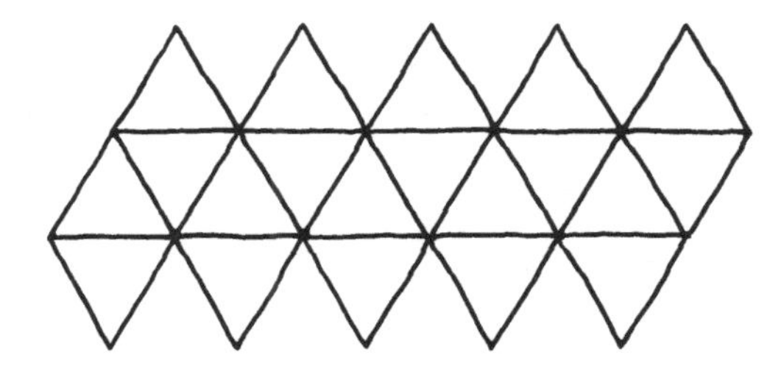

Step 1 Make a net for an icosahedron with each edge approximately $4\frac{3}{16}$ inches (10.67 cm) long.

Step 2 Cut out the net and assemble it. Use a hanger to enclose your icosahedron between two transparencies. Then hang up your inscribed icosahedron.

Investigate

1. Compare your methods for constructing the different Platonic solids.
2. Imagine that you could inflate your inscribed Platonic solids until they had spherical shapes. Compare your flat-sided solids with their "blown-up" counterparts. Find some similarities and differences between them.

Explore More

3. Order your five Platonic solids according to their volumes, starting with the smallest volume and ending with the largest. Explain how you determined the order.
   The table below gives the area of a face of each solid you constructed, and the distance of a face from the center of the circumscribed sphere.

	Area	Distance	Volume
Tetrahedron	119.18 cm^2	3.39 cm	
Cube	137.59 cm^2	5.87 cm	
Octahedron	89.54 cm^2	5.87 cm	
Dodecahedron	90.18 cm^2	8.07 cm	
Icosahedron	49.30 cm^2	8.07 cm	

4. Describe some other solids that can be inscribed in a sphere.
5. Johannes Kepler (1571–1630) was a famous German mathematician and astronomer. He tried to prove that spheres inscribed in and circumscribed around the five Platonic solids described the orbits of planets around the sun. Later Kepler realized that the orbits of the planets are elliptical. Read about Kepler's ideas and describe them in more detail.

How can you inscribe the Platonic solids in a sphere?

Student Audience: High School

Prerequisites: This adventure is closely connected with Adventure 9.5, "How can you "blow up" a Platonic solid to tile a sphere?" Students will need heavy paper and scissors to make these constructions.

Class Time: 2 hours

Construction/Investigation

Your completed Platonic solids (the tetrahedron, the cube, the octahedron, the dodecahedron, and the icosahedron) should look like this:

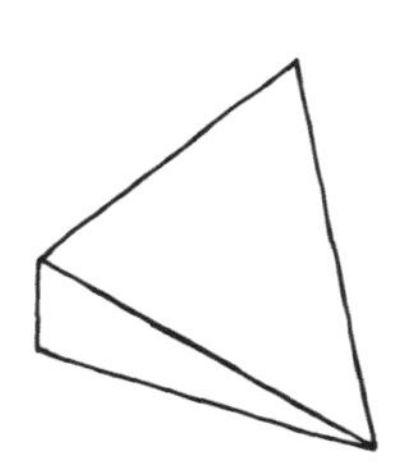

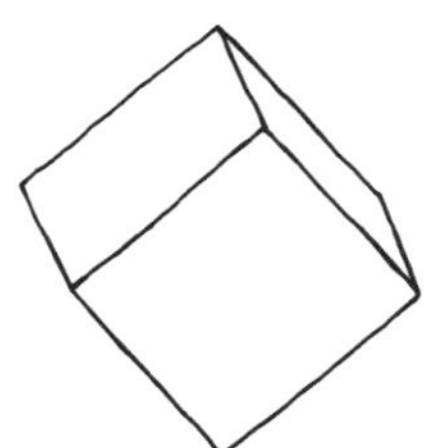

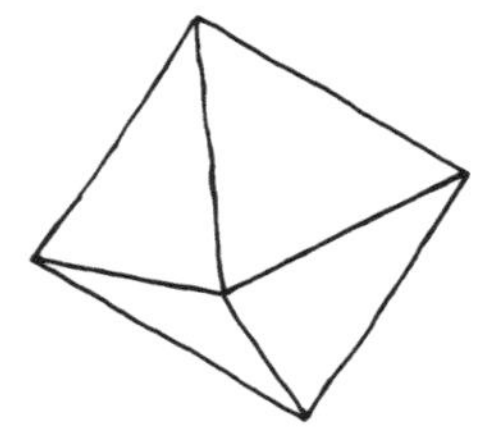

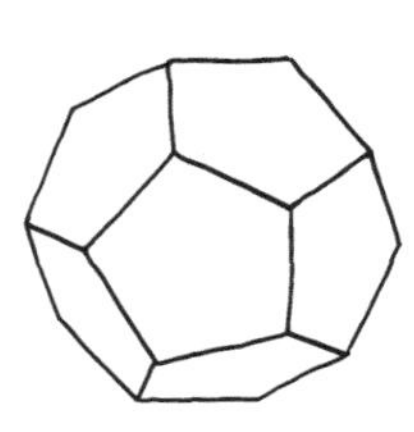

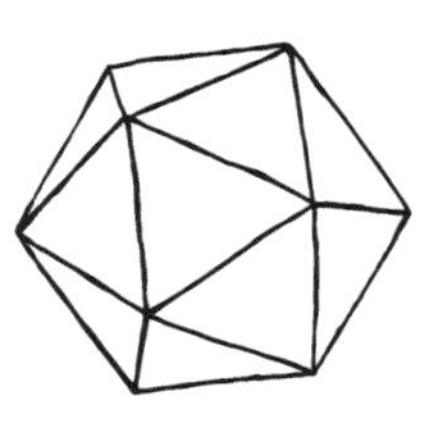

2. Here are some similarities: The equilateral triangles of the spherical tetrahedron correspond to equilateral triangles of the flat-sided tetrahedron. The number of faces, edges, and vertices is the same on the flat-sided tetrahedron as on the "blown-up" one.

   Here are some differences: The measures of the edges of the two tetrahedrons are not the same. The angle between two adjacent edges of the flat-edged tetrahedron differs from the angle between two adjacent edges of the spherical tetrahedron.

Explore More

3. Pick one face of a Platonic solid and connect each of its vertices with the center of the sphere. You get a pyramid with a regular polygon as its base. The volume of such a pyramid is the area of its base multiplied by the height of the pyramid and divided by 3. You have as many pyramids in a solid as that solid has faces. The volumes of the solids, in increasing order, are: tetrahedron, 538 cm^3; octahedron, 1402 cm^3; cube, 1614 cm^3; icosahedron, 2652 cm^3; and dodecahedron, 2912 cm^3.

ADVENTURE 9.5

How can you "blow up" the Platonic solids to tile a sphere?

There are five tilings of the sphere using exactly one type of regular polygon as a tile. If you imagine inflating the Platonic solids until they are spherical, you will get an idea of what they look like. We name each tessellation after its corresponding solid: the spherical octahedron; the spherical hexahedron, or cube; the spherical tetrahedron; the spherical dodecahedron; and the spherical icosahedron.

- Construct all five spherical Platonic solids on your sphere.

Construction on the Sphere

Use a different color for each construction. Rather than constructing all five solids on the same sphere, you may want to construct the first three on a pair of transparencies and the last two directly on the sphere or on another pair of transparencies.

Step 1 **Spherical octahedron**: Draw three great circles so that each great circle is perpendicular to the other two. These three great circles form the spherical octahedron.

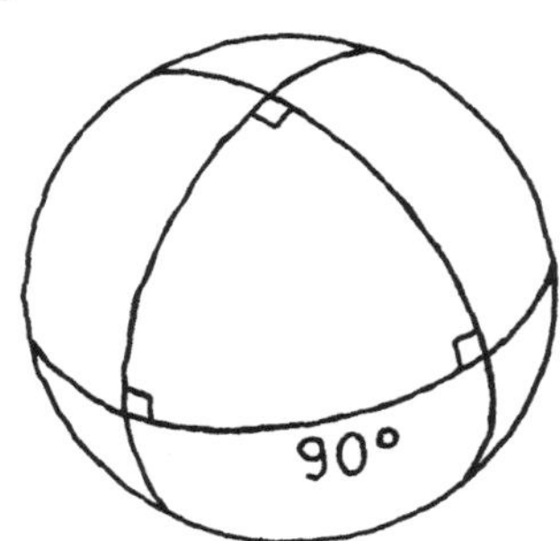

Step 2 **Spherical hexahedron or cube**: Construct the centroid (intersection of the medians) of each triangle in your spherical octahedron. Connect each centroid to the three adjacent centroids. The result is the spherical hexahedron, or cube.

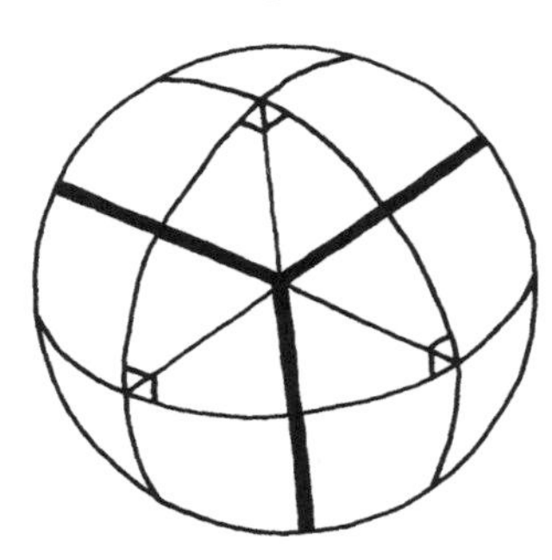

Step 3 **Spherical tetrahedron**: Pick one face of the spherical cube and mark two diagonally opposite vertices. Now look at the opposite face and mark the two vertices that do not lie on the great circle passing through the points already marked. Finally, connect each point you have marked with the other three. You have constructed the spherical tetrahedron.

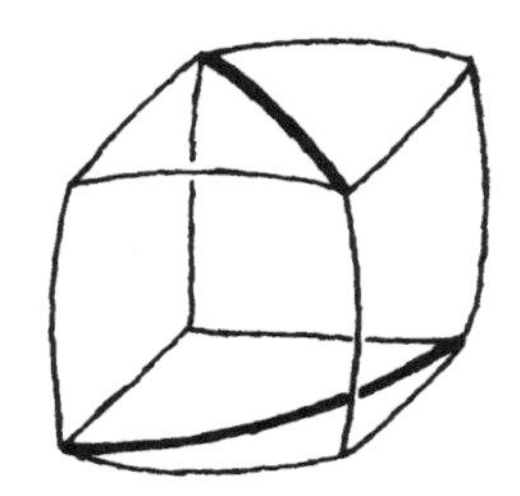

Step 4 **Spherical dodecahedron**: Take one edge of the spherical cube. (This edge should measure approximately 70.5°.) Construct a spherical equilateral triangle having this side. Construct the centroid of this equilateral triangle. Use a different-colored pen to draw the three arcs connecting the vertices of the triangle to its centroid. These are three edges of the spherical dodecahedron. Any two adjacent edges of

this tessellation have an angle of measure 120° between them. Using this information, and keeping in mind that all the edges are the same length, finish constructing a face of the spherical dodecahedron. Continue this process around the sphere to construct the other faces.

Step 5 **Spherical icosahedron**: Construct perpendicular bisectors to each edge of the spherical dodecahedron so that they intersect in the center of each face of the spherical dodecahedron. You have constructed the spherical icosahedron.

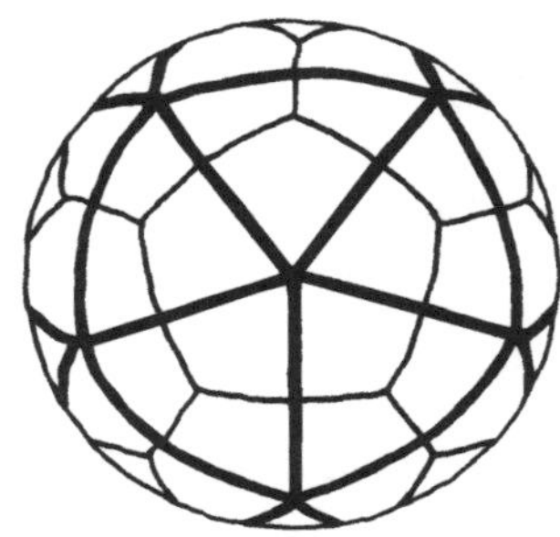

Explore More

1. Cut out a regular polygon from a spherical Platonic solid you drew on a transparency. Use this cutout as a template to create a tessellation of regular polygons on another Lénárt Sphere.

2. Each tessellation using regular polygons has a companion tessellation, which is called its **dual**. The dual tessellation is drawn by connecting centers of adjacent tiles in the original tessellation.

   a. What is the dual of a spherical octahedron?

   b. What is the dual of a spherical cube?

   c. What is the dual of a spherical tetrahedron?

   d. What is the dual of a spherical dodecahedron?

   e. What is the dual of a spherical icosahedron?

3. **a.** Create a chart similar to the one below and fill in the missing information.

	Number of faces	Number of vertices	Number of edges
Spherical octahedron			
Spherical cube			
Spherical tetrahedron			
Spherical dodecahedron			
Spherical icosahedron			

   b. Find the patterns in the chart that relate a solid and its dual.

   c. Find a pattern that relates the number of faces with the number of vertices and the number of edges in a solid.

4. **a.** How many different pure tessellations can you make on the plane by using regular polygons?

   b. How many different pure tessellations can you make on the sphere by using regular polygons? (Hint: There are more than five.)

How can you "blow up" the Platonic solids to tile a sphere?

Student Audience: High School

Prerequisites: Students should know the terms **median**, **centroid**, and **equilateral triangle** on the sphere.

Class Time: 45–80 minutes

Tips for the Adventure

We suggest that you divide this adventure into two parts, as indicated in the Student's Guide. The constructions will get very complicated and may be confusing to students if all five solids are constructed on one sphere. This adventure may take students more than one class period, so it is wise to plan on doing Steps 1 to 3 during one class period and Steps 4 and 5 during another class period. At the end of their first session, students should measure and record the length of one side of the spherical cube, which is approximately 70.53°. They will need this measurement to begin Step 4.

Construction on the Sphere

It is useful to select the colors and point sizes of the marking pens so that each new spherical tile dominates the former ones. Construction details can be drawn by using extra-fine-tip pens; the edges of the solids can be drawn with medium-tip pens.

Step 3: This figure shows how to connect four vertices of a flat-sided cube to make a tetrahedron.

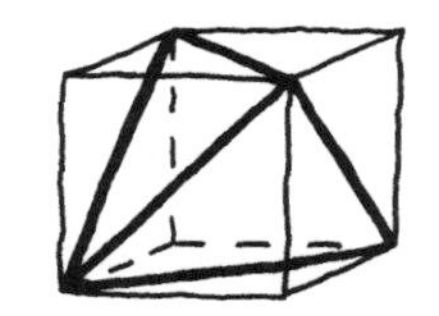

Step 4: If we begin with a side of the spherical cube and construct an equilateral triangle on it, then we can go on to construct the tile of the spherical dodecahedron, as shown in the following figures.

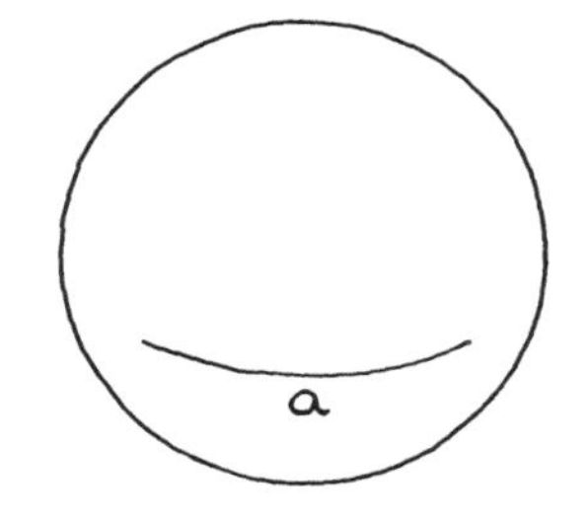

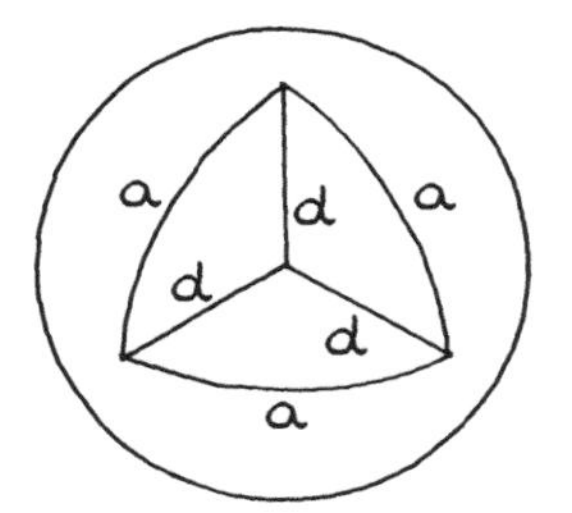

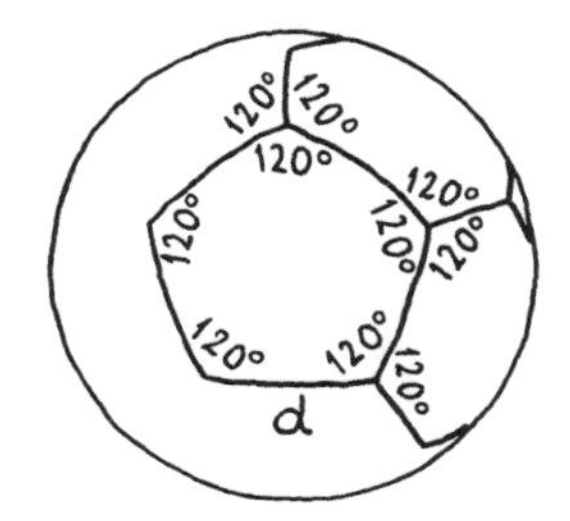

The vertices on the sphere determine the five Platonic solids (the tetrahedron, the cube, the octahedron, the dodecahedron, and the icosahedron).

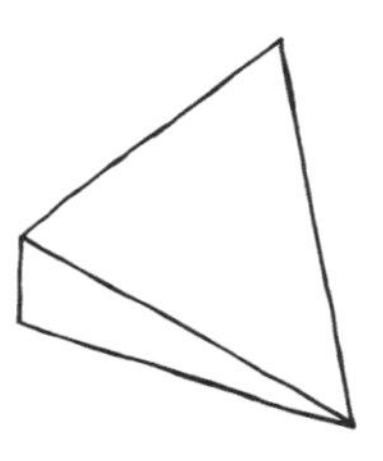 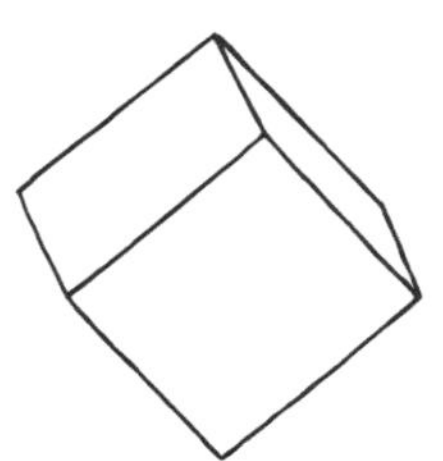 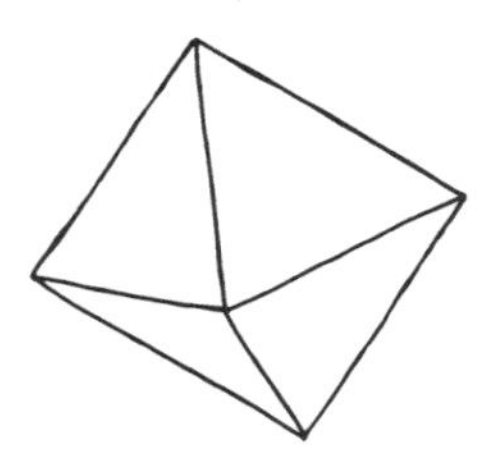 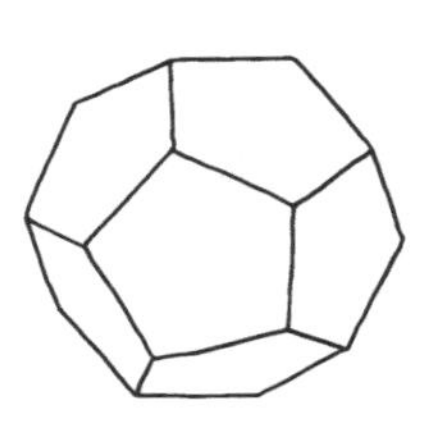 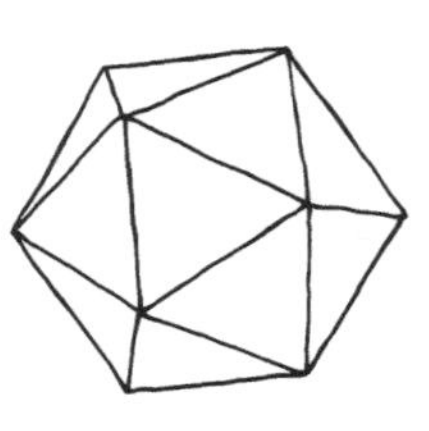

Explore More

2. The pairs of duals are octahedron-cube, tetrahedron-tetrahedron, and dodecahedron-icosahedron.

3. We get the following formula for each tile: Faces + Vertices = Edges + 2. This is a special case of Euler's formula for networks, which is just as valid on the sphere as it is on the plane.

4. **a.** On the plane there are three pure tessellations, made of equilateral triangles, squares, and regular hexagons, respectively.

b. On the sphere, we have pure tessellations made from the five spherical Platonic tiles, and we have an infinite number of tessellations made from congruent biangles.

CHAPTER 10
Polar Triangles

Chapter 10: Polar Triangles

Adventure 10.1: How do you construct a polar triangle?

Adventure 10.2: How are the angles and the sides related in a pair of polar triangles?

Adventure 10.3: What is special about the altitudes of polar triangles?

Adventure 10.4: What is special about the angle bisectors in a triangle and the perpendicular bisectors of its sides?

Adventure 10.5: What is special about lines through the midpoints of the sides of a triangle?

Polar triangles do not exist on the plane in the simple form in which they exist on the sphere because a plane has no pole points or equators. To create a polar triangle, start with a spherical triangle and imagine every side as an arc of an equator. Then construct the pole that is on the same side of each equator as the spherical triangle. Connect these three poles to form a triangle. Pairs of corresponding polar triangles have many interesting properties. This chapter explores some of these properties.

Adventure 10.1 introduces polar triangles and is a good introduction to Adventures 10.2 through 10.5. In Adventure 10.2, students discover a simple but fascinating relationship between the sides and the angles of a triangle and its polar mate. Adventures 10.3 through 10.5 deal with concurrency in triangles and polar triangles: In Adventure 10.3, students explore the concurrency of altitudes; in Adventure 10.4, students explore the concurrency of angle bisectors and perpendicular bisectors; and in Adventure 10.5, students explore the concurrency of medians and other special segments connecting midpoints. Adventure 10.1 is the only prerequisite for Adventures 10.2 through 10.5.

The Teacher's Guides contain construction hints and answers to questions in the Student's Guides.

ADVENTURE 10.1

How do you construct a polar triangle?

For every triangle on the sphere, there is a related triangle called a *polar triangle.* In this adventure you will construct such a triangle. In the adventures that follow you will discover some of the interesting properties of polar triangles.

- Draw a spherical triangle. Each side of your spherical triangle is part of a great circle that has two corresponding pole points. For each side of your spherical triangle, choose the pole point that is on the same side of the great circle as the triangle itself. Connect these three pole points to construct a polar triangle.
- What interesting properties can you discover about your spherical triangle and its corresponding polar triangle?

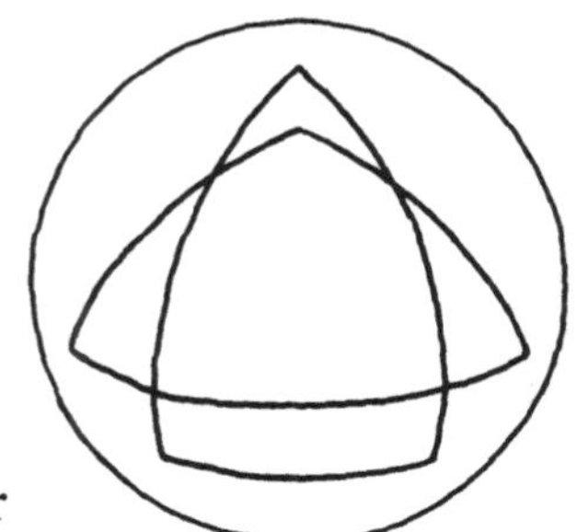

ADVENTURE 10.2

How are the angles and the sides related in a pair of polar triangles?

In Adventure 10.1, you learned how to construct a pair of polar triangles.

- Explore the relationship between the angles and the sides of a triangle and its corresponding polar triangle.

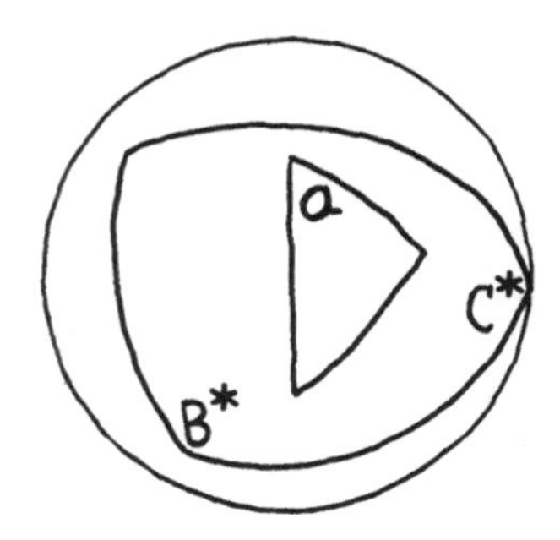

ADVENTURE 10.3

What is special about the altitudes of polar triangles?

An *altitude* of a triangle is a line that passes through a vertex of the triangle and is perpendicular to the side opposite the vertex.

- Investigate some properties of the three altitudes of a triangle on the plane.
- Construct and investigate the three altitudes of a spherical triangle and the three altitudes of its corresponding polar triangle.

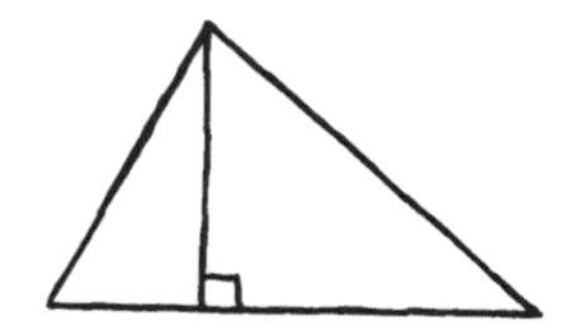

ADVENTURE 10.4

What is special about the angle bisectors in a triangle and the perpendicular bisectors of its sides?

The *perpendicular bisector* of a triangle's side is the perpendicular line that passes through the midpoint of that side.

An *angle bisector* in a triangle is a line that passes through one of the triangle's vertices and bisects the angle at that vertex.

- Investigate the properties of the angle bisectors and the perpendicular bisectors of the sides of planar and spherical triangles.
- Investigate these properties in spherical triangles and their corresponding polar triangles.

ADVENTURE 10.5

What is special about lines through the midpoints of the sides of a triangle?

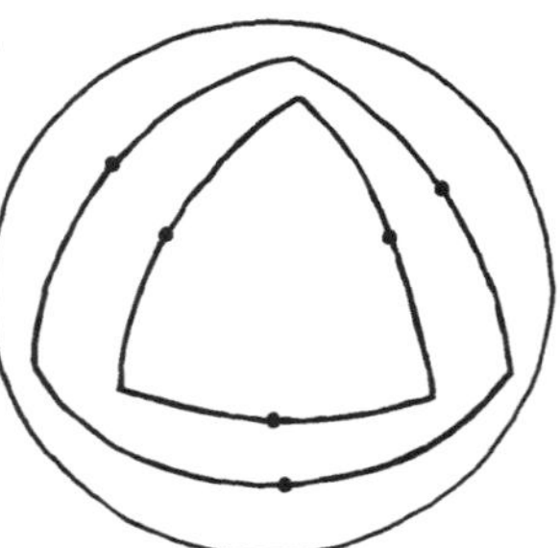

The *median* of a triangle is the segment connecting a vertex with the midpoint of the opposite side.

- Investigate the medians of triangles on the plane and on the sphere.
- Construct and investigate the great circles connecting the midpoints of the sides of a spherical triangle with the corresponding midpoints of the sides of its polar mate.

ADVENTURE 10.1

How do you construct a polar triangle?

For every triangle on the sphere, there is a related triangle called a **polar triangle**. In this adventure you will construct such a triangle.

- Draw a spherical triangle. Each side of your spherical triangle is part of a great circle that has two corresponding pole points. For each side of your spherical triangle, choose the pole point that is on the same side of the great circle as the triangle itself. Connect these three pole points to construct a polar triangle.
- What interesting properties can you discover about your spherical triangle and its corresponding polar triangle?

Construction on the Sphere

Step 1 Draw a triangle. Label its vertices *A*, *B*, and *C*.

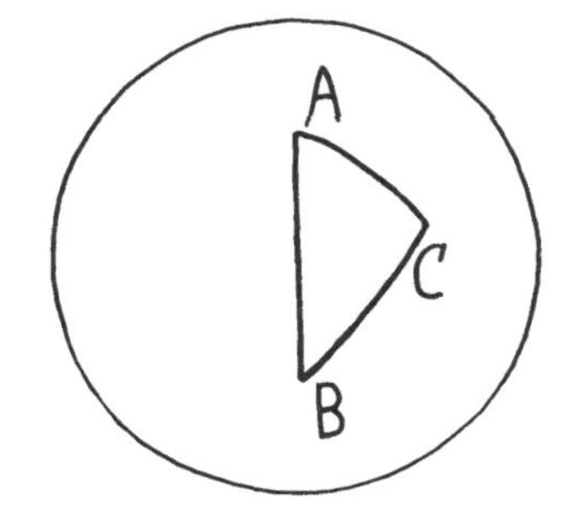

Step 2 Consider side *AB* and the great circle through side *AB*. Notice that the great circle *AB* divides the whole sphere into two hemispheres. One of these hemispheres contains triangle *ABC*. The other hemisphere is blank. With great circle *AB* as the equator, draw the pole point that lies in the hemisphere containing the triangle. Label this pole point C^*.

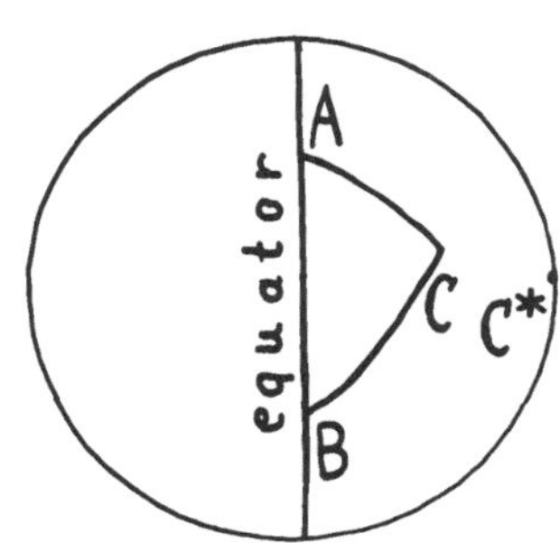

Step 3 Repeat Step 2 for side *BC*. Label the pole point A^*.

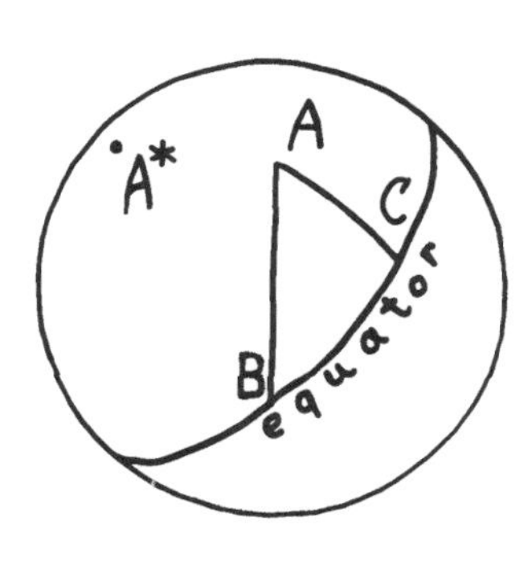

Step 4 Repeat Step 2 for side *CA*. Label the pole point B^*.

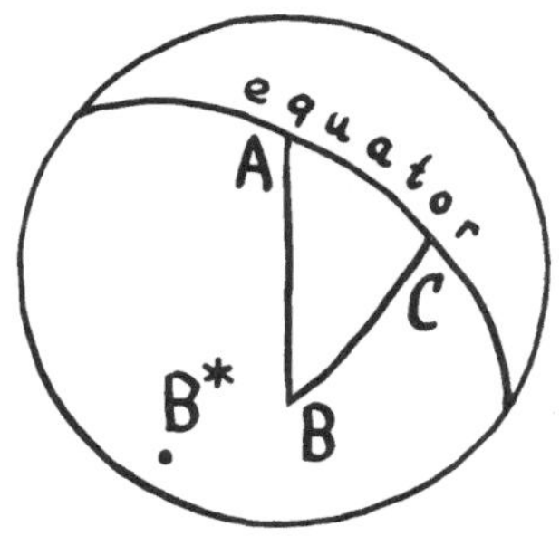

Step 5 Connect points A^*, B^*, and C^*. You have just constructed triangle ABC's polar triangle, $A^*B^*C^*$.

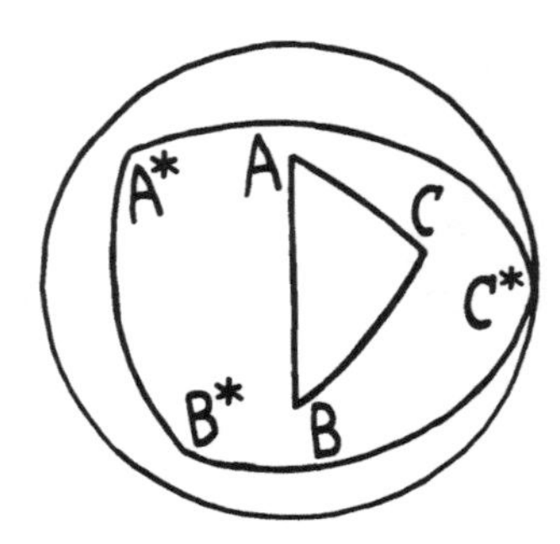

Investigate

1. Construct the polar triangle of triangle $A^*B^*C^*$. What do you find?

Explore More

2. Try to find triangles that resemble their polar triangles as much as possible. Can you find a triangle that is exactly the same as its polar triangle?
3. Follow the steps for constructing the polar triangle but make one change: For each new vertex, use the pole point in the hemisphere that does *not* contain the original triangle. How does this triangle compare to a real polar triangle?
4. Can the method of constructing a polar triangle be applied to any spherical quadrilateral in order to construct a polar quadrilateral?

How do you construct a polar triangle?

Student Audience: Middle School/High School/College

Prerequisites: It is useful to review the correspondence between poles and equators with some concrete examples of points and great circles. Students can use the center of the mini-protractor at the top of the ruler's saddle to find the pole point of the great circle that lies along the base edge of the spherical ruler.

Class Time: 20–30 minutes. You may want to do this adventure in the same class period that you do Adventure 1.4, "How can you construct equators and pole points?"

Construction/Investigation on the Sphere

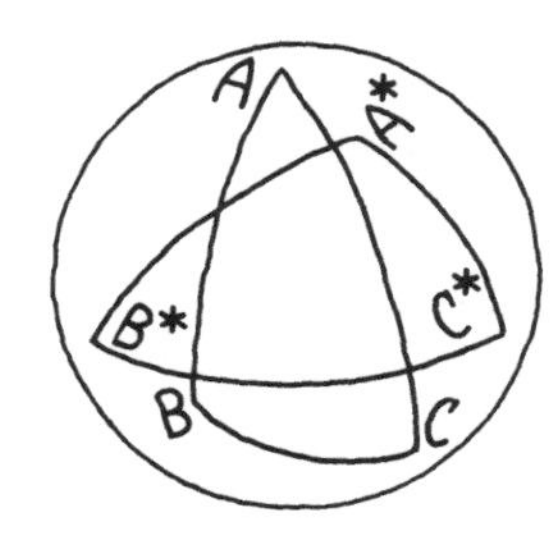

Students tend to draw triangles that are nearly equilateral. These triangles lead to easier and simpler constructions than other types. However, it is also worth trying wilder types. For example, long and skinny triangles result in a construction of quite another structure, as shown.

1. The polar triangle of triangle $A^*B^*C^*$ will be triangle ABC. In other words, the polar triangle of the polar triangle is the original triangle.

Explore More

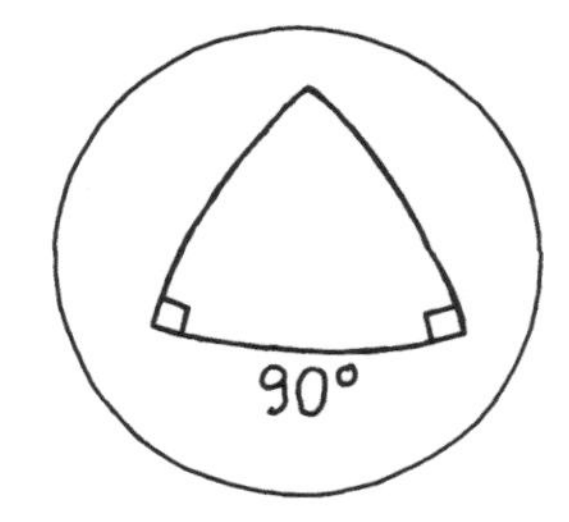

2. There is only one type of triangle that coincides with its polar triangle: the triangle with three right angles. You can construct such a triangle by drawing a 90° arc and constructing two perpendiculars at its endpoints.

3. This triangle is the reflexive partner of the real polar triangle. These two triangles are congruent because their corresponding sides and angles are congruent. They cannot be placed on each other so that they exactly coincide with each other, unless they are isosceles triangles.

4. Only for nonconcave quadrilaterals. For a concave quadrilateral, we can always find a side with a great circle that cuts into the spherical quadrilateral. So we do not know which of the two pole points of this great circle should be chosen for a vertex of the polar quadrilateral.

ADVENTURE 11.1

What happens to a point if you reflect it across three perpendicular great circles in succession?

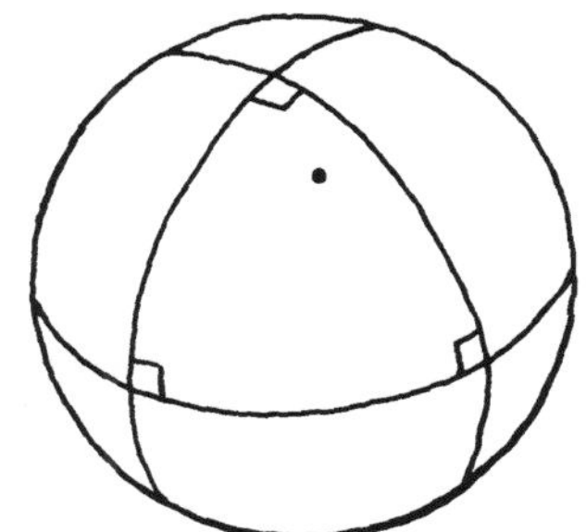

- Construct three great circles on the sphere so that each of them is perpendicular to the other two. Investigate what happens to a point when you reflect it successively across each of the three great circles.
- What happens to a triangle when you reflect it successively across three perpendicular great circles?

ADVENTURE 11.2

What shapes can you create if you reflect a point across the sides of an octant?

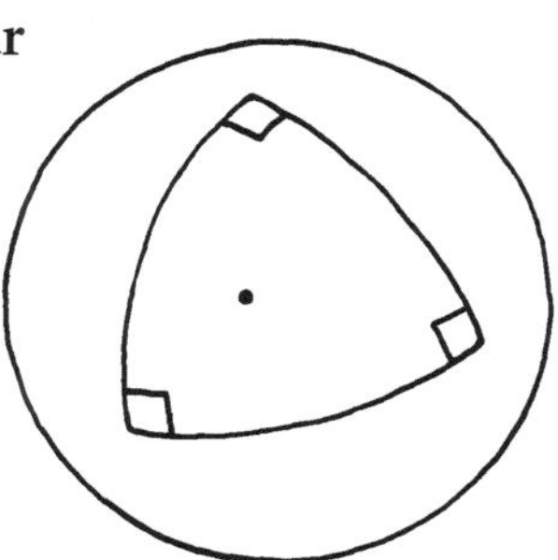

You may have reflected shapes before, using straight lines as your mirrors. You follow the same procedure to reflect a shape across a great circle on the sphere. In this adventure you will use the three arcs of an octant.

Draw a point inside an octant. Reflect the point through the sides of the octant to get three new points. Connect these points to form a triangle.

- Prove that this triangle is circumscribed around the octant.
- What properties of this triangle can you discover?

ADVENTURE 11.1

What happens to a point if you reflect it across three perpendicular great circles in succession?

- Construct three great circles on the sphere so that each of them is perpendicular to the other two. Investigate what happens to a point when you reflect it successively across each of the three great circles.
- What happens to a triangle when you reflect it successively across three perpendicular great circles?

Construction on the Sphere

Step 1 Construct three great circles so that each is perpendicular to the other two. Label these great circles *a*, *b*, and *c*.

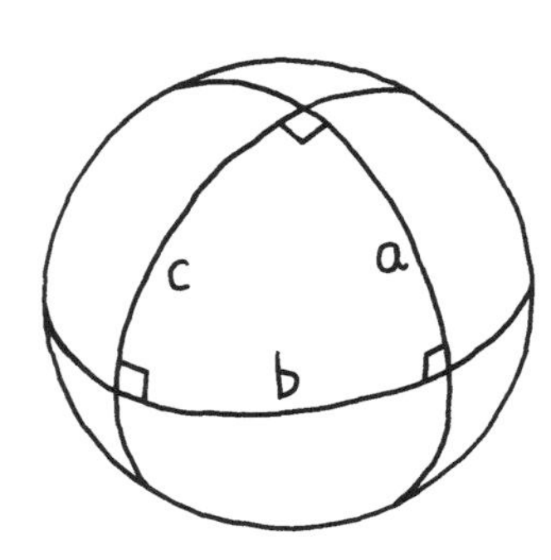

Step 2 Draw a point *P* that does not lie on any of the three great circles. Reflect this point *P* through three great circles. Reflect this point *P* through great circle *a* and label its image point *Q*. Reflect point *Q* through great circle *b* and label its image point *R*. Finally, reflect point *R* through great circle *c* and label its image point *P′*.

Investigate

1. Measure the distance between points *P* and *P′* and describe your results.
2. Choose another order for the three great circles, say *b*, *c*, *a*. Reflect point *P* through great circles *b*, *c*, and *a* in that order. Label the endpoint *S*. Measure the distance between points *P* and *S*. What do you find?
3. Pick another point and find its image point after the same three reflections. Describe your results.
4. Summarize your findings from these constructions.

Explore More

5. Follow the steps in Construction on the Sphere but reflect a triangle instead of a single point.
   a. Trace your original triangle onto a transparency.
   b. Try to move the transparency so that the tracing of your original triangle exactly covers its final image. Explain your results.

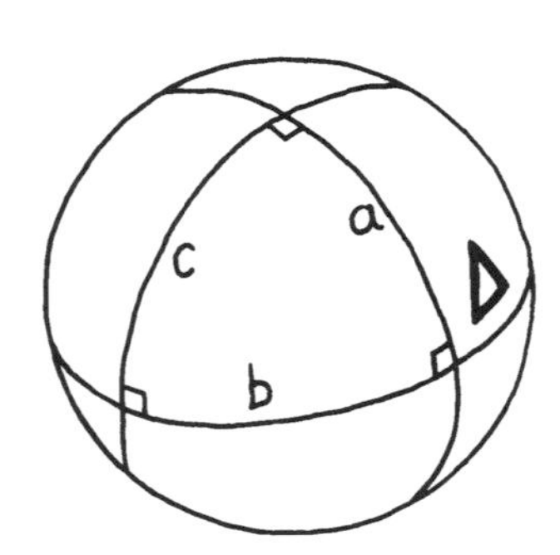

ADVENTURE 11.1

What happens to a point if you reflect it across three perpendicular great circles in succession?

Student Audience: High School/College

Prerequisites: Students should know that you reflect a point across a great circle on the sphere in the same way that you reflect a point over a line on the plane. Construct a perpendicular from the point to the great circle, determine the distance of the point from the great circle, and measure this distance on the perpendicular at the other side of the great circle, as shown.

Class Time: 20–45 minutes

Construction/Investigation on the Sphere

4. Whatever initial point is given, and whatever order of the three perpendiculars is chosen, the final point will be the opposite of the initial point. Their distance will measure 180°.

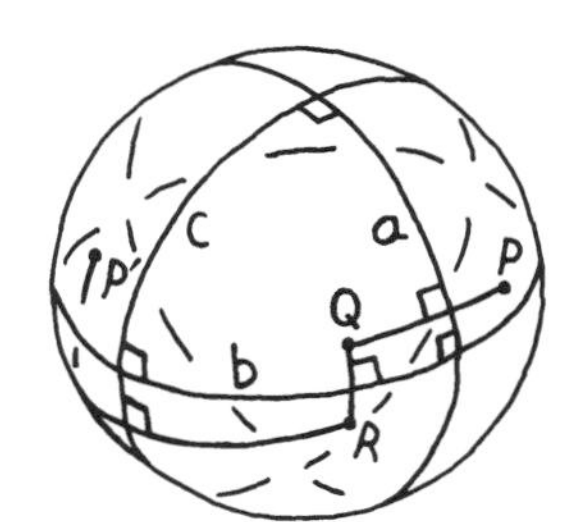

Explore More

5. The final figure will be the reflexive triangle of the initial triangle; that is, each vertex of the final triangle is the opposite point of a vertex in the original triangle. The two triangles coincide with each other if and only if the initial triangle is an isosceles triangle, because the triangle has undergone an odd number of reflections.

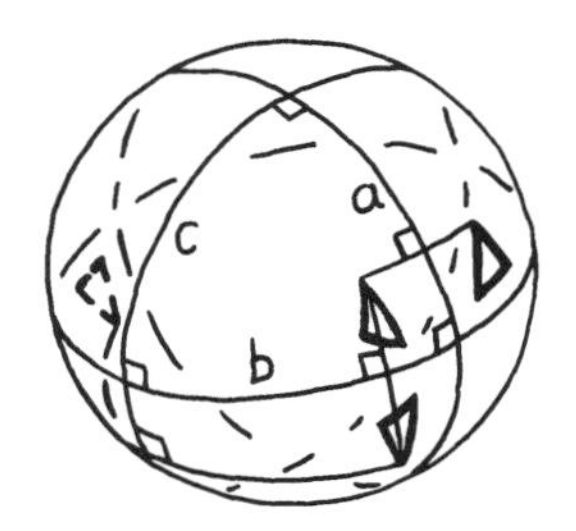

ADVENTURE 11.2

What shapes can you create if you reflect a point across the sides of an octant?

You may have reflected shapes before, using straight lines as your mirrors. You follow the same procedure to reflect a shape across a great circle on the sphere. In this adventure you will use the three arcs of an octant as mirrors to perform three reflections. The results of these reflections demonstrate an interesting property of the octant.

- Perform the construction below. Make conjectures about the angle and side measurements in your construction and try to prove your conjectures.

Construction on the Sphere

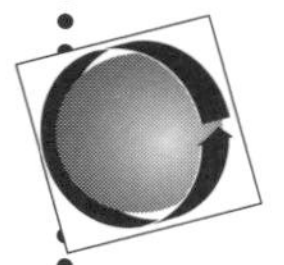

Step 1 Construct an octant. Label its vertices *K, L,* and *M*.

Step 2 Draw a point *O* inside triangle *KLM* and connect this point with the three vertices *K, L,* and *M*.

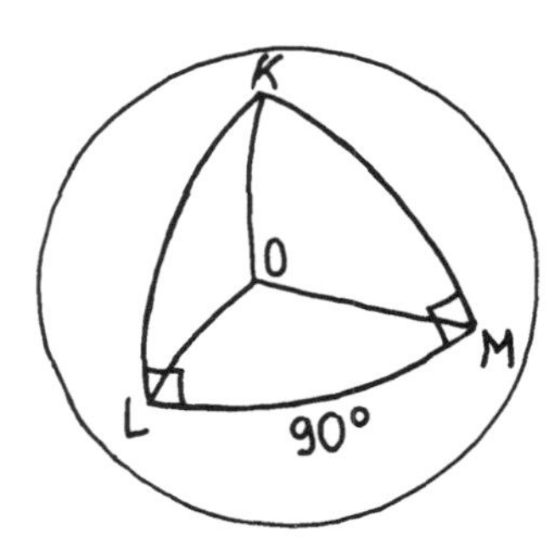

Step 3 Reflect triangle *KLO* across side *KL* to create triangle *KLP*. Then reflect triangle *LMO* across side *LM* to create triangle *LMQ*. Finally, reflect triangle *MKO* across side *MK* to create triangle *MKR*.

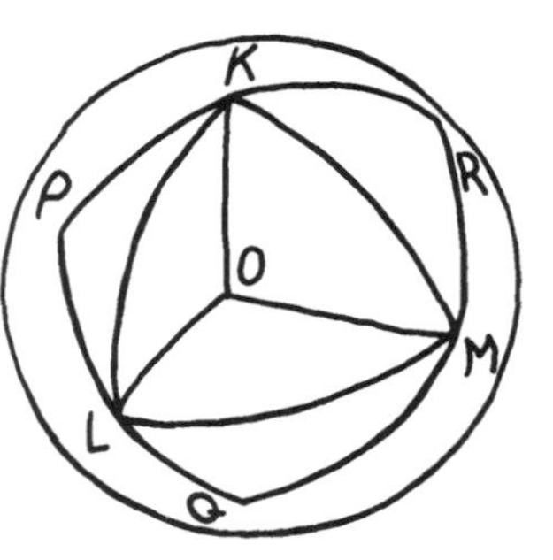

Investigate

1. Measure the angles at vertices *K, L,* and *M*. What can you say about the sum of angle measures at these three vertices?
2. Is *PQR* a triangle or is *PLQMRK* a hexagon?
3. Measure the angles at vertices *P, Q,* and *R*. What is the sum of these three angle measures?
4. Measure the parts into which point *K* divides side *PR*. Do the same for point *L* and side *QP*, and point *M* and side *RQ*. What do you find? What kind of points are *K, L,* and *M* in triangle *PQR*?

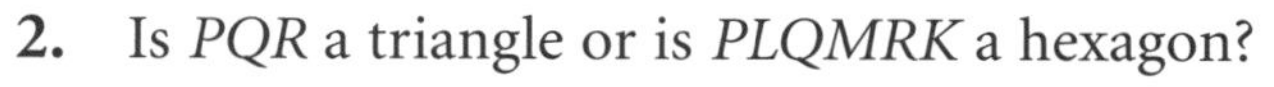

Explore More

5. The reflection of a triangle has the same side, angle, and area measurements as the original triangle. This is true on the sphere as well as the plane. For example, triangle *KLP* has the same side, angle, and area measurements as triangle *KLO*. Use this property of reflections to prove that *PLQMRK* is really a triangle.
6. Prove that the measures of the angles of triangle *PQR* add up to 360°.
7. Prove that points *K, L,* and *M* are the midpoints of the sides of triangle *PQR*.
8. **a.** What can you say about the area of triangle *KLM* compared with the area of triangle *PQR*?

   b. Can you imagine a result like that for a triangle on the plane?

What shapes can you create if you reflect a point across the sides of an octant?

Student Audience: High School/College

Prerequisites: Students should know or be introduced to the way to reflect a triangle across one of its sides on the sphere. As used in this adventure, the method of reflecting a triangle is the same as it is on the plane.

Class Time: 20–50 minutes

Construction/Investigation on the Sphere

1. The sum of the angle measures at each of the vertices *K*, *L*, and *M* is 180°.
2. Each of the arcs *PR*, *RQ*, and *QP* is the arc of a great circle, so *PQR* is a triangle.
3. The sum of the measures of the angles at vertices *P*, *Q*, and *R* is 360°.
4. Points *K*, *L*, and *M* are the midpoints of sides *PR*, *RQ*, and *QP* of triangle *PQR*.

Some of these constructions are not possible on the plane, such as a triangle with three right angles and a triangle whose sum of angle measures is 360°.

Explore More

5. Two triangles that are reflections of each other have congruent pairs of sides and congruent pairs of angles. The sum of the angle measures of the two shaded angles at vertex *K* is 90°, so the whole angle measure is twice this sum. Thus the sum of angle measures at vertex *K* is exactly 180°, so the angle measure between arcs *KP* and *KR* is 180°. In other words, arcs *KP* and *KR* are on the same great circle. The same reasoning applies for the angles at vertices *L* and *M*. Thus points *P*, *Q*, and *R* are three vertices of a triangle, not a hexagon.

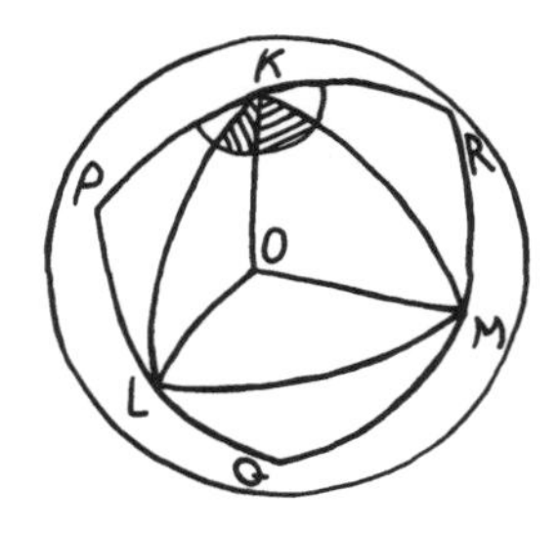

6. The three angles at point *O* are reflected onto the angles at vertices *P*, *Q*, and *R*. Because the three angle measures at point *O* add up to 360°, the sum of angle measures in triangle *PQR* is 360°.
7. Another consequence of the reflections is that arc *KO* is congruent with arcs *KP* and *KR*. Thus point *K* is the midpoint of side *PR*. Accordingly, points *K*, *L*, and *M* are the midpoints of the sides of triangle *PQR*, and triangle *PQR* is called a duplex of triangle *KLM*.
8. Two reflexive triangles have the same area. Thus the whole area of triangle *PQR* is twice that of triangle *KLM*. We could begin the construction with any one of infinitely many different points in triangle *KLM*. Each of these points determines another duplex triangle *PQR*. Thus there are infinitely many triangles that have the same midpoints *K*, *L*, and *M*. This is not possible on the plane because a given planar triangle *KLM* has only one duplex triangle (a triangle whose sides have midpoints *K*, *L*, and *M*) instead of an infinite number. Also, the area of the planar duplex triangle is four times the area of the original triangle, not twice the area.

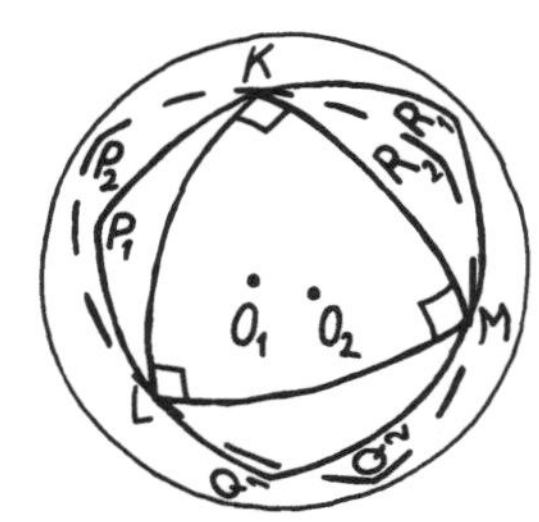

Appendix A

Five-Day Units in Spherical Geometry

These units are suggestions for groupings of adventures. The five-day time frame is very approximate. When students find a topic interesting to think about and explore, let them take their time with it and don't worry about completing the entire unit over the given time frame. Students have sometimes spent several class periods pondering a single sentence from an adventure.

Basic geometric concepts

Adventure 1.1
Adventure 1.2
Adventure 1.3
Adventure 1.5
Adventure 2.1

Changing your planar axioms to use on the sphere

Adventure 1.1
Adventure 1.2
Adventure 1.3
Adventure 2.1
Adventure 3.4

Parallel and intersecting lines

Adventure 1.2
Adventure 2.1
Adventure 3.2
Adventure 6.1

Triangles

Adventure 1.2
Adventure 1.5
Adventure 3.2
Adventure 3.3
Adventure 3.4
Adventure 3.5
(This may take more than five days. To shorten this list, skip 3.2 and 3.3 and use them as references for 3.4. Do 3.5 if you have time.)

For the units that follow, students should know that a great circle is the spherical equivalent of a straight line on the plane. To review this concept in depth, start with Adventure 1.2. Additionally, students need to know that distance on a sphere is measured along a great circle and that the units on their spherical ruler are degrees. Use Adventure 1.3 to explore distance on a sphere in more depth.

Right triangles

Adventure 2.2
Adventure 3.5
Adventure 8.3
And look at the perpendicularity adventures in the list below.

Perpendicularity

Adventure 2.2
Then choose from:
Adventure 2.3
Adventure 8.2
Adventure 11.1
Adventure 11.2
Adventure 6.1

Similarity and congruence

Adventure 4.1
Adventure 3.5 (See the Explore More section.)
Adventure 4.2
Adventure 4.3
Adventure 3.2 (See the references to reflexive triangles.)

Circles

Adventure 5.1
Adventure 5.2
Adventure 5.3
Adventure 6.3 (You may need to refer to some ideas from Adventure 6.2.)
Adventure 8.1

Area

Adventure 6.1
Adventure 6.2
Adventure 6.3
Look at Adventure 9.3, Explore More #2.

Maps of the earth

Adventure 7.1
Then choose from the other adventures in Chapter 7 (Mapping the Earth). Individuals or groups can work on different adventures, then present their finished products to the whole class. This chapter provides a good opportunity to integrate your math curriculum with geography or social studies.

Constructions on the sphere with surprising results

Adventure 6.1
Adventure 8.1
Adventure 8.2
Adventure 8.3

Tessellations

Adventure 9.1
Then choose from the other adventures in Chapter 9 (Tessellations). Individuals or groups can work on different adventures, then present their finished products to the whole class. These constructions are easier if you use the small spherical protractor made in Adventure 1.5. This chapter provides a good opportunity to integrate mathematics and art.

Polar triangles

(These are triangles that exist only on the sphere.)
Adventure 1.4
Adventure 10.1
Adventure 10.2
Then choose from:
Adventure 10.3
Adventure 10.4
Adventure 10.5

Appendix B

Traditional Geometry: A Correlation Chart

Use the first column of the chart to locate the topic you are currently teaching. Use the second column to find corresponding adventures in spherical geometry to use as enrichment units. Then check the prerequisites for those units, found in the Teacher's Guide, to see what your students need to know before they start the adventure.

Topic in traditional geometry	Supplementary adventures in spherical geometry
Introducing geometry	
Points	1.1 What is the simplest shape?
Lines	1.2 Can you draw a straight line on a sphere?
Distance	1.3 How do you measure distance?
	0.1 What color is the bear?
Inductive reasoning	
	In all of these adventures students make their initial discoveries by using inductive reasoning. In a few places they use deductive reasoning to prove some of their more interesting conjectures.
Deductive reasoning	
	Almost every adventure involves challenging a fundamental axiom of plane geometry and establishing an appropriate replacement axiom for spherical geometry. In a sense this entire book is about deductive reasoning. The first six chapters focus more on the tension between the two different axiomatic systems. Some of the adventures in Chapter 10 (Polar Triangles) ask students to prove their results. The same is true for Adventures 8.1 and 8.2 in Chapter 8 (Surprises on the Sphere).
Definitions	
	There are many places in these adventures where students will appreciate the importance of a precise geometric definition. Here are a few such places.
	0.1 What color is the bear?
	1.3 How do you measure distance?
	3.1 Is it possible to make a polygon with only two sides?
	3.3 How many triangles can have the same three vertices?
	3.4 What is the sum of the angles of a triangle?
	4.1 Can you construct similar polygons?
	9.1 What are some tessellations on the sphere?

Topic in traditional geometry	Supplementary adventures in spherical geometry
Angles	
Angle measure	1.5 How can you use a protractor to measure angles on a sphere?
Vertical angles	2.2 What do perpendicular lines look like on a sphere? (See the Explore More section.)
Perpendicularity	2.2 What do perpendicular lines look like on the sphere? 2.3 How many perpendiculars can two lines have in common? 0.1 What color is the bear?
Parallel lines	
Parallel lines versus intersecting lines	2.1 How many points can two lines share?
Parallel postulate	2.1 How many points can two lines share? (See the Explore More section.)
Triangles	
Definition of a triangle	3.1 Is it possible to make a polygon with only two sides? 3.2 What regions can you create using three lines? 3.3 How many triangles can have the same three vertices? 3.4 What is the sum of the angle measures of a triangle? 11.2 What shapes can you create if you reflect a point across the sides of an octant? Look at Chapter 10 (Polar Triangles) to learn about a triangle that can only exist on a sphere, especially: 10.1 How do you construct a polar triangle? 10.2 How are the angles and the sides related in a pair of polar triangles?
Sum of the measures of the angles of a triangle	3.4 What is the sum of the angle measures of a triangle? 3.5 Can a triangle have more than one right angle? 6.2 How can you measure the area of a triangle? 8.1 What is special about triangles inscribed on a diameter of a circle? 8.2 What are some properties of a triangle inscribed in an octant?
AAS triangle congruence property	3.5 Can a triangle have more than one right angle? 4.3 What conditions guarantee congruence of spherical triangles?
SSS, ASA, and SAS triangle congruence properties	4.3 What conditions guarantee congruence of spherical triangles?

Topic in traditional geometry	Supplementary adventures in spherical geometry
Triangles (continued)	
SSA congruence property for right triangles	3.5 Can a triangle have more than one right angle?
	4.3 What conditions guarantee congruence of spherical triangles?
AAA triangle similarity property	4.2 What is special about two triangles whose corresponding angles are congruent?
	4.3 What conditions guarantee congruence of spherical triangles?
Altitudes of a triangle	10.3 What is special about the altitudes of polar triangles?
Angle bisectors in a triangle	10.4 What is special about the angle bisectors in a triangle and the perpendicular bisectors of its sides?
	9.2 How can you construct a soccer ball?
	9.3 How can you tile the sphere with three different types of regular polygons?
	8.2 What are some properties of a triangle inscribed in an octant?
Perpendicular bisectors of the sides of a triangle	10.4 What is special about the angle bisectors in a triangle and the perpendicular bisectors of its sides?
	9.2 How can you construct a soccer ball?
Medians of a triangle	10.5 What is special about lines through the midpoints of the sides of a triangle?
Right triangles	
Right triangles	3.5 Can a triangle have more than one right angle?
	8.3 How can you construct Napier's pentagon?
	The octant is a spherical triangle with three right angles, so the adventures about the octant are relevant, too. A few examples are:
	8.2 What are some properties of a triangle inscribed in an octant?
	11.1 What happens to a point if you reflect it across three perpendicular great circles in succession?
	11.2 What shapes can you create if you reflect a point across the sides of an octant?
Pythagorean theorem	3.5 Can a triangle have more than one right angle? (See the Explore More section.)
Coordinate geometry	
	7.2 Where in the world are you?

Topic in traditional geometry	Supplementary adventures in spherical geometry
Geometric constructions	
Constructing perpendicular bisectors	9.2 How can you construct a soccer ball?
	9.5 How can you "blow up" the Platonic solids to tile a sphere?
Constructing angle bisectors	9.2 How can you construct a soccer ball?
	9.3 How can you tile the sphere with three different types of regular polygons?
	9.5 How can you "blow up" the Platonic solids to tile a sphere?
Constructing points of concurrence	9.1 What are some tessellations on the sphere?
	9.2 How can you construct a soccer ball?
	9.3 How can you tile the sphere with three different types of regular polygons?
	9.5 How can you "blow up" the Platonic solids to tile a sphere?
	10.3 What is special about the altitudes of polar triangles?
	10.4 What is special about the angle bisectors in a triangle and the perpendicular bisectors of its sides?
	10.5 What is special about lines through the midpoints of the sides of a triangle?
Constructing equilateral triangles	9.2 How can you construct a soccer ball?
	9.4 How can you inscribe the Platonic solids in a sphere?
Similarity	
Similar polygons	4.1 Can you construct similar polygons?
	4.2 What is special about two triangles whose corresponding angles are congruent?
	6.1 Can you always use square units to measure area?
AAA similarity property	4.2 What is special about two triangles whose corresponding angles are congruent?
Area	
Units of area	6.1 Can you always use square units to measure area?
Area of a circle	6.3 How can you approximate the area of a circle?
Area of a polygon	6.2 How can you measure the area of a triangle?
	9.2 How can you construct a soccer ball? (See problem 2.)
Surface area of a sphere	6.2 How can you measure the area of a triangle? (See the Explore More section.)

Topic in traditional geometry	Supplementary adventures in spherical geometry
Quadrilaterals	
Squares	6.1 Can you always use square units to measure area?
	9.1 What are some tessellations on the sphere?
	9.2 How can you construct a soccer ball?
	9.3 How can you tile the sphere with three different types of regular polygons?
	9.4 How can you inscribe the Platonic solids in a sphere?
	9.5 How can you "blow up" the Platonic solids to tile a sphere?
Area of a quadrilateral	6.2 How can you measure the area of a triangle? (See the Explore More section.)
Sum of the measures of the angles of a quadrilateral	3.4 What is the sum of the angle measures of a triangle? (See the Explore More section.)
Tessellations	
Regular tessellations	3.1 Is it possible to make a polygon with only two sides? (See the Explore More section.)
	9.1 What are some tessellations on the sphere?
	9.2 How can you construct a soccer ball?
	9.3 How can you tile the sphere with three different types of regular polygons?
	9.4 How can you inscribe the Platonic solids in a sphere? (See problem 2.)
	9.5 How can you "blow up" the Platonic solids to tile a sphere?
Pure tessellations	3.1 Is it possible to make a polygon with only two sides? (See the Explore More section.)
	9.1 What are some tessellations on the sphere?
	9.4 How can you inscribe the Platonic solids in a sphere? (See problem 2.)
	9.5 How can you "blow up" the Platonic solids to tile a sphere?
Semipure tessellations	9.1 What are some tessellations on the sphere?
	9.2 How can you construct a soccer ball?
	9.3 How can you tile the sphere with three different types of regular polygons?
Volume	
	9.4 How can you inscribe the Platonic solids in a sphere? (See the Explore More section.)

Topic in traditional geometry	Supplementary adventures in spherical geometry
Circles	
Tangents	5.1 What are some properties of a circle on a sphere?
Radii	5.1 What are some properties of a circle on a sphere?
Diameters	5.1 What are some properties of a circle on a sphere?
	5.3 What is the ratio of the circumference of a circle to its diameter?
	8.1 What is special about triangles inscribed on a diameter of a circle?
Chords	5.1 What are some properties of a circle on a sphere?
π	5.3 What is the ratio of the circumference of a circle to its diameter?
	6.3 How can you approximate the area of a circle?
Area of a circle	6.3 How can you approximate the area of a circle?
Inscribed angle theorem	5.1 What are some properties of a circle on a sphere? (See the Explore More section.)
Triangle inscribed in a semicircle	8.1 What is special about triangles inscribed on a diameter of a circle?
Transformational geometry	
Reflections	11.1 What happens to a point if you reflect it across three perpendicular great circles in succession?
	11.2 What shapes can you create if you reflect a point across the sides of an octant?
	9.4 How can you inscribe the Platonic solids in a sphere? (Students can use reflections to construct the nets for the Platonic solids, especially if they are making the nets on the computer.)
Other transformations	9.4 How can you inscribe the Platonic solids in a sphere? (Students use transformations to construct their templates.)
	All the adventures in Chapter 9 (Tessellations) provide opportunities to discuss transformations of the different tiles.
Solid geometry	
	9.1 What are some tessellations on the sphere?
	9.2 How can you construct a soccer ball?
	9.3 How can you tile the sphere with three different types of regular polygons?
	9.4 How can you inscribe the Platonic solids in a sphere?
	9.5 How can you "blow up" the Platonic solids to tile a sphere?

About the Author

I come from literature. My family was interested in poems and plays by profession and by inclination. Mostly, mathematics was mentioned among us with sacred horror. I spent my childhood reading books that my parents and grandmother had given me, written by authors from around the world. I wanted to become a poet. Even now, I strongly feel that my literary roots have determined most of what I have done or thought in mathematics and in other parts of my life.

I made my first step toward natural sciences when I studied geography. I copied maps from my school atlas, or, which I much preferred to copying, drew fancy maps of fancy islands and continents. While drawing these maps, I felt as though I was traveling the world over. Next came chemistry and, later on, physics. I liked experimenting very much. It was a pity, I thought, that I could not conduct real research with my "Little Chemist" kit! Then my mother gave me a selection of Galileo's *Dialogo* to read. This book struck me because I felt that Galileo's way of thinking was very close to my heart. (Later on, when I had some problems in my life, my dear mother often said: "That guy, Galileo; he confused your head!")

I already had a deep respect for mathematics at that time, but still I was not in love with it. Why? First, it appeared to be very distant from reality, from the actual experimentation I liked so much. Second, I was, and still am, very slow in the uptake and could not quickly solve math problems. Third, the mathematicians-to-be in my secondary school constituted a private world of their own, with no access afforded to an outsider from literature or chemistry. So I went to learn chemistry and physics at the university.

I was twenty-two years old when I finally decided to study mathematics. I found the same composition of imagination and common sense in this subject that I admired in my favorite poets. I started to work on a theory of axioms based on spherical geometry. After several years' work, I found an old professor, Ferenc Kárteszi, who was the first to help me work out and publish my ideas.

When talking about my work, we often discussed the educational potential of the material. So with his recommendation, I began to go about my native Hungary, teaching and demonstrating my project in primary and secondary schools, in colleges and universities.

I was happy to see that the students and their teachers appreciated my ideas. However, it soon became clear that the project would not be successful without real spheres! Even for university students, it was necessary to draw on a sphere to understand the geometry. But what sphere?

We tried Ping-Pong balls, lampshades, glass balloons from the chemistry lab, black globes from the geography lab, wooden bowls, electric bulbs, and the like. None of these proved really satisfactory, so I tried to design a special device for the purpose. A Hungarian company called TANÉRT seemed to be interested in the production, so I negotiated with the company, went on with the educational project, and tried to improve the design.

Step by step, I came to realize that this idea occupied the larger part of my life. My wife and two sons have always been tolerant and patient with a husband and father writing his papers in the kitchen or drawing endlessly on a plastic sphere. My younger son once remarked: "Dad, I will maybe also spend my life with something like your sphere, but then I won't have a family!"

Over the years, political and economic changes have caused many Hungarian companies to collapse, and TANÉRT went under. An American woman, Eileen Osmond Savdié, who has a literary and technical background, tried to come to my rescue. She heard about the project, and she caught fire. Although she tried her best to help me, she couldn't do so. I was desperate.

Then a miracle happened. It originated from Julianna Radnai-Szendrei, a colleague of mine who helped me a great deal in my work after the death of my old professor. In 1988, she introduced me to a well-known American mathematics educator, Marion Walter, at the sixth meeting of the International Congress on Mathematical Education in Budapest. Four years later, at the next ICME congress, Marion Walter introduced me to Steven and Peter Rasmussen of Key Curriculum Press. The Rasmussens took up the project and the sphere.

As I see now, my previous efforts were only sufficient to produce the raw material for this project. It was Key Curriculum Press that organized my ideas and made them a reality. Despite thousands of miles between Berkeley and Budapest, they have surrounded me with a working team that has helped enormously to turn my sketch into a real product. Thanks to the brilliant designer Lou Temesvary for his contribution. Thanks to manufacturers Lawrence Lin and Marshall Montgomery and to computer cartographer Joseph Roubal. And thanks to the Seattle teacher Masha Albrecht for her many original ideas and sense of reality.

Now I am happy and excited to see that the Lénárt Sphere materials are on their way to the most competent audience: the community of students and teachers.

As Farkas Bolyai put it, each idea has its own particular epoch to come into existence. There certainly must be many teachers around the world who are working on some version of comparative geometry between the plane and the sphere. I had the good luck to meet David Henderson of Cornell University. He has not only elaborated on an educational method similar to, and in many respects richer than, my own, but he has also, to my surprise, shared my interest in the human aspects of this mathematical concept. Another congenial spirit, Jan van den Brink from the Freudenthal Institute, Utrecht, focuses on the multicultural aspects of spherical geometry and its connection with other subjects.

I hope that the project and the construction materials give a boost to the work of all the teachers who are already involved with spherical geometry. I believe the project represents but the first steps in a field of limitless potentials.

I hope most that this project has something very important to say to all students with all kinds of interests, not only to the mathematically enthusiastic. My aim in this project has been to reveal the mathematics that I have loved to learn and teach. Mathematics is not a cold and austere idol of perfectness. It is a living body, just as human as those who have created or are just creating it. It is not at all infallible but always ready to correct its faults and turn them into advantage. It is not to be feared or hated. In its highest moments, it is simple and wild and beautiful.

I wish you much fun! And good luck!

István Lénárt
H-1145, Amerikai út 40/a
Budapest, Hungary
100324.436@compuserve.com or h12572len@ella.hu
October, 1995

For Further Reading

Burger, Dionys. *Sphereland: A Fantasy About Curved Spaces and an Expanding Universe.* Translated from the Dutch. Harper and Row, New York, 1983. A sequel to Abbott's *Flatland,* this is "a pleasant fantasy" on important questions of geometry and physics.

Coxeter, H. S. M. *Introduction to Geometry,* 2nd ed. John Wiley, New York, 1969. A collection of diverse topics in classical and modern geometry, with relatively few, but valuable, hints at spherical geometry.

Greenberg, Marvin Jay. *Euclidean and Non-Euclidean Geometries: Development and History,* 3rd ed. W. H. Freeman, New York, 1993. Readable at the high school level. Its dedication says: "The moral of this book is: Check your premises."

Henderson, David W. *Experiencing Geometry: On Plane and Sphere.* Prentice Hall, Englewood Cliffs, New Jersey, 1995. Written mainly for college and university students, this book provides a collection of well-structured topics in comparative geometry, including surfaces different from the plane and the sphere, and provides an extremely rich selection of concrete examples of students' work on the problems raised in the book.

Hilbert, David, and Stefan Cohn-Vossen. *Geometry and the Imagination.* Translated from the German. Chelsea, New York, 1952. A comprehensive presentation of geometry, including the geometry of spheres and other surfaces, as it was seen by two leading mathematicians of the first half of the twentieth century.

Lénárt, István. "Alternative Models on the Drawing Ball." *Educational Studies in Mathematics* 24 (1993), 277–312. A description of an experiment with middle and high school students, and a theoretical foundation for applying alternative models in mathematics education—the plane and sphere, different number systems, or different algebraic structures, for example. The Drawing Ball is, of course, the same as the Lénárt Sphere!

Osserman, Robert. *Poetry of the Universe.* Doubleday, New York, 1995. "Physics in a human voice" with many references to non-Euclidean geometries.

Rosenfeld, Boris A. *A History of Non-Euclidean Geometry.* Translated from the Russian. Springer-Verlag, New York, 1988. A comprehensive work with a separate chapter about spherical geometry.

Runion, Garth E., and James R. Lockwood. *Deductive Systems: Finite and Non-Euclidean Geometries.* National Council of Teachers of Mathematics, Reston, Virginia, 1978. Readable at the high school level.

Serra, Michael. *Discovering Geometry: An Inductive Approach.* Key Curriculum Press, Berkeley, California, 1989. Written for high school students. We frequently used this book as a source of reference for conjectures and definitions on the plane.

Todhunter, Isaac. *Spherical Trigonometry.* Macmillan, London, 1886. The first edition was published in 1859. A well-written book that deals mainly with spherical trigonometry but that also includes many useful details in synthetic spherical geometry.

van den Brink, Jan. "Spherical Geometry Lessons." *Mathematics Teaching* 147 (June 1994), 26–33. Lessons in spherical geometry for high school students, building upon the basic elements in continuous comparison with plane geometry. Interesting connections with geographical and cultural topics.

———. "Geometry Education in the Midst of Theories." *For the Learning of Mathematics* 15 (1) (February 1995).

———, and Marja Meeder. *Mecca.* Translated from the Dutch. Freudenthal Institute, Utrecht, the Netherlands, 1993

Wenninger, Magnus J. *Spherical Models.* Cambridge University Press, New York, 1979. With many illustrations and detailed instructions about designing and constructing the models.

Ordering Lénárt Sphere Materials and Replacement Parts

To order additional Lénárt Sphere materials (including transparencies, hangers, posters, and marking pens) or replacement parts call Key Curriculum Press at 1-510-548-2304 or write to Key Curriculum Press, P.O. Box 2304, Berkeley, CA 94702, USA.

Catalog no.	Catalog item	Contents
53104	Lénárt Sphere Construction Materials Basic Set	1 sphere, 1 torus, 4 hemispherical transparencies, 1 hanger, 1 spherical straightedge/ruler/protractor, 1 spherical compass, 1 center locator, 4 Vis-à-Vis Wet-Erase marking pens, 4 compass collars, 1 *Living Earth on the Lénárt Sphere* poster, 1 *Getting Started with the Lénárt Sphere* booklet
53105	Lénárt Sphere Construction Materials Classroom Set	8 Lénárt Sphere Basic Sets
53126	Lénárt Sphere Transparency and Hanger Set	16 hemispherical transparencies, 4 hangers
53127	Vis-à-Vis Wet-Erase Extra Fine Point Pens	8 marking pens (black, red, blue, green, yellow, orange, brown, and purple)
53128	Vis-à-Vis Wet-Erase Fine Point Pens	8 marking pens (black, red, blue, green, yellow, orange, brown, and purple)
53130	Vis-à-Vis Permanent Extra Fine Point Pens	8 marking pens (black, red, blue, green, yellow, orange, brown, and purple)
53131	Vis-à-Vis Permanent Fine Point Pens	8 marking pens (black, red, blue, green, yellow, orange, brown, and purple)
53103	*Non-Euclidean Adventures on the Lénárt Sphere*	Book of blackline masters and teacher's guides for 43 classroom investigations in spherical geometry

Part no.	Replacement part	Quantity
53132	Sphere	1
53133	Torus	1
53129	Hemispherical transparency	1
53139	Hanger	1
53134	Spherical straightedge/ruler/protractor	1
53135	Spherical compass	1 arc and 1 mandrel (no collars)
53136	Compass collars (for gripping Vis-à-Vis and Stabilo marking pens)	1 set of four
53137	Center locator	1
53140	*The Living Earth on the Lénárt Sphere* poster (folded)	1
53106	*Getting Started with the Lénárt Sphere* booklet	1